THE WORLD
OF PHYSICS

THE WORLD OF PHYSICS

Readings in the nature, history, and challenge of physics edited and introduced by **ARTHUR BEISER,** *Associate Professor of Physics, New York University*

with a foreword by Edward U. Condon

McGRAW-HILL *Book Company, Inc.*
New York Toronto London **1960**

Library of Congress Catalog Card Number: 60-13759

II

ACKNOWLEDGMENTS

The kind permission of the following individuals and organizations to reprint copyrighted material is hereby gratefully acknowledged.

Simon and Schuster, Inc., and George Allen & Unwin, Ltd., for "The Rise of Science," from *History of Western Philosophy*, copyright 1945 by Bertrand Russell. The Estate of Albert Einstein and Leopold Infeld for "Conservation of Energy," from *The Evolution of Physics*, copyright 1938 by Albert Einstein and Leopold Infeld. Prentice-Hall, Inc., for "Entropy," from *Matter, Earth and Sky* by George Gamow, copyright 1958 by Prentice-Hall, Inc. Science, for "Superfluids" by K. Mendelssohn, which appeared Jan. 31, 1958, in *Science*. William Sloane Associates, for "Special Relativity," from *The World and Dr. Einstein*, copyright 1948 by Harper & Brothers; copyright 1948, 1950, 1957 by Lincoln Barnett. Curtis Brown, Ltd., for "The Discovery of Radium," from *Pierre Curie*, copyright 1923 by Marie Curie. Physics Today, for "History of the Cyclotron" by M. Stanley Livingston, which appeared October, 1959, in *Physics Today*, copyright 1959 by American Institute of Physics. Controller of Her Britannic Majesty's Stationery Office, for "The Birth of Atomic Energy," which appeared as part of Appendix 7 of *Atomic Energy for Military Purposes* by Henry Smyth, Princeton University Press, 1948. Science, for "Quantum Physics" by Edward U. Condon, which appeared Feb. 18, 1955, in *Science*. Endeavour, for "Elementary Particles" by Abdus Salam, which appeared April, 1958, in

Endeavour. American Scientist, for "Origin and Implications of Cosmic Radiation" by Serge A. Korff, which appeared September, 1957, in *American Scientist,* copyright 1957 by The Society of the Sigma Xi. Scientific American, for "Fusion Power" by Richard F. Post, which appeared December, 1957, in *Scientific American,* copyright 1957 by Scientific American, Inc. Random House, Inc., for "Scientific Space Exploration," from *Space Handbook: Astronautics and Its Applications* by Robert W. Buchheim and the Staff of the RAND Corporation, copyright 1959 by the RAND Corporation.

Edward U. Condon

Foreword

I envy the young students of today who are just starting to learn physics. Enormous progress has been made in three and a half centuries—and particularly in the last half century—in accumulating new observations, in devising new experimental techniques, and in forming new clarifying theoretical ideas. Despite all this, the subject shows no sign of closing in on itself or of ceasing to grow. Exciting new vistas of discovery are opening up in every direction—in the study of elementary particles and their laws of interaction, in the study of extraordinary properties of matter at extremely low temperatures, in the application of our knowledge of atomic physics to understanding conditions in the space between sun and planets, within nebulae, and in the interiors of stars, in the development of the not-yet-existent technology of fusion power, and in a host of other things.

Not only will all these things be greatly clarified in the next decade or two by reason of researches now in progress, but there will also be many other realms which I do not include only because they have not been thought of yet. The pace of activity in physics now is unparalleled by that of any previous period in human history. This fact becomes evident by a comparison of developments even within the span of our own century. Max Planck first introduced in 1900 the idea that the energy in a radiation field can change only by discrete amounts, which we now call quanta. A search of the literature indicates that this idea brought forth almost no response until 1905, when Einstein pointed out its significance for understanding the photoelectric effect. Contrast this time lag with the recent revision of the idea of parity conservation in nuclear physics: a revolutionary idea was introduced by Lee and Yang in the summer of 1956, and this immediately triggered off a whole series of important experimental and theoretical developments, so that this topic had reached a new level of completion just three years later.

It must be admitted that this enormous activity raises problems for the student. So much is going on, and so much is being published about it, that it becomes extremely difficult to gain a general perspective of the main lines of growth of the science both in the historical past and in the present. I think that much of our teaching suffers from too great an emphasis on details within the older branches of the subject. As a result, thousands of college students annually go through a one-year course in college physics without having had anything happen to them that gives them a sense of the high adventure in the research laboratories today.

There is a reason for this. It is argued that all the time of the introductory course is needed just to lay a sound foundation in the basic concepts of mechanics, heat, electromagnetism, and optics. All these basic ideas are so important that none of them can be crowded out. The result is often an introduction that is rather dehumanized in two respects. To save time in the study of the older parts of the subject, the story of their historical development is neglected, and a condensed, formal, deductive presentation is adopted. This type of introduction may be highly efficient for communication of such knowledge to persons already motivated to learn it, but it deprives the student of a sense of growing human achievement, the successes and failures, the flashes of insight mixed with bumbling error which have marked the actual development of the science. The other respect is that the course usually concludes with almost nothing having been said about twentieth-century physics, and certainly nothing said of the physics of the current decade. The result is that the student does not get from his course (although the eager ones will have bootlegged some of it from newspapers and popular-science journals) a real appreciation of the excitement of current progress in the field.

One way to remedy this lack is through a well-selected group of readings on special topics, indicating the way in which ideas about them have grown and developed and communicating some feel for the personalities, thoughts, and problems of those who really made history. Professor Beiser has chosen this path in the collection which he presents in this book. He starts with the immortal account by Galileo of the work on falling bodies upon which Newton later built in arriving at his laws of motion. Lord Russell then gives a general setting of the significance for human affairs of the development of science. In the next few selections we are given an insight into the three major developments of nineteenth-century physics: the recognition of the broad applicability of the principle of conservation of energy, the introduction of probability ideas into the study of the chaotic molecular motion that is heat, and the development of the idea of a field for describing electric and magnetic interactions.

The rest of the selections give us a survey of the leading developments of twentieth-century physics. Here one gets a sense of the moving boundary between what may be called the old physics and the new physics. The special theory of relativity and the ideas of quantum mechanics, both of which seemed so strange and revolutionary about thirty years ago, have now become part of the standard content of the subject. The discovery of natural radioactive elements also seems to belong to the distant past now that many people work in biochemical laboratories with a large variety of radioactive atoms, all produced artificially. It is hard to realize that less than forty years ago the women of America raised a subscription to buy 1 gram of radium for Marie Curie, while today the problem of safe disposal of vast quantities of radioactive wastes from large-scale nuclear reactors is a major task for industrial hygiene.

Other selections confront us with the current story of some main lines of progress, from the cyclotron through the wartime atomic-energy project, the efforts to realize fusion power, the discovery of more and more elementary particles, the peculiar behavior of superfluids, the study of cosmic radiation, and the problems of exploration of interplanetary space. The story of wartime atomic-energy work is told by a selection from the official British statement issued jointly with the American Smyth Report just after the bombings of Hiroshima and Nagasaki. The British report and the American report gave, respectively, the story of the accomplishments of two national groups. Neither one by itself gives a complete presentation, but the wider circulation of the Smyth report in this country has given many people an inadequate appreciation of the British contributions to the joint venture. The resulting bias in public understanding was probably unintentional, but it exists nevertheless, and the choice of this selection may help to restore needed balance.

The last group of selections shows that we stand on the threshold of vast and exciting new developments. One of the strongest reasons for desiring immortality would be to be allowed to take part in the growth. Whether such immortality is in any sense available to us we do not know, but we can have a vicarious part in the world to come through the contribution we make to the growth of our students.

CONTENTS

THE WORLD
OF PHYSICS

I often say that when you can measure what you are speaking about, and express it in numbers, you know something about it; but when you cannot express it in numbers, your knowledge is of a meagre and unsatisfactory kind; it may be the beginning of knowledge, but you have scarcely, in your thoughts, advanced to the stage of Science, whatever the matter may be.

LORD KELVIN

Life would be stunted and narrow if we could feel no significance in the world around us beyond that which can be weighed and measured with the tools of the physicist or described by the metrical symbols of the mathematician.

SIR ARTHUR EDDINGTON

Arthur Beiser

INTRODUCTION

Physics, the basic science from which all other sciences devolve, has as its province the world of things and actions. It is, above all, a human endeavor, and its sometimes daring, often profound, and usually successful assaults on a reticent Nature constitute human triumphs. The moments of triumph are only part of the story, for in his quest for knowledge the physicist more often experiences moments of confusion and discouragement. Nevertheless, the efforts of a true scientist continue despite setbacks; not only is it impossible to make an omelet without cracking eggs, but it is often valuable to identify incorrect methods of approach so that others will not fall into the same traps.

Physics is also great fun. Though the fundamental nature of the questions it considers is apparent on slight acquaintance, the deep pleasure its practitioners experience is not always obvious. Yet the latter is surely a major reason for the enormous development of physics in this century. Physics has a way of becoming an addiction, of swelling from a casual interest into a passion that excludes almost everything else. That so few people experience this passion is partly because of the intellectual ability and discipline required and partly because the more rapturous aspects of physics are seldom displayed to novices and outsiders. It is the purpose of this volume to convey something of the flavor of physics by presenting various aspects of classical, modern, and contemporary physics as seen by different observers from different points of view. It is hoped that the selections will be read out of curiosity and that they will stimulate the reader's imagination, for curiosity and imagination are the physicist's chief tools in his search for order in the universe we inhabit.

It is almost impossible to draw definite boundaries separating the physical sciences from one another. The central theme of physics is the nature of matter and the fundamental interactions—gravitational, electromagnetic, nuclear, and so on—it exhibits; that of chemistry is the combination of different species of matter into composite substances; that of geology and the other earth sciences is our planet, from core to outer atmosphere; and that of astronomy is the structure and evolution of the universe. These themes are different, but their pursuit leads to considerable overlapping. Thus astrophysics, geophysics, geochemistry, physical chemistry, and chemical physics are all established professions. The principles and concepts of physics, however, underlie the other disciplines of physical science, and as the latter grow more sophisticated, they draw that much more upon physics for the tools of discovery.

The physics of today is a direct descendant of Galileo's studies of moving bodies, first published as *Two New Sciences* in 1638. For Galileo, physics began and ended with experiment: the first step in investigating nature must be empirical observation, then the intermediate steps of formulating a hypothesis and extracting from the hypothesis whatever consequences are implicit in it, and finally the confrontation of these consequences with further experiment. Galileo's notion of how inquiries into the physical universe should be conducted was the antithesis of the introspective scholastic philosophy, and when its power was appreciated, it replaced this philosophy to become the universal approach of science. The vast theoretical structure of physics has its ultimate roots in experiment, and whether its validity extends beyond the limits of the data in hand only further data can say.

This bald statement of the scientific method is simple enough, but nostalgia tends to cloud matters when the time comes for it to be ruthlessly applied. Examples from the past abound: a striking one is the reluctance of Max Planck to accept the modifications in classical physics required by his own quantum theory of radiation. Closer to the present, the inadequate experimental support for the general theory of relativity is only now occasioning the concern it has long cried out for. Oddly enough, then, it is the innovator in science, unwilling to accept an existing doctrine beyond its verified domain, who is the true conservative. The "revolutions" that have taken place in physics are more apparent than real, since they almost always represent the filling of an unrecognized void in our knowledge. New ideas characteristically enter the world of physics with a bang, circle among established ideas (perhaps knocking over a few of the flimsier of them) for a time, and eventually occupy niches that, in retrospect, should have been recognized as vacant all along. Thus the quantum theory of radiation has replaced the electromagnetic theory only in those regions where it never was proper to apply the latter. Even when a theory of restricted scope is revealed as a special case of a more general one, those elements of the former that are valid must be included, implicitly or explicitly, in the latter.

The most remarkable achievements of physics have been in realms distant from our personal experience. Nobody has ever seen an electron or a photon, yet so convincing is the agreement between those quantities we can measure with theories built upon the existence of electrons and photons that their reality is unquestioned. It is worth pondering the exact sense in which the assumptions of modern physics have meaning. In the late nineteenth century the great Ludwig Boltzmann is supposed to have given a lecture on atoms and molecules at which the physicist-philosopher Ernst Mach was present. At the end of the lecture Mach rose and said, "You do not know that molecules exist." "I *know* that there are molecules," replied Boltzmann. "You *do not*," said Mach, and sat down.

Currently the word "physics" suggests a good deal more than

the scholarly pursuit of a certain type of knowledge for its own sake. The atomic bomb is not alone in elevating physics to its present eminence. The modern world is characterized by rapid and profound changes of many kinds, and physics is responsible, directly or indirectly, for most of the engines of these changes. No major power is without a vast scientific establishment in which physics is emphasized, and even minor powers find it expedient to follow suit. Scientific research, and physics research in particular, has accordingly been transformed from a private to a public occupation. The consequences for the spirit of science fall into two categories, one concerning the philosophy of research and the other the position of the scientist in society.

Once an individual of talent could, with sufficient luck, ingenuity, and sacrifice, follow his intellectual fancy whither it led him. While this is still true in principle, as a practical matter a considerable degree of external control is now imposed upon scientific investigation. The control may be direct via political or economic influences, or it may be indirect via social ones. Even when there is a free choice of subject, projects involving collective efforts with definite goals and timetables are encouraged, not the kind of speculative research carried on by an individual staring out the window with paper and pencil handy. It remains to be seen whether the contemporary approach to science, so efficient at carrying existing ideas to their logical conclusions, has a comparable capacity to engender new ideas. There are signs, however, of a return to sanity in the way science is carried on, though the recognition that the scientist is closer to an artist than to an engineer is still not widespread.

Now that science has become so intimate a part of our lives, the scientist can no longer hold himself aloof from the uses society sees fit to develop from his efforts. An automotive engineer is not necessarily the best driver of a car, but he may well have things of value to say regarding the use of a car. Similarly, while the scientific innovator is seldom the best exploiter of his creations, the insights that led to his achievement do not always stop right there. In recognition of this, the participation of scientists in appropriate areas of government is already a reality, and this participation must grow as science and the technology it gives birth to continue to develop. For the sake of the general welfare as well as his own, the physicist must be, perhaps even more than his fellow scientists, politically conscious and willing to express himself in public and fight for his beliefs.

Still, despite the new complications that surround it, physics remains fun. A deliberate attempt was made in choosing selections for *The World of Physics* to present different viewpoints as well as different topics—yet the official prose of the British Information Services and the RAND Corporation reflects the exhilaration to be found in physics no less than do the personal recollections of Marie Curie and M. Stanley Livingston. If the reader derives from this book even a trace of the intense pleasure originally associated with the endeavors it recounts, the efforts of the editor will have been repaid.

Modern science began with Galileo. Born in Pisa in 1564, Galileo entered the University of Pisa as a medical student, became interested in mathematics and physical science, and made so striking an impression that he was appointed to the chair of mathematics when he was only twenty-six. But the independence of thought that led Galileo to his great work in astronomy and mechanics was accompanied by an intolerance of fools, a trait no more endearing to the universities of the sixteenth century than to those of the twentieth century. Galileo was forced to resign his chair at Pisa, and after a time he secured a professorship at Padua. This was a fortunate choice, for Padua was under the protection of Venice, unique among the Italian states for its refusal to accept the authority of the monastic orders and the Inquisition. There Galileo stayed for twenty years, becoming famous throughout Europe for his experiments and lectures. At Padua he championed the Copernican system and invented the telescope, ultimately becoming so involved with correspondence, visitors, and the construction of hundreds of telescopes that he had no time left for creative work. In 1610 Galileo returned to Tuscany as Court Mathematician and Philosopher to his friend Cosimo II, the Grand Duke, attracted by the promise of time to pursue his own interests. This move was a serious mistake, for his enemies in Pisa and Florence saw to it that he was brought before the Inquisition and ordered to renounce the heresy that the earth moved. Copernicus's masterpiece **De revolutionibus orbium coelestium** was placed on the Index, not to be withdrawn until 1835.

When his friend Cardinal Maffeo Barberini became Pope in 1623, Galileo optimistically began work on **Dialogues on the Two Principal Systems.** Until then, despite the prohibition on **De revolutionibus,** the

Copernican system had continued to be widely discussed under the polite fiction that it was no more than a scheme for simplifying computations. With tactless vigor Galileo asserted its literal truth, and he ridiculed the objections of the Jesuits and Aristotelians. His preface began,

> There was promulgated at Rome, some years ago, a salutary edict, in which to obviate the perilous scandals of the present age silence has been imposed on the Pythagorean opinion of the motion of the earth. There are some people so rash as to believe that this decree was not the result of a judicious examination but of a passion too little informed; and complaints have been heard that Councillors totally ignorant of astronomical observations ought not, with a precipitate prohibition, to cut the wings of speculative men of intellect.

Not surprisingly, **Dialogues on the Two Principal Systems** was banned and its author was summoned for trial before the Inquisition. These acts of the Church, which were provoked by Galileo, must therefore be considered as among his most significant contributions, for they made it clear forever that intellectual tyranny is as unacceptable as physical tyranny. Following his humiliating public renunciation of his ideas, Galileo, old, ill, and forbidden to teach or write, returned to Tuscany. There he wrote **Two New Sciences,** a treatise on his many years' work in physics, which he said contained "results which I consider the most important of all my studies." The printing of any work by Galileo was forbidden by the Church, **nullo excepto,** but he managed to get the manuscript to Holland, where it was published in 1638. In 1642 Galileo died at the age of seventy-eight.

Two New Sciences was written in the form of a conversation among three men, Salviati, a spokesman for Galileo, Simplicio, a spokesman for the Aristotelian point of view, and Sagredo, an impartial man of intelligence. The excerpts that follow are from the translation by Henry Crew and Alfonso de Salvio (Macmillan, 1914, and Dover Publications). The involved geometrical proofs of Propositions I and II have been omitted since they are found, in simpler algebraic form, in all physics textbooks.

Galileo Galilei

FALLING BODIES

SALVIATI: I greatly doubt that Aristotle ever tested by experiment whether it be true that two stones, one weighing ten times as much the other, if allowed to fall, at the same instant, from a height of, say, 100 cubits, would so differ in speed that when the heavier had reached the ground, the other would not have fallen more than 10 cubits.

SIMPLICIO: His language would seem to indicate that he had tried the experiment, because he says: *We see the heavier;* now the word *see* shows that he had made the experiment.

SAGREDO: But I, Simplicio, who have made the test can assure you that a cannon ball weighing one or two hundred pounds, or even more, will not reach the ground by as much as a span ahead of a musket ball weighing only half a pound, provided both are dropped from a height of 200 cubits.

SALVIATI: But, even without further experiment, it is possible to prove clearly, by means of a short and conclusive argument, that a heavier body does not move more rapidly than a lighter one provided both bodies are of the same material and in short such as those mentioned by Aristotle. But tell me, Simplicio, whether you admit that each falling body acquires a definite speed fixed by nature, a velocity which cannot be increased or diminished except by the use of force or resistance.

SIMPLICIO: There can be no doubt but that one and the same body moving in a single medium has a fixed velocity which is determined by nature and which cannot be increased except by the addition of momentum or diminished except by some resistance which retards it.

SALVIATI: If then we take two bodies whose natural speeds are different, it is clear that on uniting the two, the more rapid one will be partly retarded by the slower, and the slower will be somewhat hastened by the swifter. Do you not agree with me in this opinion?

SIMPLICIO: You are unquestionably right.

SALVIATI: But if this is true, and if a large stone moves with a speed of, say, eight while a smaller moves with a speed of four, then when they are united, the system will move with a speed less than eight; but the two stones when tied together make a stone larger than that which before moved with a speed of eight. Hence the heavier body moves with less speed than the lighter; an effect which is contrary to your supposition. Thus you see how, from your assumption that the heavier body moves more rapidly than the lighter one, I infer that the heavier body moves more slowly.

SIMPLICIO: I am all at sea because it appears to me that the smaller stone when added to the larger increases its weight and by adding weight I do not see how it can fail to increase its speed or, at least, not to diminish it.

SALVIATI: Here again you are in error, Simplicio, because it is not true that the smaller stone adds weight to the larger.

SIMPLICIO: This is, indeed, quite beyond my comprehension.

SALVIATI: It will not be beyond you when I have once shown you the mistake under which you are laboring. Note that it is necessary to distinguish between heavy bodies in motion and the same bodies at rest. A large stone placed in a balance not only acquires additional weight by having another stone placed upon it, but even by the addition of a handful of hemp its weight is augmented six to ten ounces according to the quantity of hemp. But if you tie the hemp to the stone and allow them to fall freely from some height, do you believe that the hemp will press down upon the stone and thus accelerate its motion or do you think the motion will be retarded by a partial upward pressure? One always feels the pressure upon his shoulders when he prevents the motion of a load resting upon him; but if one descends just as rapidly as the load would fall how can it gravitate or press upon him? Do you not see that this would be the same as trying to strike a man with a lance when he is running away from you with a speed which is equal to, or even greater, than that with which you are following him? You must therefore conclude that, during free and natural fall, the small stone does not press upon the larger and consequently does not increase its weight as it does when at rest.

SIMPLICIO: But what if we should place the larger stone upon the smaller?

SALVIATI: Its weight would be increased if the larger stone moved more rapidly; but we have already concluded that when the small stone moves more slowly it retards to some extent the speed of the larger, so that the combination of the two, which is a heavier body than the larger of the two stones, would move less rapidly, a conclusion which is contrary to your hypothesis. We infer therefore that large and small bodies move with the same speed provided they are of the same specific gravity.

SIMPLICIO: Your discussion is really admirable; yet I do not find it easy to believe that a bird-shot falls as swiftly as a cannon ball.

SALVIATI: Why not say a grain of sand as rapidly as a grindstone? But, Simplicio, I trust you will not follow the example of many others who divert the discussion from its main intent and fasten upon some statement of mine which lacks a hair's-breadth of the truth and, under this hair, hide the fault of another which is as big as a ship's cable. Aristotle says that "an iron ball of one hundred pounds falling from a height of one hundred cubits reaches the ground before a one-pound ball has fallen a single cubit." I say that they arrive at the same time. You find, on making the experiment, that the larger outstrips the smaller by two finger-breadths, that is, when the larger has reached the ground, the other is short of it by two finger-breadths; now you would not hide behind these two fingers the ninety-nine cubits of Aristotle, nor would you mention my small error and at the same time pass over in silence his very large one. Aristotle declares that bodies of different weights, in the same medium, travel (in so far as their motion depends upon gravity) with speeds which are proportional to their weights; this he illustrates by use of bodies in which it is possible to perceive the pure and unadulterated effect of gravity, eliminating other considerations, for example, figure as being of small importance, influences which are greatly dependent upon the medium which modifies the single effect of gravity alone. Thus we observe that gold, the densest of all substances, when beaten out into a very thin leaf, goes floating through the air; the same thing happens with stone when ground into a very fine powder. But if you wish to maintain the general proposition you will have to show that the same ratio of speeds is preserved in the case of all heavy bodies, and that a stone of twenty pounds moves ten times as rapidly as one of two; but I claim that this is false and that, if they fall from a height of fifty or a hundred cubits, they will reach the earth at the same moment.

SIMPLICIO: Perhaps the result would be different if the fall took place not from a few cubits but from some thousands of cubits.

SALVIATI: If this were what Aristotle meant you would burden him with another error which would amount to a falsehood; because, since there is no such sheer height available on earth, it is clear that Aristotle could not have made the experiment; yet he wishes to give us the impression of his having performed it when he speaks of such an effect as one which we see.

SIMPLICIO: In fact, Aristotle does not employ this principle, but uses the other one which is not, I believe, subject to these same difficulties.

SALVIATI: But the one is as false as the other; and I am surprised that you yourself do not see the fallacy and that you do not perceive that if it were true that, in media of different densities and different resistances, such as water and air, one and the same body moved in air more rapidly than in water, in proportion as the density of water is greater than that of air, then it would follow that any body which falls through air ought also to fall through water. But this conclusion is false inasmuch as many bodies which descend in air not only do not descend in water, but actually rise.

SIMPLICIO: I do not understand the necessity of your inference; and in addition I will say that Aristotle discusses only those bodies which fall in both media, not those which fall in air but rise in water.

SALVIATI: The arguments which you advance for the Philosopher are such as he himself would have certainly avoided so as not to aggravate his first mistake. But tell me now whether the density of the water, or whatever it may be that retards the motion, bears a definite ratio to the density of air which is less retardative; and if so fix a value for it at your pleasure.

SIMPLICIO: Such a ratio does exist; let us assume it to be ten; then, for a body which falls in both these media, the speed in water will be ten times slower than in air.

SALVIATI: I shall now take one of those bodies which fall in air but not in water, say a wooden ball, and I shall ask you to assign to it any speed you please for its descent through air.

SIMPLICIO: Let us suppose it moves with a speed of twenty.

SALVIATI: Very well. Then it is clear that this speed bears to some smaller speed the same ratio as the density of water bears to that of air; and the value of this smaller speed is two. So that really if we follow exactly the assumption of Aristotle we ought to infer that the wooden ball which falls in air, a substance ten times less-resisting than water, with a speed of twenty would fall in water with a speed of two, instead of coming to the surface from the bottom as it does; unless perhaps you wish to reply, which I do not believe you will, that the rising of the wood through the water is the same as its falling with a speed of two. But since the wooden ball does not go to the bottom, I think you will agree with me that we can find a ball of another material, not wood, which does fall in water with a speed of two.

SIMPLICIO: Undoubtedly we can; but it must be of a substance considerably heavier than wood.

SALVIATI: That is it exactly. But if this second ball falls in water with a speed of two, what will be its speed of descent in air? If you hold to the rule of Aristotle you must reply that it will move at the rate of twenty; but twenty is the speed which you yourself have already assigned to the wooden ball; hence this and the other heavier ball will each move through air with the same speed. But now how does the Philosopher harmonize this result with his other, namely, that bodies of different weight move through the same medium with different speeds—speeds which are proportional to their weights? But without going into the matter more deeply, how have these common and obvious properties escaped your notice? Have you not observed that two bodies which fall in water, one with a speed a hundred times as great as that of the other, will fall in air with speeds so nearly equal that one will not surpass the other by as much as one hundredth part? Thus, for example, an egg made of marble will descend in water one hundred times more rapidly than a hen's egg, while in air falling from a height of twenty cubits the one will fall short of the other by less than four finger-breadths. In short, a heavy body which sinks through ten cubits of water in three hours will traverse ten cubits of air in one or two pulse-beats; and if the heavy body be a ball of lead it will easily traverse the ten cubits of water in less than double the time required for ten cubits of air. And here, I am sure, Simplicio, you find no ground for difference or objection. . . .

We have already seen that the difference of speed between bodies of different specific gravities is most marked in those media which are the most resistant: thus, in a medium of quicksilver, gold not merely sinks to the bottom more rapidly than lead but it is the only substance that will descend at all; all other metals and stones rise to the surface and float. On the other hand the variation of speed in air between balls of gold, lead, copper, porphyry, and other heavy materials is so slight that in a fall of 100 cubits a ball of gold would surely not outstrip one of copper by as much as four fingers. Having observed this I came to the conclusion that in a medium totally devoid of resistance all bodies would fall with the same speed. . . .

We pass now to a new and more discriminating consideration of naturally accelerated motion, such as that generally experienced by heavy falling bodies; following is the title and introduction.

Naturally Accelerated Motion. And first of all it seems desirable to find and explain a definition best fitting natural phenomena. For anyone may invent an arbitrary type of motion and discuss its properties; thus, for instance, some have imagined helices and conchoids as described by certain motions which are not met with in nature, and have very commendably established the properties which these curves possess in virtue of their definitions; but we have decided to consider the phenomena of bodies falling with an acceleration such as actually occurs in nature and to make this definition of accelerated motion exhibit the essential features of observed accelerated motions. And this, at last, after repeated efforts we trust we have succeeded in doing. In this belief we are confirmed mainly by the consideration that experimental results are seen to agree with and exactly correspond with those properties which have been, one after another, demonstrated by us. Finally, in the investigation of naturally accelerated motion we were led, by hand as it were, in following the habit and custom of nature herself, in all her various other processes, to employ only those means which are most common, simple and easy.

For I think no one believes that swimming or flying can be accomplished in a manner simpler or easier than that instinctively employed by fishes and birds.

When, therefore, I observe a stone initially at rest falling from an elevated position and continually acquiring new increments of speed, why should I not believe that such increases take place in a manner which is exceedingly simple and rather obvious to everybody? If now we examine the matter carefully we find no addition or increment more simple than that which repeats itself always in the same manner. This we readily understand when we consider the intimate relationship between time and motion; for just as uniformity of motion is defined by and conceived through equal times and equal spaces (thus we call a motion uniform when equal distances are traversed during equal time-intervals), so also we may, in a similar manner, through equal time-intervals, conceive additions of speed as taking place without complication; thus we may picture to our mind a motion as uniformly and continuously accelerated when, during any equal intervals of time whatever, equal increments of speed are given to it. Thus if any equal intervals of time whatever have elapsed, counting from the time at which the moving body left its position of rest and began to descend, the amount of speed acquired during the first two time-intervals will be double that acquired during the first time-interval alone; so the amount added during three of these time-intervals will be treble; and that in four, quadruple that of the first time-interval. To put the matter more clearly, if a body were to continue its motion with the same speed which it had acquired during the first time-interval and were to retain this same uniform speed, then its motion would be twice as slow as that which it would have if its velocity had been acquired during *two* time-intervals.

And thus, it seems, we shall not be far wrong if we put the increment of speed as proportional to the increment of time; hence the definition of motion which we are about to discuss may be stated as follows: A motion is said to be uniformly accelerated, when starting from rest, it acquires, during equal time-intervals, equal increments of speed.

SAGREDO: Although I can offer no rational objection to this or indeed to any other definition, devised by any author whomsoever, since all definitions are arbitrary, I may nevertheless without offense be allowed to doubt whether such a definition as the above, established in an abstract manner, corresponds to and describes that kind of accelerated motion which we meet in nature in the case of freely falling bodies. . . .

SALVIATI: This definition established, the Author makes a single assumption, namely, *The speeds acquired by one and the same body moving down planes of different inclinations are equal when the heights of these planes are equal.* By the height of an inclined plane we mean the perpendicular let fall from the upper end of the plane upon the horizontal line drawn through the lower end of the same plane. Thus, to illustrate, let the line *AB* be horizontal, and let the planes *CA* and *CD* be inclined to it; then the Author calls the perpendicular *CB* the "height" of the planes *CA* and *CD;* he supposes that the speeds acquired by one and the same body, descending along the planes *CA* and *CD* to the terminal points *A* and *D* are equal since the heights of these planes are the same, *CB;* and also it must be understood that this speed is that which would be acquired by the same body falling from *C* to *B*.

SAGREDO: Your assumption appears to me so reasonable that it ought to be conceded without question, provided of course there are no chance or outside resistances, and that the planes are hard and smooth, and that the figure of the moving body is perfectly round, so that neither plane nor moving body is rough. All resistance and opposition having been

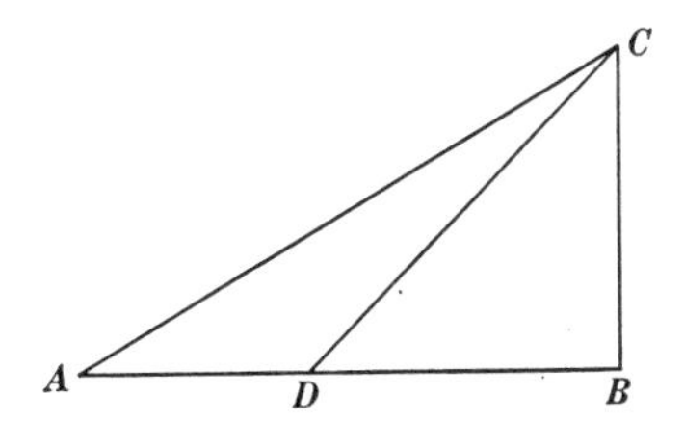

Figure 1

removed, my reason tells me at once that a heavy and perfectly round ball descending along the lines *CA*, *CD*, *CB* would reach the terminal points *A*, *D*, *B*, with equal momenta.

SALVIATI: Your words are very plausible; but I hope by experiment to increase the probability to an extent which shall be little short of a rigid demonstration.

Imagine this page to represent a vertical wall, with a nail driven into it; and from the nail let there be suspended a lead bullet of one or two ounces by means of a fine vertical thread, *AB*, say from four to six feet long, on this wall draw a horizontal line *DC*, at right angles to the vertical thread *AB*, which hangs about two finger-breadths in front of the wall. Now bring the thread *AB* with the attached ball into the position *AC* and set it free; first it will be observed to descend along the arc *CBD*, to pass the point *B*, and to travel along the arc *BD*, till it almost reaches the horizontal *CD*, a slight shortage being caused by the resistance of the air and the string; from this we may rightly infer that the ball in its descent through the arc *CB* acquired a momentum on reaching *B*, which was just sufficient to carry it through a similar arc *BD* to the same height. Having repeated this experiment many times, let us now drive a nail into the wall close to the perpendicular *AB*, say at *E* or *F*, so that it projects out some five or six finger-breadths in order that the thread, again

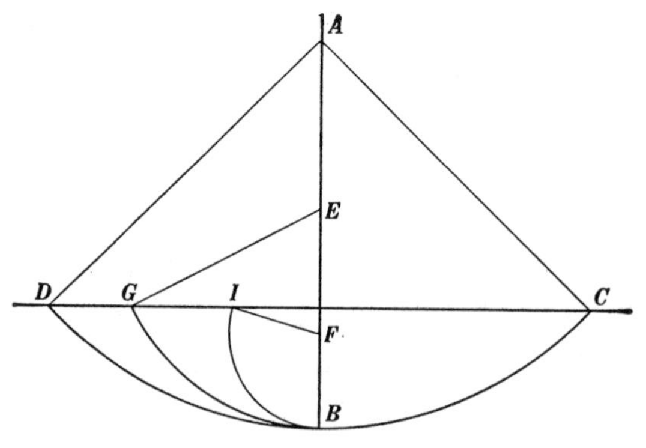

Figure 2

carrying the bullet through the arc *CB*, may strike upon the nail *E* when the bullet reaches *B*, and thus compel it to traverse the arc *BG*, described about *E* as center. From this we can see what can be done by the same momentum which previously starting at the same point *B* carried the same body through the arc *BD* to the horizontal *CD*. Now, gentlemen, you will observe with pleasure that the ball swings to the point *G* in the horizontal, and you would see the same thing happen if the obstacle were placed at some lower point, say at *F*, about which the ball would describe the arc *BI*, the rise of the ball always terminating exactly on the line *CD*. But when the nail is placed so low that the remainder of the thread below it will not reach to the height *CD* (which would happen if the nail were placed nearer *B* than to the intersection of *AB* with the horizontal *CD*) then the thread leaps over the nail and twists itself about it.

This experiment leaves no room for doubt as to the truth of our supposition; for since the two arcs *CB* and *DB* are equal and similarly placed, the momentum acquired by the fall through the arc *CB* is the same as that gained by fall through the arc *DB;* but the momentum acquired at *B*, owing to fall through *CB*, is able to lift the same body through the arc *BD;* therefore, the momentum acquired in the fall *BD* is equal to that which lifts the same body through the same arc from *B* to *D;* so, in general, every momentum acquired by fall through an arc is equal to that which can lift the same body through the same arc. But all these momenta which cause a rise through the arcs *BD*, *BG*, and *BI* are equal, since they are produced by the same momentum, gained by fall through *CB*, as experiment shows. Therefore all the momenta gained by fall through the arcs *DB*, *GB*, *IB* are equal.

SAGREDO: The argument seems to me so conclusive and the experiment so well adapted to establish the hypothesis that we may, indeed, consider it as demonstrated.

SALVIATI: I do not wish, Sagredo, that we trouble ourselves too much about this matter, since we are going to apply this principle mainly in motions which occur on plane surfaces, and not upon curved, along which acceleration varies in a manner greatly different from that which we have assumed for planes.

So that, although the above experiment shows us that the descent of the moving body through the arc *CB* confers upon it momentum just sufficient to carry it to the same height through any of the arcs *BD, BG, BI,* we are not able, by similar means, to show that the event would be identical in the case of a perfectly round ball descending along planes whose inclinations are respectively the same as the chords of these arcs. It seems likely, on the other hand, that, since these planes form angles at the point *B*, they will present an obstacle to the ball which has descended along the chord *CB*, and starts to rise along the chord *BD, BG, BI.*

In striking these planes some of its momentum will be lost and it will not be able to rise to the height of the line *CD;* but this obstacle, which interferes with the experiment, once removed, it is clear that the momentum (which gains in strength with descent) will be able to carry the body to the same height. Let us then, for the present, take this as a postulate, the absolute truth of which will be established when we find that the inferences from it correspond to and agree perfectly with experiment. The Author having assumed this single principle passes next to the propositions which he clearly demonstrates:

Proposition I. The time in which any space is traversed by a body starting from rest and uniformly accelerated is equal to the time in which that same space would be traversed by the same body moving at a uniform speed whose value is the mean of the highest speed and the speed just before acceleration began.

Proposition II. The spaces described by a body falling from rest with a uniformly accelerated motion are to each other as the squares of the time-intervals employed in traversing these distances.

SIMPLICIO: I am convinced that matters are as described, once having accepted the definition of uniformly accelerated motion. But as to whether this acceleration is that which one meets in nature in the case of falling bodies, I am still doubtful; and it seems to me, not only for my own sake but also for all those who think as I do, that this would be the proper moment to introduce one of those experiments—and there are many of them, I understand—which illustrate in several ways the conclusions reached.

SALVIATI: The request which you, as a man of science, make, is a very reasonable one; for this is the custom—and properly so—in those sciences where mathematical demonstrations are applied to natural phenomena, as is seen in the case of perspective, astronomy, mechanics, music, and others where the principles, once established by well-chosen experiments, become the foundations of the entire superstructure. I hope therefore it will not appear to be a waste of time if we discuss at considerable length this first and most fundamental question upon which hinge numerous consequences of which we have in this book only a small number, placed there by the Author, who has done so much to open a pathway hitherto closed to minds of speculative turn. So far as experiments go they have not been neglected by the Author; and often, in his company, I have attempted in the following manner to assure myself that the acceleration actually experienced by falling bodies is that above described.

A piece of wooden moulding or scantling, about 12 cubits long, half a cubit wide, and three finger-breadths thick, was taken; on its edge was cut a channel a little more than one finger in breadth; having made this groove very straight, smooth, and polished, and having lined it with parchment, also as smooth and polished as possible, we rolled along it a hard, smooth, and very round bronze ball. Having placed this board in a sloping position, by lifting one end some one or two cubits above the other, we rolled the ball, as I was just saying, along the channel, noting, in a manner presently to be described, the time required to make the descent. We repeated this experiment more than once in order to measure the time with an accuracy such that the deviation between two observations never exceeded one-tenth of a pulse-beat. Having performed this operation and having assured ourselves of its reliability, we now rolled the ball only one-quarter the length of the channel; and having measured the time of its descent, we found it precisely one-half of the former. Next we tried other distances, comparing the time for the whole length with that for the half, or with that for two-thirds, or three-fourths, or indeed for any fraction; in such experiments, repeated a full hundred times, we always found that the spaces traversed were to each other as the squares of the times, and this was true for all inclinations of the plane, i.e., of the channel, along which we rolled the ball. We also observed that the times of descent, for various inclinations of the plane, bore to one another precisely that ratio which, as we shall see later, the Author had predicted and demonstrated for them.

For the measurement of time, we employed a large vessel of water placed in an elevated position; to the bottom of this vessel was soldered a pipe of small diameter giving a thin jet of water, which we collected in a small glass during the time of each descent, whether for the whole length of the channel or for a part of its length; the water thus collected was weighed, after each descent, on a very accurate balance; the differences and ratios of these weights gave us the differences and ratios of the times, and this with such accuracy that although the operation was repeated many, many times, there was no appreciable discrepancy in the results.

SIMPLICIO: I would like to have been present at these experiments; but feeling confidence in the care with which you performed them, and in the fidelity with which you relate them, I am satisfied and accept them as true and valid.

Although Bertrand Russell is best known as a philosopher, his interests have always spanned a broad range: three of his earliest books were **German Social Democracy** (1896), **The Philosophy of Leibniz** (1899), and **Principles of Mathematics** (1903). His most famous work is perhaps his collaboration with A. N. Whitehead on the three volumes of **Principia mathematica** (1910), an analysis of mathematics as a branch of logic that is so thorough and intense that, despite its considerable influence, it is largely unread. His biographer, Alan Wood, has noted that **Principia mathematica** would not have been possible had Russell not had sufficient private means to permit him to concentrate on it, since research grants seldom go for unconventional studies: "It is hard, for example, to imagine Russell going to a local educational authority, explaining that 'I feel uneasy about the foundations of mathematics,' and getting enough money to live on for fifteen years while he investigated them."

The Rise of Science, concerned with the birth of the modern scientific viewpoint in the seventeenth century, is a chapter in Russell's magnificent **A History of Western Philosophy.** His purpose in writing the **History** was "to exhibit philosophy as an integral part of social and political life: not as the isolated speculations of remarkable individuals, but as both an effect and a cause of the character of the various communities in which different systems flourished." Why a concern for science in a history of philosophy? Simply because

> . . . the conceptions of life and the world which we call "philosophical" are a product of two factors: one, inherited religious and ethical conceptions; the other, the sort of investigation which may be called "scientific," using this word in its broadest sense. Individual philosophers have differed widely in regard to the proportions in which these two factors entered into their systems, but it is the presence of both, in some degree, that characterizes philosophy. . . . Philosophy, as I shall understand the word, is something intermediate between theology and science. Like theology, it consists of speculations on matters as to which definite knowledge has, so far, been unascertainable; but like science, it appeals to human reason rather than to authority, whether that of tradition or that of revelation. All **definite** knowledge—so I should contend—belongs to science; all **dogma** as to what surpasses definite knowledge belongs to theology. But between theology and science there is a No Man's Land, exposed to attack from both sides; this No Man's Land is philosophy.

For the details of Russell's life and career the reader is referred to Wood's **Bertrand Russell: The Passionate Skeptic** (Simon and Schuster, 1958), and for a briefer impression to T. S. Eliot's **Mr. Apollinax.**

Bertrand Russell

THE RISE OF SCIENCE

Almost everything that distinguishes the modern world from earlier centuries is attributable to science, which achieved its most spectacular triumphs in the seventeenth century. The Italian Renaissance, though not medieval, is not modern; it is more akin to the best age of Greece. The sixteenth century, with its absorption in theology, is more medieval than the world of Machiavelli. The modern world, so far as mental outlook is concerned, begins in the seventeenth century. No Italian of the Renaissance would have been unintelligible to Plato or Aristotle; Luther would have horrified Thomas Aquinas, but would not have been difficult for him to understand. With the seventeenth century it is different: Plato and Aristotle, Aquinas and Occam, could not have made head or tail of Newton.

The new conceptions that science introduced profoundly influenced modern philosophy. Descartes, who was in a sense the founder of modern philosophy, was himself one of the creators of seventeenth-century science. Something must be said about the methods and results of astronomy and physics before the mental atmosphere of the time in which modern philosophy began can be understood.

Four great men—Copernicus, Kepler, Galileo, and Newton—are pre-eminent in the creation of science. Of these, Copernicus belongs to the sixteenth century, but in his own time he had little influence.

Copernicus (1473–1543) was a Polish ecclesiastic, of unimpeachable orthodoxy. In his youth he travelled in Italy, and absorbed something of the atmosphere of the Renaissance. In 1500 he had a lectureship or professorship of mathematics in Rome, but in 1503 he returned to his native land, where he was a canon of Frauenburg. Much of his time seems to have been spent in combating the Germans and reforming the currency, but his leisure was devoted to astronomy. He came early to believe that the sun is at the centre of the universe, and that the earth has a twofold motion: a diurnal rotation, and an annual revolution about the sun. Fear of ecclesiastical censure led him to delay publication of his views, though he allowed them to become known. His chief work, *De revolutionibus orbium cœlestium*, was published in the year of his death (1543), with a preface by his friend Osiander saying that the heliocentric theory was only put forward as a hypothesis. It is uncertain how far Copernicus sanctioned this statement, but the question is not very important, as he himself made similar statements in the body of the book. The book is dedicated to the Pope, and escaped official Catholic condemnation until the time of Galileo. The Church in the lifetime of Copernicus was more liberal than it became after the Council of Trent, the Jesuits, and the revived Inquisition had done their work.

The atmosphere of Copernicus's work is not modern; it might rather be described as Pythagorean. He takes it as axiomatic that all celestial motions must be circular and uniform, and like the Greeks he allows himself to be influenced by æsthetic motives. There are still epicycles in his system, though their centres are at the sun, or, rather, near the sun. The fact that the sun is not exactly in the centre marred the simplicity of his theory. He does not seem to have known of Aristarchus's heliocentric theory, but there is nothing in his speculations that could not have occurred to a Greek astronomer. What was important in his work was the dethronement of the earth from its geometrical pre-eminence.

In the long run, this made it difficult to give to man the cosmic importance assigned to him in the Christian theology, but such consequences of his theory would not have been accepted by Copernicus, whose orthodoxy was sincere, and who protested against the view that his theory contradicted the Bible.

There were genuine difficulties in the Copernican theory. The greatest of these was the absence of stellar parallax. If the earth at any one point of its orbit is 186,000,000 miles from the point at which it will be in six months, this ought to cause a shift in the apparent positions of the stars, just as a ship at sea which is due north from one point of the coast will not be due north from another. No parallax was observed, and Copernicus rightly inferred that the fixed stars must be very much more remote than the sun. It was not till the nineteenth century that the technique of measurement became sufficiently precise for stellar parallax to be observed, and then only in the case of a few of the nearest stars.

Another difficulty arose as regards falling bodies. If the earth is continually rotating from west to east, a body dropped from a height ought not to fall to a point vertically below its starting-point, but to a point somewhat further west, since the earth will have slipped away a certain distance during the time of the fall. To this difficulty the answer was found by Galileo's law of inertia, but in the time of Copernicus no answer was forthcoming.

There is an interesting book by E. A. Burtt, called *The Metaphysical Foundations of Modern Physical Science* (1925), which sets forth with much force the many unwarrantable assumptions made by the men who founded modern science. He points out quite truly that there were in the time of Copernicus no known facts which compelled the adoption of his system, and several which militated against it. "Contemporary empiricists, had they lived in the sixteenth century, would have been the first to scoff out of court the new philosophy of the universe." The general purpose of the book is to discredit modern science by suggesting that its discoveries were lucky accidents springing by chance from superstitions as gross as those of the Middle Ages.

I think this shows a misconception of the scientific attitude: it is not *what* the man of science believes that distinguishes him, but *how* and *why* he believes it. His beliefs are tentative, not dogmatic; they are based on evidence, not on authority or intuition. Copernicus was right to call his theory a hypothesis; his opponents were wrong in thinking new hypotheses undesirable.

The men who founded modern science had two merits which are not necessarily found together: immense patience in observation, and great boldness in framing hypotheses. The second of these merits had belonged to the earliest Greek philosophers; the first existed, to a considerable degree, in the later astronomers of antiquity. But no one among the ancients, except perhaps Aristarchus, possessed both merits, and no one in the Middle Ages possessed either. Copernicus, like his great successors, possessed both. He knew all that could be known, with the instruments existing in his day, about the apparent motions of the heavenly bodies on the celestial sphere, and he perceived that the diurnal rotation of the earth was a more economical hypothesis than the revolution of all the celestial spheres. According to modern views, which regard all motion as relative, simplicity is the only gain resulting from his hypothesis, but this was not his view or that of his contemporaries. As regards the earth's annual revolution, there was again a simplification, but not so notable a one as in the case of the diurnal rotation. Copernicus still needed epicycles, though fewer than were needed in the Ptolemaic system. It was not until Kepler discovered his laws that the new theory acquired its full simplicity.

Apart from the revolutionary effect on cosmic imagination, the great merits of the new astronomy were two: first, the recognition that what had been believed since ancient times might be false; second, that the test of scientific truth is patient collection of facts, combined with bold guessing as to laws binding the facts together. Neither merit is so fully developed in Copernicus as in his successors, but both are already present in a high degree in his work.

Some of the men to whom Copernicus communicated his theory were German Lutherans, but when Luther came to know of it, he was profoundly shocked. "People give ear," he said, "to an upstart astrologer who strove to show that the earth revolves, not the heavens or the firmament, the sun and the moon. Whoever wishes to appear clever must devise some new system, which of all systems is of course the very best. This fool wishes to reverse the entire science of astronomy; but sacred Scripture tells us that Joshua commanded the sun to stand still, and not the earth." Calvin, similarly, demolished Copernicus with the text: "The world also is stablished, that it cannot be moved" (Ps. XCIII, 1), and exclaimed: "Who will venture to place the authority of Copernicus above that of the Holy Spirit?" Protestant clergy were as least as bigoted as Catholic ecclesiastics; nevertheless there soon came to be much more liberty of speculation in Protestant than in Catholic countries, because in Protestant countries the clergy had less power. The important aspect of Protestantism was schism, not heresy, for schism led to national Churches, and national Churches were not strong enough to control the lay government. This was wholly a gain, for the Churches, everywhere, opposed as long as they could practically every innovation that made for an increase of happiness or knowledge here on earth.

Copernicus was not in a position to give any conclusive evidence in favour of his hypothesis, and for a long time astronomers rejected it. The next astronomer of importance was Tycho Brahe (1546–1601), who adopted an intermediate position: he held that the sun and moon go round the earth, but the planets go round the sun. As regards theory he was not very original. He gave, however, two good reasons against Aristotle's view that everything above the moon is unchanging. One of these was the appearance of a new star in 1572, which was found to have no daily parallax, and must therefore be more distant than the moon. The other reason was derived from observation of comets, which were also found to be distant. The reader will remember Aristotle's doctrine that change and decay are confined to the sublunary sphere; this, like everything else that Aristotle said on scientific subjects, proved an obstacle to progress.

The importance of Tycho Brahe was not as a theorist, but as an observer, first under the patronage of the king of Denmark, then under the Emperor Rudolf II. He made a star catalogue, and noted the positions of the planets throughout many years. Towards the end of his life Kepler, then a young man, became his assistant. To Kepler his observations were invaluable.

Kepler (1571–1630) is one of the most notable examples of what can be achieved by patience without much in the way of genius. He was the first important astronomer after Copernicus to adopt the heliocentric theory, but Tycho Brahe's data showed that it could not be quite right in the form given to it by Copernicus. He was influenced by Pythagoreanism, and more or less fancifully inclined to sun-worship, though a good Protestant. These motives no doubt gave him a bias in favour of the heliocentric hypothesis. His Pythagoreanism also inclined him to follow Plato's *Timaeus* in supposing that cosmic significance must attach to the five regular solids. He used them to suggest hypotheses to his mind; at last, by good luck, one of these worked.

Kepler's great achievement was the discovery of his three laws of planetary motion. Two of these he published in 1609, and the third in 1619. His first law states: The planets describe elliptic orbits, of which the sun occupies one focus. His second law states: The line joining a planet to the sun sweeps out equal areas in equal times. His third law states: The square of the period of revolution of a planet is proportioned to the cube of its average distance from the sun.

Something must be said in explanation of the importance of these laws.

The first two laws, in Kepler's time, could only be *proved* in the case of Mars; as regards the other planets, the observations were compatible with them, but not such as to establish them definitely. It was not long, however, before decisive confirmation was found.

The discovery of the first law, that the planets move in ellipses, required a greater effort of emancipation from tradition than a modern man can easily realize. The one thing upon which all astronomers, without exception, had been agreed, was that all celestial motions are circular, or compounded of circular motions. Where circles were found inadequate to explain planetary motions, epicycles were used. An epicycle is the curve traced by a point on a circle which rolls on another circle. For example: take a big wheel and fasten it flat on the ground; take a smaller wheel which has a nail through it, and roll the smaller wheel (also flat on the ground) round the big wheel, with the point of the nail touching the ground. Then the mark of the nail in the ground will trace out an epicycle. The orbit of the moon, in relation to the sun, is roughly of this kind: approximately, the earth describes a circle round the sun, and the moon meanwhile describes a circle round the earth. But this is only an approximation. As observation grew more exact, it was found that no system of epicycles would exactly fit the facts. Kepler's hypothesis, he found, was far more closely in accord with the recorded positions of Mars than was that of Ptolemy, or even that of Copernicus.

The substitution of ellipses for circles involved the abandonment of the æsthetic bias which had governed astronomy ever since Pythagoras. The circle was a perfect figure, and the celestial orbs were perfect bodies—originally gods, and even in Plato and Aristotle closely related to gods. It seemed obvious that a perfect body must move in a perfect figure. Moreover, since the heavenly bodies move freely, without being pushed or pulled, their motion must be "natural." Now it was easy to suppose that there is something "natural" about a circle, but not about an ellipse. Thus many deep-seated prejudices had to be discarded before Kepler's first law could be accepted. No ancient, not even Aristarchus of Samos, had anticipated such an hypothesis.

The second law deals with the varying velocity of the planet at different points of its orbit. If S is the sun, and P_1, P_2, P_3, P_4, P_5 are successive positions of the planet at equal intervals of time—say at intervals of a month—then Kepler's law states that the areas

P_1SP_2, P_2SP_3, P_3SP_4, P_4SP_5 are all equal. The planet therefore moves fastest when it is nearest to the sun, and slowest when it is farthest from it. This, again, was shocking; a planet ought to be too stately to hurry at one time and dawdle at another.

The third law was important because it compared the movements of different planets, whereas the first two laws dealt with the several planets singly. The third law says: If r is the average distance of a planet from the sun, and T is the length of its year, then r^3 divided by T^2 is the same for all the different planets. This law afforded the proof (as far as the solar system is concerned) of Newton's law of the inverse square for gravitation. But of this we shall speak later.

Galileo (1564–1642) is the greatest of the founders of modern science, with the possible exception of Newton. He was born on about the day on which Michelangelo died, and he died in the year in which Newton was born. I commend these facts to those (if any) who still believe in metempsychosis. He is important as an astronomer, but perhaps even more as the founder of dynamics.

Galileo first discovered the importance of *acceleration* in dynamics. "Acceleration" means change of velocity, whether in magnitude or direction; thus a body moving uniformly in a circle has at all times an acceleration towards the centre of the circle. In the language that had been customary before his time, we might say that he treated uniform motion in a straight line as alone "natural," whether on earth or in the heavens. It had been thought "natural" for heavenly bodies to move in circles, and for terrestrial bodies to move in straight lines; but moving terrestrial bodies, it was thought, would gradually cease to move if they were let alone. Galileo held, as against this view, that every body, if let alone, will continue to move in a straight line with uniform velocity; any change, either in the rapidity or the direction of motion, requires to be explained as due to the action of some "force." This principle was enunciated by Newton as the "first law of motion." It is also called the law of inertia. I shall return to its purport later, but first something must be said as to the detail of Galileo's discoveries.

Galileo was the first to establish the law of falling bodies. This law, given the concept of "acceleration," is of the utmost simplicity. It says that, when a body is falling freely, its acceleration is constant, except in so far as the resistance of the air may interfere; further, the acceleration is the same for all bodies, heavy or light, great or small. The complete proof of this law was not possible until the air pump had been invented, which was about 1654. After this, it was possible to observe bodies falling in what was practically a vacuum, and it was found that feathers fell as fast as lead. What Galileo proved was that there is no measurable difference between large and small lumps of the same substance. Until his time it had been supposed that a large lump of lead would fall much quicker than a small one, but Galileo proved by experiment that this is not the case. Measurement, in his day, was not such an accurate business as it has since become; nevertheless he arrived at the true law of falling bodies. If a body is falling freely in a vacuum, its velocity increases at a constant rate. At the end of the first second, its velocity will be 32 feet per second; at the end of another second, 64 feet per second; at the end of the third, 96 feet per second; and so on. The acceleration, i.e., the rate at which the velocity increases, is always the same; in each second, the increase of velocity is (approximately) 32 feet per second.

Galileo also studied projectiles, a subject of importance to his employer, the duke of Tuscany. It had been thought that a projectile fired horizontally will move horizontally for a while, and then suddenly begin to fall vertically. Galileo showed that, apart from the resistance of the air, the horizontal velocity would remain constant, in accordance with the law of inertia, but a vertical velocity would be added, which would grow according to the law of falling bodies. To find out how the projectile will move during some short time, say a second, after it has been in flight for some time, we proceed as follows: First, if it were not falling, it would cover a certain horizontal distance, equal to that which it covered in the first second of its flight. Second, if it were not moving horizontally, but merely falling, it would fall vertically with a velocity proportional to the time since the flight began. In fact, its change of place is what it would be if it first moved horizontally for a second with the initial velocity, and then fell vertically for a second with a velocity proportional to the time during which it has been in flight. A simple calculation shows that its consequent course is a parabola, and this is confirmed by observation except in so far as the resistance of the air interferes.

The above gives a simple instance of a principle which proved immensely fruitful in dynamics, the principle that, when several forces act simultaneously, the effect is as if each acted in turn. This is part of a more general principle called the parallelogram law. Suppose, for example, that you are on the deck of a moving ship, and you walk across the deck. While you are walking the ship has moved on, so that, in relation to the water, you have moved both forward and across the direction of the ship's motion. If you want to know where you will have got to in relation to the water, you may suppose that first you stood still while the ship moved, and then, for an equal time, the ship stood still while you walked across it. The same principle applies to forces. This makes it possible to work out the total effect of a number of forces, and makes it feasible to analyse physical phenomena, discovering the separate laws of the several forces to which moving bodies are subject. It was Galileo who introduced this immensely fruitful method.

In what I have been saying, I have tried to speak, as nearly as possible, in the language of the seventeenth century. Modern language is different in important respects, but to explain what the seventeenth century achieved it is desirable to adopt its modes of expression for the time being.

The law of inertia explained a puzzle which, before Galileo, the Copernican system had been unable to explain. As observed above, if you drop a stone from the top of a tower, it will fall at the foot of the tower, not somewhat to the west of it; yet, if the earth is rotating, it ought to have slipped away a certain distance during the fall of the stone. The reason this does not happen is that the stone retains the velocity of rotation which, before being dropped, it shared with everything else on the earth's surface. In fact, if the tower were high enough, there would be the opposite effect to that expected by the opponents of Copernicus. The top of the tower, being further from the centre of the earth than the bottom, is moving faster, and therefore the stone should fall slightly to the east of the foot of the tower. This effect, however, would be too slight to be measurable.

Galileo ardently adopted the heliocentric system; he corresponded with Kepler, and accepted his discoveries. Having heard that a Dutchman had lately invented a telescope, Galileo made one himself, and very quickly discovered a number of important things. He found that the Milky Way consists of a multitude of separate stars. He observed the phases of Venus, which Copernicus knew to be implied by his theory, but which the naked eye was unable to perceive. He discovered the satellites of Jupiter, which, in honour of his employer, he called "sidera medicea." It was found that these satellites obey Kepler's laws. There was, however, a difficulty. There had always been seven heavenly bodies, the five planets and the sun and moon; now seven is a sacred number. Is not the Sabbath the seventh day? Were there not the seven-branched candlesticks and the seven churches of Asia? What, then, could be more appropriate than that there should be seven heavenly bodies? But if we have to add Jupiter's four moons, that makes eleven—a number which has no mystic properties. On this ground the traditionalists denounced the telescope, refused to look through it, and maintained that it revealed only delusions. Galileo wrote to Kepler wishing they could have a good laugh together at the stupidity of "the mob"; the rest of his letter makes it plain that "the mob" consisted of the professors of philosophy, who tried to conjure away Jupiter's moons, using "logic-chopping arguments as though they were magical incantations."

Galileo, as every one knows, was condemned by the Inquisition, first privately in 1616, and then publicly in 1633, on which latter occasion he recanted, and promised never again to maintain that the earth rotates or revolves. The Inquisition was successful in putting an end to science in Italy, which did not revive there for centuries. But it failed to prevent men of science from adopting the heliocentric theory, and did considerable damage to the Church by its stupidity. Fortunately there were Protestant countries, where the clergy, however anxious to do harm to science, were unable to gain control of the State.

Newton (1642–1727) achieved the final and complete triumph for which Copernicus, Kepler, and Galileo had prepared the way. Starting from his three laws of motion—of which the first two are due to Galileo—he proved that Kepler's three laws are equivalent to the proposition that every planet, at every moment, has an acceleration towards the sun which varies inversely as the square of the distance from the sun. He showed that accelerations towards the earth and the sun, following the same formula, explain the moon's motion, and that the acceleration of falling bodies on the earth's surface is again related to that of the moon according to the inverse square law. He defined "force" as the cause of change of motion, i.e., of acceleration. He was thus able to enunciate his law of universal gravitation: "Every body attracts every other with a force directly proportional to the product of their masses and inversely proportional to the square of the distance between them." From this formula he was able to deduce everything in planetary theory: the motions of the planets and their satellites, the orbits of comets, the tides. It appeared later that even the minute departures from elliptical orbits on the part of the planets were deducible from Newton's law. The triumph was so complete that Newton was in danger of becoming another Aristotle, and imposing an insuperable barrier to progress. In England, it was not till a century after his death that men freed themselves from his authority sufficiently to do important original work in the subjects of which he had treated.

The seventeenth century was remarkable, not only in astronomy and dynamics, but in many other ways connected with science.

Take first the question of scientific instruments. The compound microscope was invented just before the seventeenth century, about 1590. The telescope was invented in 1608, by a Dutchman named Lippershey, though it was Galileo who first made serious use of it for scientific purposes. Galileo also invented the thermometer—at least, this seems most probable. His pupil Toricelli invented the barometer. Guericke (1602–86) invented the air pump. Clocks, though not new, were greatly improved in the seventeenth century, largely by the work of Galileo. Owing to these inventions, scientific observation became immensely more exact and more extensive than it had been at any former time.

Next, there was important work in other sciences than astronomy and dynamics. Gilbert (1540–1603) published his great book on the magnet in 1600. Harvey (1578–1657) discovered the circulation of the blood, and published his discovery in 1628. Leeuwenhoek (1632–1723) discovered spermatozoa, though another man, Stephen Hamm, had discovered them, apparently, a few months earlier; Leeuwenhoek also discovered protozoa or unicellular organisms, and even bacteria. Robert Boyle (1627–91) was, as children were taught when I was young, "the father of chemistry and son of the Earl of Cork"; he is now chiefly remembered on account of "Boyle's Law," that in a given quantity of gas at a given temperature, pressure is inversely proportional to volume.

I have hitherto said nothing of the advances in pure mathematics, but these were very great indeed, and were indispensable to much of the work in the physical sciences. Napier published his invention of logarithms in 1614. Co-ordinate geometry resulted from the work of several seventeenth-century mathematicians, among whom the greatest contribution was made by Descartes. The differential and integral calculus was invented independently by Newton and Leibniz; it is the instrument for almost all higher mathematics. These are only the most outstanding achievements in pure mathematics; there were innumerable others of great importance.

The consequence of the scientific work we have been considering was that the outlook of educated men was completely transformed. At the beginning of the century, Sir Thomas Browne took part in trials for witchcraft; at the end, such a thing would have been impossible. In Shakespeare's time, comets were still portents; after the publication of Newton's *Principia* in 1687, it was known that he and Halley had calculated the orbits of certain comets, and that they were as obedient as the planets to the law of gravitation. The reign of law had established its hold on men's imaginations, making such things as magic and sorcery incredible. In 1700 the mental outlook of educated men was completely modern; in 1600, except among a very few, it was still largely medieval.

In the remainder of this chapter I shall try to state briefly the philosophical beliefs which appeared to follow from seventeenth-century science, and some of the respects in which modern science differs from that of Newton.

The first thing to note is the removal of almost all traces of animism from the laws of physics. The Greeks, though they did not say so explicitly, evidently considered the power of movement a sign of life. To common-sense observation it seems that animals move themselves, while dead matter only moves when impelled by an external force. The soul of an animal, in Aristotle, has various functions, and one of them is to move the animal's body. The sun and planets, in Greek thinking, are apt to be gods, or at least regulated and moved by gods. Anaxagoras thought otherwise, but was impious. Democritus thought otherwise, but was neglected, except by the Epicureans, in favour of Plato and Aristotle. Aristotle's forty-seven or fifty-five unmoved movers are divine spirits, and are the ultimate source of all the motion in the universe. Left to itself, any inanimate body would soon become motionless; thus the operation of soul on matter has to be continuous if motion is not to cease.

All this was changed by the first law of motion. Lifeless matter, once set moving, will continue to move for ever unless stopped by some external cause. Moreover the external causes of change of motion turned out to be themselves material, whenever they could be definitely ascertained. The solar system, at any rate, was kept going by its own momentum and its own laws; no outside interference was needed. There might still seem to be need of God to set the mechanism working; the planets, according to Newton, were originally hurled by the hand of God. But when He had done this, and decreed the law of gravitation, everything went on by itself without further need of divine intervention. When Laplace suggested that the same forces which are now operative might have caused the planets to grow out of the sun, God's share in the course of nature was pushed still further back. He might remain as Creator, but even that was doubtful, since it was not clear that the world had a beginning in time. Although most of the men of science were models of piety, the outlook suggested by their work was disturbing to orthodoxy, and the theologians were quite justified in feeling uneasy.

Another thing that resulted from science was a profound change in the conception of man's place in the universe. In the medieval world, the earth was the centre of the heavens, and everything had a purpose concerned with man. In the Newtonian world, the earth was a minor planet of a not specially distinguished star; astronomical distances were so vast that the earth, in comparison, was a mere pin-point. It seemed unlikely that this immense apparatus was all designed for the good of certain small creatures on this pin-point. Moreover purpose, which had since Aristotle formed an intimate part of the conception of science, was not thrust out of scientific procedure. Any one might still believe that the heavens exist to declare the glory of God, but no one could let this belief intervene in an astronomical calculation. The world might have a purpose, but purposes could no longer enter into scientific explanations.

The Copernican theory should have been humbling to human pride, but in fact the contrary effect was produced, for the triumphs of science revived human pride. The dying ancient world had been obsessed with a sense of sin, and had bequeathed this as an oppression to the Middle Ages. To be humble before God was both right and prudent, for God would punish pride. Pestilences, floods, earthquakes, Turks, Tartars, and comets perplexed the gloomy centuries, and it was felt that only greater and greater humility would avert these real or threatened calamities. But it became impossible to remain humble when men were achieving such triumphs:

> Nature and Nature's laws lay hid in night.
> God said "Let Newton be," and all was light.

And as for damnation, surely the Creator of so vast a universe had something better to think about than sending men to hell for minute theological errors. Judas Iscariot might be damned, but not Newton, though he were an Arian.

There were of course many other reasons for self-satisfaction. The Tartars had been confined to Asia, and the Turks were ceasing to be a menace. Comets had been humbled by Halley, and as for earthquakes, though they were still formidable, they were so interesting that men of science could hardly regret them. Western Europeans were growing rapidly richer, and were becoming lords of all the world: they had conquered North and South America, they were powerful in Africa and India, respected in China and feared in Japan. When to all this were added the triumphs of science, it is no wonder that the men of the seventeenth century felt themselves to be fine fellows, not the miserable sinners that they still proclaimed themselves on Sundays.

There are some respects in which the concepts of modern theoretical physics differ from those of the Newtonian system. To begin with, the conception of "force," which is prominent in the seventeenth century, has been found to be superfluous. "Force," in Newton, is the cause of change of motion, whether in magnitude or direction. The motion of cause is regarded as important, and force is conceived imaginatively as the sort of thing that we experience when we push or pull. For this reason it was considered an objection to gravitation that it acted at a distance, and Newton himself conceded that there must be some medium by which it was transmitted. Gradually it was found that all the equations could be written down without bringing in forces. What was observable was a certain relation between acceleration and configuration; to say that this relation was brought about by the intermediacy of "force" was to add nothing to our knowledge. Observation shows that planets have at all times an acceleration towards the sun, which varies inversely as the square of their distance from it. To say that this is due to the "force" of gravitation is merely verbal, like saying that opium makes people sleep because it has a dormitive virtue. The modern physicist, therefore, merely states formulæ which determine accelerations, and avoids the word "force" altogether. "Force" was the faint ghost of the vitalist view as to the causes of motions, and gradually the ghost has been exorcized.

Until the coming of quantum mechanics, nothing happened to modify in any degree what is the essential purport of the first two laws of motion, namely this: that the laws of dynamics are to be stated in terms of accelerations. In this respect, Copernicus and Kepler are still to be classed with the ancients; they sought laws stating the shapes of the orbits of the heavenly bodies. Newton made it clear that laws stated in this form could never be more than approximate. The planets do not move in *exact* ellipses, because of the perturbations caused by the attractions of other planets. Nor is the orbit of a planet ever exactly repeated, for the same reason. But the law of gravitation, which deals with accelerations, was very simple, and was thought to be quite exact until two hundred years after Newton's time. When it was emended by Einstein, it still remained a law dealing with accelerations.

It is true that the conservation of energy is a law dealing with velocities, not accelerations. But in calculations which use this law it is still accelerations that have to be employed.

As for the changes introduced by quantum mechanics, they are very profound, but still, to some degree, a matter of controversy and uncertainty.

There is one change from the Newtonian philosophy which must be mentioned now, and that is the abandonment of absolute space and time. The reader will remember a mention of this question in connection with Democritus. Newton believed in a space composed of points, and a time composed of instants, which had an existence independent of the bodies and events that occupied them. As regards space, he had an empirical argument to support his view, namely that physical phenomena enable us to distinguish absolute rotation. If the water in a bucket is rotated, it climbs up the sides and is depressed in the centre; but if the bucket is rotated while the water is not, there is no such effect. Since his day, the experiment of Foucault's pendulum has been devised, giving what has been considered a demonstration of the earth's rotation. Even on the most modern views, the question of absolute rotation presents difficulties. If all motion is relative, the difference between the hypothesis that the earth rotates and the hypothesis that the heavens revolve is purely verbal; it is no more than the difference between "John is the father of James" and "James is the son of John." But if the heavens revolve, the stars move faster than light, which is considered impossible. It cannot be said that the modern answers to this difficulty are completely satisfying, but they are sufficiently satisfying to cause almost all physicists to accept the view that motion and space are purely relative. This, combined with the amalgamation of space and time into space-time, has considerably altered our view of the universe from that which resulted from the work of Galileo and Newton. But of this, as of quantum theory, I will say no more at this time.

For so fundamental a concept in physical science, conservation of energy had a curiously delayed recognition. Not that suspicions of the true nature of heat did not antedate by many years the formal discarding of the caloric theory of heat, but they were not taken seriously by the elders of science, and the identity of heat and energy had to be literally forced upon them. The first explicit statement of conservation of energy was made by a German physician, Robert Mayer, in 1842. Nobody paid attention to his work, he received scant credit for priority when the idea was at last accepted, and he went mad. Less unhappy is the story of James Prescott Joule, who inherited a brewery. The MKS unit of energy bears his name owing to his careful measurements of the mechanical equivalent of heat. The final independent discoverer of conservation of energy was Hermann von Helmholtz, the greatest of the three, who applied it quantitatively to problems in electricity, magnetism, chemistry, and astronomy in addition to the more obvious fields of mechanics and heat.

The complex of ideas involved in conservation of energy is described with particular clarity in **The Evolution of Physics** (Simon and Schuster, 1938), from which the following selection is taken. In this book Einstein and his distinguished collaborator Infeld set out "to sketch in broad outline the attempts of the human mind to find a connection between the world of ideas and the world of phenomena. We have tried to show the active forces which compel science to invent ideas corresponding to the reality of our world." Despite its age, **The Evolution of Physics** may still be read with profit. Einstein, the greatest physicist since Newton, died in 1955. Infeld is still active in theoretical physics in his native Poland.

Albert Einstein and Leopold Infeld

CONSERVATION OF ENERGY

The most fundamental concepts in the description of heat phenomena are *temperature* and *heat.* It took an unbelievably long time in the history of science for these two to be distinguished, but once this distinction was made, rapid progress resulted. Although these concepts are now familiar to everyone we shall examine them closely, emphasizing the differences between them.

Our sense of touch tells us quite definitely that one body is hot and another cold. But this is a purely qualitative criterion, not sufficient for a quantitative description and sometimes even ambiguous. This is shown by a well-known experiment: we have three vessels containing, respectively, cold, warm and hot water. If we dip one hand into the cold water and the other into the hot, we receive a message from the first that it is cold and from the second that it is hot. If we then dip both hands into the same warm water we receive two contradictory messages, one from each hand. For the same reason an Eskimo and a native of some equatorial country meeting in New York on a spring day would hold different opinions as to whether the climate was hot or cold. We settle all such questions by the use of a thermometer, an instrument designed in a primitive form by Galileo. Here again that familiar name! The use of a thermometer is based on some obvious physical assumptions. We shall recall them by quoting a few lines from lectures given about a hundred and fifty years ago by Black, who contributed a great deal toward clearing up the difficulties connected with the two concepts, heat and temperature:

> By the use of this instrument we have learned, that if we take 1000, or more, different kinds of matter, such as metals, stones, salts, woods, feathers, wool, water and a variety of other fluids, although they be all at first of different *heats*, let them be placed together in the same room without a fire, and into which the sun does not shine, the heat will be communicated from the hotter of these bodies to the colder, during some hours perhaps, or the course of a day, at the end of which time, if we apply a thermometer to them all in succession, it will point precisely to the same degree.

The italicized world *heats* should, according to present-day nomenclature, be replaced by the word *temperatures.*

A physician taking the thermometer from a sick man's mouth might reason like this: "The thermometer indicates its own temperature by the length of its column of mercury. We assume that the length of the mercury column increases in proportion to the increase in temperature. But the thermometer was for a few minutes in contact with my patient, so that both patient and thermometer have the same temperature. I conclude, therefore, that my patient's temperature is that registered on the thermometer." The doctor probably acts mechanically, but he applies physical principles without thinking about it.

But does the thermometer contain the same amount of heat as the body of the man? Of course not. To assume that two bodies contain equal quantities of heat just because their temperatures are equal would, as Black remarked, be

> . . . taking a very hasty view of the subject. It is confounding the quantity of heat in different bodies with its general strength or intensity, though it is plain that these are two different things, and should always be distinguished, when we are thinking of the distribution of heat.

An understanding of this distinction can be gained by considering a very simple experiment. A pound of water placed over a gas flame takes some time to change from room temperature to the boiling point. A much longer time is required for heating twelve pounds, say, of water in the same vessel by means of the same flame. We interpret this fact as indicating that now more of "something" is needed and we call this "something"—*heat.*

A further important concept, *specific heat,* is gained by the following experiment: let one vessel contain a pound of water and another a pound of mercury, both to be heated in the same way. The mercury gets hot much more quickly than the water, showing that less "heat" is needed to raise the temperature by one degree. In general, different amounts of "heat" are required to change by one degree, say from 40 to 41 degrees Fahrenheit, the temperatures of different substances such as water, mercury, iron, copper, wood, etc., all of the same mass. We say that each substance has its individual *heat capacity*, or *specific heat.*

Once having gained the concept of heat we can investigate its nature more closely. We have two bodies, one hot, the other cold, or more precisely, one of a higher temperature than the other. We bring them into contact and free them from all other external influences. Eventually they will, we know, reach the same temperature. But how does this take place? What happens between the instant they are brought into contact and the achievement of equal temperatures? The picture of heat "flowing" from one body to another suggests itself, like water flowing from a higher level to a lower. This picture, though primitive, seems to fit many of the facts, so that the analogy runs:

Water–heat
Higher level–higher temperature
Lower level–lower temperature

The flow proceeds until both levels, that is, both temperatures, are equal. This naïve view can be made more useful by quantitative considerations. If definite masses of water and alcohol, each at a definite temperature, are mixed together, a knowledge of the specific heats will lead to a prediction of the final temperature of the mixture. Conversely, an observation of the final temperature, together with a little algebra, would enable us to find the ratio of the two specific heats.

We recognize in the concept of heat which appears here a similarity to other physical concepts. Heat is, according to our view, a substance, such as mass in mechanics. Its quantity may change or not, like money put aside in a safe or spent. The amount of money in a safe will remain unchanged so long as the safe remains locked, and so will the amounts of mass and heat in an isolated body. The ideal thermos bottle is analogous to such a safe. Furthermore, just as the mass of an isolated system is unchanged even if a chemical transformation takes place, so heat is conserved even though it flows from one body to another. Even if heat is not used for raising the temperature of a body but for melting ice, say, or changing water into steam, we can still think of it as a substance and regain it entirely by freezing the water or liquefying the steam. The old names, latent heat of melting or vaporization, show that these concepts are drawn from the picture of heat as a substance. Latent heat is temporarily hidden, like money put away in a safe, but available for use if one knows the lock combination.

But heat is certainly not a substance in the same sense as mass. Mass can be detected by means of scales, but what of heat? Does a piece of iron weigh more when red-hot than when ice-cold? Experiment shows that it does not. If heat is a substance at all, it is a weightless one. The "heat-substance" was usually called *caloric* and is our first acquaintance among a whole family of weightless substances. Later we shall have occasion to follow the history of the family, its rise and fall. It is sufficient now to note the birth of this particular member.

The purpose of any physical theory is to explain as wide a range of phenomena as possible. It is justified in so far as it does make events understandable. We have seen that the substance theory explains many of the heat phenomena. It will soon become apparent, however, that this again is a false clew, that heat cannot be regarded as a substance, even weightless. This is clear if we think about some simple experiments which marked the beginning of civilization.

We think of a substance as something which can be neither created nor destroyed. Yet primitive man created by friction sufficient heat to ignite wood. Examples of heating by friction are, as a matter of fact, much too numerous and familiar to need recounting. In all these cases some quantity of heat is created, a fact difficult to account for by the substance theory. It is true that a supporter of this theory could invent arguments to account for it. His reasoning would run something like this: "The substance theory can explain the apparent creation of heat. Take the simplest example of two pieces of wood rubbed one against the other. Now rubbing is something which influences the wood and changes its properties. It is very likely that the properties are so modified that an unchanged quantity of heat comes to produce a higher temperature than before. After all, the only thing we notice is the rise in temperature. It is possible that the friction changes the specific heat of the wood and not the total amount of heat."

At this stage of the discussion it would be useless to argue with a supporter of the substance theory, for this is a matter which can be settled only by experiment. Imagine two identical pieces of wood and suppose equal changes of temperature are induced by different methods; in one case by friction and in the other by contact with a radiator, for example. If the two pieces have the same specific heat at the new temperature the whole substance theory must break down. There are very simple methods for determining specific heats, and the fate of the theory depends on the result of just such measurements. Tests which are capable of pronouncing a verdict of life or death on a theory occur frequently in the history of physics, and are called *crucial* experiments. The crucial value of an experiment is revealed only by the way the question is formulated, and only one theory of the phenomena can be put on trial by it. The determination of the specific heats of two bodies of the same kind, at equal temperatures attained by friction and heat flow respectively, is a typical example of a crucial experiment. This experiment was performed about a hundred and fifty years ago by Rumford, and dealt a death blow to the substance theory of heat.

An extract from Rumford's own account tells the story:

> It frequently happens, that in the ordinary affairs and occupations of life, opportunities present themselves of contemplating some of the most curious operations of Nature; and very interesting philosophical experiments might often be made, almost without trouble or expense, by means of machinery contrived for the mere mechanical purposes of the arts and manufactures.
>
> I have frequently had occasion to make this observation; and am persuaded, that a habit of keeping the eyes open to every thing that is going on in the ordinary course of the business of life has oftener led, as it were by accident, or in the playful excursions of the imagination, put into action by contemplating the most common appearances, to useful doubts, and sensible schemes for investigation and improvement, than all the more intense meditations of philosophers, in the hours expressly set apart for study. . . .
>
> Being engaged, lately, in superintending the boring of cannon, in the workshops of the military arsenal at Munich, I was struck with the very considerable degree of Heat which a brass gun acquires, in a short time, in being bored; and with the still more intense Heat (much greater than that of boiling water, as I found by experiment) of the metallic chips separated from it by the borer. . . .
>
> From whence comes the Heat actually produced in the mechanical operation above mentioned?
>
> Is it furnished by the metallic chips which are separated by the borer from the solid mass of metal?
>
> If this were the case, then, according to the modern doctrines of latent Heat, and of caloric, the capacity ought not only to be changed, but the change undergone by them should be sufficiently great to account for all the Heat produced.
>
> But no such change had taken place; for I found, upon taking equal quantities, by weight, of these chips, and of thin slips of the same block of metal separated by means of a fine saw and putting

> them, at the same temperature (that of boiling water), into equal quantities of cold water (that is to say, at the temperature of 59½ ° F.) the portion of water into which the chips were put was not, to all appearance, heated either less or more than the other portion, in which the slips of metal were put.

Finally we reach his conclusion:

> And, in reasoning on this subject, we must not forget to consider that most remarkable circumstance, that the source of the Heat generated by friction, in these Experiments, appeared evidently to be *inexhaustible.*
>
> It is hardly necessary to add, that anything which any *insulated* body, or system of bodies, can continue to furnish *without limitation*, cannot possibly be a *material substance*; and it appears to me to be extremely difficult, if not quite impossible, to form any distinct idea of anything, capable of being excited and communicated, in the manner the Heat was excited and communicated in these Experiments, except it be MOTION.

Thus we see the breakdown of the old theory, or to be more exact, we see that the substance theory is limited to problems of heat flow. Again, as Rumford has intimated, we must seek a new clew. To do this, let us leave for the moment the problem of heat and return to mechanics.

The Roller-coaster. Let us trace the motion of that popular thrill-giver, the roller-coaster. A small car is lifted or driven to the highest point of the track. When set free it starts rolling down under the force of gravity, and then goes up and down along a fantastically curved line, giving the occupants a thrill by the sudden changes in velocity. Every roller-coaster has its highest point, that from which it starts. Never again, throughout the whole course of the motion will it reach the same height. A complete description of the motion would be very complicated. On the one hand is the mechanical side of the problem, the changes of velocity and position in time. On the other there is friction and therefore the creation of heat, on the rail and in the wheels. The only significant reason for dividing the physical process into

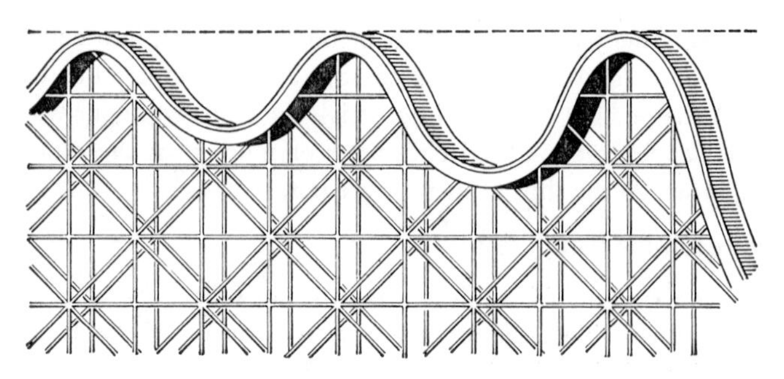

Figure 1

these two aspects is to make possible the use of the concepts previously discussed. The division leads to an idealized experiment, for a physical process in which only the mechanical aspect appears can be only imagined but never realized.

For the idealized experiment we may imagine that someone has learned to eliminate entirely the friction which always accompanies motion. He decides to apply his discovery to the construction of a roller-coaster, and must find out for himself how to build one. The car is to run up and down, with its starting point, say, at one hundred feet above ground level. He soon discovers by trial and error that he must follow a very simple rule: he may build his track in whatever path he pleases so long as no point is higher than the starting point. If the car is to proceed freely to the end of the course its height may attain a hundred feet as many times as he likes, but never exceed it. The initial height can never be reached by a car on an actual track because of friction, but our hypothetical engineer need not consider that.

Let us follow the motion of the idealized car on the idealized roller-coaster as it begins to roll downward from the starting point. As it moves its distance from the ground diminishes, but its speed increases. This sentence at first sight may remind us of one from a language lesson: "I have no pencil, but you have six oranges." It is not so stupid, however. There is no connection between my having no pencil and your having six oranges, but there is a very real correlation between the distance of the car from the ground and its speed. We can calculate the speed of the car at any moment if we know how high it happens to be above the ground, but we omit this point here because of its quantitative character which can best be expressed by mathematical formulae.

At its highest point the car has zero velocity and is one hundred feet from the ground. At the lowest possible point it is no distance from the ground, and has its greatest velocity. These facts may be expressed in other terms. At its highest point the car has *potential energy* but no *kinetic energy* or energy of motion. At its lowest point it has the greatest kinetic energy and no potential energy whatever. At all intermediate positions, where there is some velocity and some elevation, it has both kinetic and potential energy. The potential energy increases with the elevation, while the kinetic energy becomes greater as the velocity increases. The principles of mechanics suffice to explain the motion. Two expressions for energy occur in the mathematical description, each of which changes, although the sum does not vary. It is thus possible to introduce mathematically and rigorously the concepts of potential energy, depending on position, and kinetic energy, depending on velocity. The introduction of the two names is, of course, arbitrary and justified only by convenience. The sum of the two quantities remains unchanged, and is called a constant of the motion. The total energy, kinetic plus potential, is like a substance, for example, money kept intact as to amount but changed continually from one currency to another, say from dollars to pounds and back again, according to a well-defined rate of exchange.

In the real roller-coaster, where friction prevents the car from again reaching as high a point as that from which it started, there is still a continuous change between kinetic and potential energy. Here, however, the sum does not remain constant, but grows smaller. Now one important and courageous step more is needed to relate the mechanical and heat aspects of motion. The wealth of consequences and generalizations from this step will be seen later.

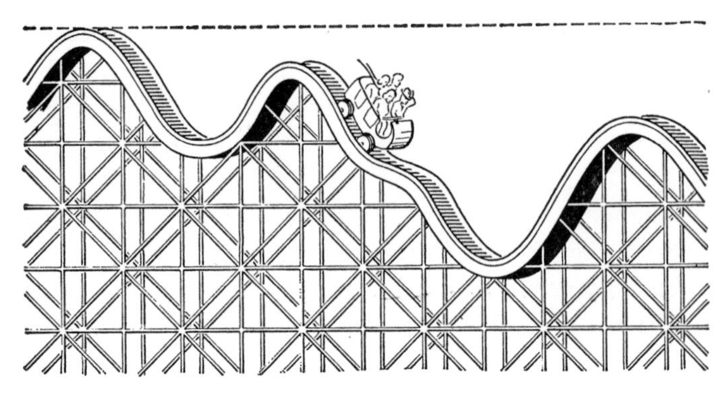

Figure 2

Something more than kinetic and potential energies is now involved, namely, the heat created by friction. Does this heat correspond to the diminution in mechanical energy, that is kinetic and potential energy? A new guess is imminent. If heat may be regarded as a form of energy, perhaps the sum of all three, heat, kinetic and potential energies, remains constant. Not heat alone, but heat and other forms of energy taken together are, like a substance, indestructible. It is as if a man must pay himself a commission in francs for changing dollars to pounds, the commission money also being saved so that the sum of dollars, pounds, and francs is a fixed amount according to some definite exchange rate.

The progress of science has destroyed the older concept of heat as a substance. We try to create a new substance, energy, with heat as one of its forms.

The Rate of Exchange. Less than a hundred years ago the new clew which led to the concept of heat as a form of energy was guessed by Mayer and confirmed experimentally by Joule. It is a strange coincidence that nearly all the fundamental work concerned with the nature of heat was done by non-professional physicists who regarded physics merely as their great hobby. There was the versatile Scotsman Black, the German physician Mayer, and the great American adventurer Count Rumford, who afterward lived in Europe, and among other activities, became Minister of War for Bavaria. There was also the English brewer Joule who, in his spare time, performed some most important experiments concerning the conservation of energy.

Joule verified by experiment the guess that heat is a form of energy, and determined the rate of exchange. It is worth our while to see just what his results were.

The kinetic and potential energy of a system together constitute its *mechanical* energy. In the case of the roller-coaster we made a guess that some of the mechanical energy was converted into heat. If this is right there must be here and in all other similar physical processes a definite *rate of exchange* between the two. This is rigorously a quantitative question, but the fact that a given quantity of mechanical energy can be changed into a definite amount of heat is highly important. We should like to know what number expresses the rate of exchange, i.e. how much heat we obtain from a given amount of mechanical energy.

The determination of this number was the object of Joule's researches. The mechanism of one of his experiments is very much like that of a weight clock. The winding of such a clock consists of elevating two weights, thereby adding potential energy to the system. If the clock is not further interfered with it may be regarded as a closed system. Gradually the weights fall and the clock runs. At the end of a certain time the weights will have reached their lowest position and the clock will have stopped. What has happened to the energy? The potential energy of the weights has changed into kinetic energy of the mechanism, and has then gradually been dissipated as heat.

A clever alteration in this sort of mechanism enabled Joule to measure the heat lost and thus the rate of exchange. In his apparatus two weights caused a paddle wheel to turn while immersed in water. The potential energy of the weights was changed into kinetic energy of the movable parts, and thence into heat which raised the temperature of the water. Joule measured this change of temperature and making use of the known specific heat

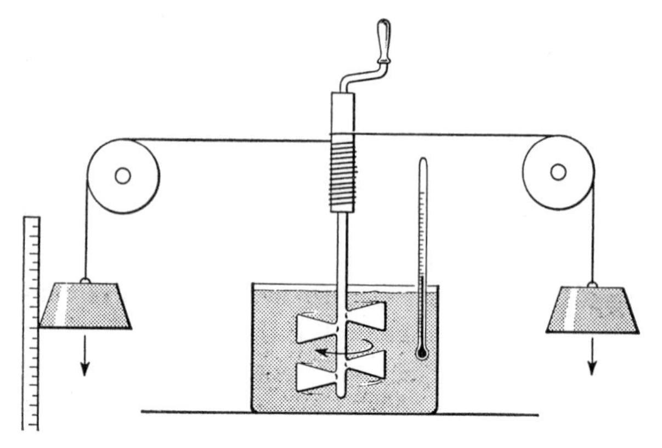

Figure 3

of water, calculated the amount of heat absorbed. He summarized the results of many trials as follows:

> 1st. That the quantity of heat produced by the friction of bodies, whether solid or liquid, is always proportional to the quantity of force [by force Joule means energy] expended. And
>
> 2nd. That the quantity of heat capable of increasing the temperature of a pound of water (weighed in vacuo and taken at between 55° and 60°) by 1° Fahr. requires for its evolution the expenditure of a mechanical force [energy] represented by the fall of 772 lb. through the space of one foot.

In other words the potential energy of 772 pounds elevated one foot above the ground is equivalent to the quantity of heat necessary to raise the temperature of one pound of water from 55° F. to 56° F. Later experimenters were capable of somewhat greater accuracy, but the mechanical equivalent of heat is essentially what Joule found in his pioneer work.

Once this important work was done, further progress was rapid. It was soon recognized that these kinds of energy, mechanical and heat, are only two of its many forms. Everything which can be converted into either of them is also a form of energy. The radiation given off by the sun is energy, for part of it is transformed into heat on the earth. An electric current possesses energy, for it heats a wire or turns the wheels of a motor. Coal represents chemical energy, liberated as heat when the coal burns. In every event in nature one form of energy is being converted into another, always at some well-defined rate of exchange. In a closed system, one isolated from external influences, the energy is conserved and thus behaves like a substance. The sum of all possible forms of energy in such a system is constant, although the amount of any one kind may be changing. If we regard the whole universe as a closed system we can proudly announce with the physicists of the nineteenth century that the energy of the universe is invariant, that no part of it can ever be created or destroyed.

Our two concepts of substance are, then, *matter* and *energy*. Both obey conservation laws: An isolated system cannot change either in mass or in total energy. Matter has weight but energy is weightless. We have therefore two different concepts and two conservation laws. Are these ideas still to be taken seriously? Or has this apparently well-founded picture been changed in the light of newer developments? It has! Further changes in the two concepts are connected with the theory of relativity. We shall return to this point later.

The Philosophical Background. The results of scientific research very often force a change in the philosophical view of problems which extend far beyond the restricted domain of science itself. What is the aim of science? What is demanded of a theory which attempts to describe nature? These questions, although exceeding the bounds of physics, are intimately related to it, since science forms the material from which they arise. Philosophical generalizations must be founded on scientific results. Once formed and widely accepted, however, they very often influence the further development of scientific thought by indicating one of the many possible lines of procedure. Successful revolt against the accepted view results in unexpected and completely different developments, becoming a source of new philosophical aspects.

These remarks necessarily sound vague and pointless until illustrated by examples quoted from the history of physics.

We shall here try to describe the first philosophical ideas on the aim of science. These ideas greatly influenced the development of physics until nearly a hundred years ago, when their discarding was forced by new evidence, new facts and theories, which in their turn formed a new background for science.

In the whole history of science from Greek philosophy to modern physics there have been constant attempts to reduce the apparent complexity of natural phenomena to some simple fundamental ideas and relations. This is the underlying principle of all natural philosophy. It is expressed even in the work of the Atomists. Twenty-three centuries ago Democritus wrote:

> By convention sweet is sweet, by convention bitter is bitter, by convention hot is hot, by convention cold is cold, by convention color is color. But in reality there are atoms and the void. That is, the objects of sense are supposed to be real and it is customary to regard them as such, but in truth they are not. Only the atoms and the void are real.

This idea remains in ancient philosophy nothing more than an ingenious figment of the imagination. Laws of nature relating subsequent events were unknown to the Greeks. Science connecting theory and experiment really began with the work of Galileo. We have followed the initial clews leading to the laws of motion. Throughout two hundred years of scientific research force and matter were the underlying concepts in all endeavors to understand nature. It is impossible to imagine one without the other because matter demonstrates its existence as a source of force by its action on other matter.

Let us consider the simplest example: two particles with forces acting between them. The easiest forces to imagine are those of attraction and repulsion. In both cases the force vectors lie on a line connecting the material points. The demand for simplicity leads to the picture of particles attracting or repelling each other; any other assumption about the direction of the acting forces would give a much more complicated picture. Can we make an equally simple assumption about the length of the force vectors? Even if we want to avoid too special assumptions we can still say one thing: The force between any two given particles depends only on the distance between them, like gravitational forces. This seems simple enough. Much more complicated forces could be imagined, such as those which might depend not only on the distance but also on the velocities of the two particles. With matter and force as our fundamental concepts we can hardly imagine simpler assumptions than that forces act along the line connecting the particles and depend only on the distance. But is it possible to describe all physical phenomena by forces of this kind alone?

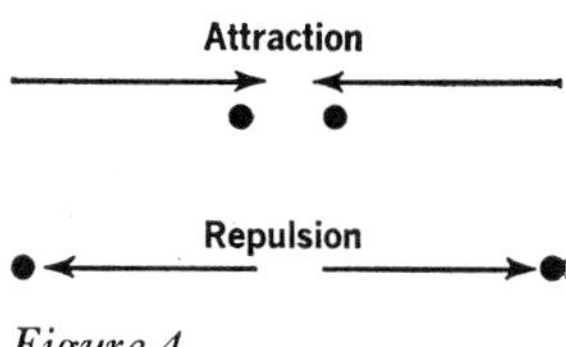

Figure 4

The great achievements of mechanics in all its branches, its striking success in the development of astronomy, the application of its ideas to problems apparently different and non-mechanical in character, all these things contributed to the belief that it *is* possible to describe all natural phenomena in terms of simple forces between unalterable objects. Throughout the two centuries following Galileo's time such an endeavor, conscious or unconscious, is apparent in nearly all scientific creation. This was clearly formulated by Helmholtz about the middle of the nineteenth century:

> Finally, therefore, we discover the problem of physical material science to be to refer natural phenomena back to unchangeable attractive and repulsive forces whose intensity depends wholly upon distance. The solubility of this problem is the condition of the complete comprehensibility of nature.

Thus, according to Helmholtz, the line of development of science is determined and follows strictly a fixed course:

> And its vocation will be ended as soon as the reduction of natural phenomena to simple forces is complete and the proof given that this is the only reduction of which the phenomena are capable.

This view appears dull and naïve to a twentieth-century physicist. It would frighten him to think that the great adventure of research could be so soon finished, and an unexciting if infallible picture of the universe established for all time.

Although these tenets would reduce the description of all events to simple forces, they do leave open the question of just how the forces should depend on distance. It is possible that for different phenomena this dependence is different. The necessity of introducing many different kinds of force for different events is certainly unsatisfactory from a philosophical point of view. Nevertheless this so-called *mechanical view*, most clearly formulated by Helmholtz, played an important role in its time. The development of the kinetic theory of matter is one of the greatest achievements directly influenced by the mechanical view.

Before witnessing its decline, let us provisionally accept the point of view held by the physicists of the past century and see what conclusions we can draw from their picture of the external world.

The Kinetic Theory of Matter. Is it possible to explain the phenomena of heat in terms of the motions of particles interacting through simple forces? A closed vessel contains a certain mass of gas, air, for example, at a certain temperature. By heating we raise the temperature, and thus increase the energy. But how is this heat connected with motion? The possibility of such a connection is suggested both by our tentatively accepted philosophical point of view and by the way in which heat is generated by motion. Heat must be mechanical energy if every problem is a mechanical one. The object of the *kinetic theory* is to present the concept of matter just in this way. According to this theory a gas is a congregation of an enormous number of particles, or *molecules*, moving in all directions, colliding with each other and changing in direction of motion with each collision. There must exist an average speed of molecules, just as in a large human community there exists an average age, or an average wealth. There will therefore be an average kinetic energy per particle.

More heat in the vessel means a greater average kinetic energy. Thus heat, according to this picture, is not a special form of energy different from the mechanical one but is just the kinetic energy of molecular motion. To any definite temperature there corresponds a definite average kinetic energy per molecule. This is, in fact, not an arbitrary assumption. We are forced to regard the kinetic energy of a molecule as a measure of the temperature of the gas if we wish to form a consistent mechanical picture of matter. This theory is more than a play of the imagination. It can be shown that the kinetic theory of gases is not only in agreement with experiment, but actually leads to a more profound understanding of the facts. This may be illustrated by a few examples.

We have a vessel closed by a piston which can move freely. The vessel contains a certain amount of gas to be kept at a constant temperature. If the piston is initially at rest in some position it can be moved upward by removing and downward by adding weight. To push the piston down force must be used acting against the inner pressure of the gas. What is the mechanism of this inner pressure according to the kinetic theory? A tremendous number of particles constituting the gas are moving in all directions. They bombard the walls and the piston, bouncing back like balls thrown against a wall. This continual bombardment by a great number of particles keeps the piston at a certain height by opposing the force of gravity acting downward on the piston and the weights. In one direction there is a constant gravitational force, in the other very many irregular blows from the molecules. The net effect on the piston of all these small irregular forces must be equal to that of the force of gravity if there is to be equilibrium.

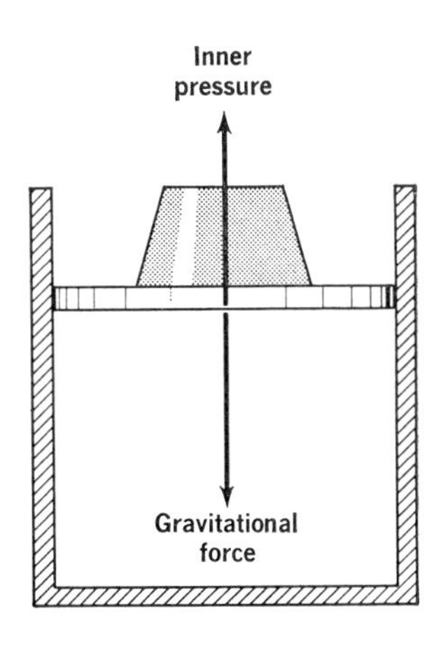

Figure 5

Suppose the piston were pushed down so as to compress the gas to a fraction of its former volume, say one-half, its temperature being kept unchanged. What, according to the kinetic theory, can we expect to happen? Will the force due to the bombardment be more or less effective than before? The particles are now packed more closely. Although the average kinetic energy is still the same, the collisions of the particles with the piston will now occur more frequently and thus the total force will be greater. It is clear from this picture presented by the kinetic theory that to keep the piston in this lower position more weight is required. This simple experimental fact is well known, but its prediction follows logically from the kinetic view of matter.

Consider another experimental arrangement. Take two vessels containing equal volumes of different gases, say hydrogen and nitrogen, both at the same temperature. Assume the two vessels are closed with identical pistons, on which are equal weights. This means, briefly, that both gases have the same volume, temperature, and pressure. Since the temperature is the same, so, according to the theory, is the average kinetic energy per particle. Since the pressures are equal, the two pistons are bombarded with the same total force. On the average every particle carries the same energy and both vessels have the same volume. Therefore, *the number of molecules in each must be the same*, although the gases are chemically different. This result is very important for the understanding of many chemical phenomena. It means that the number of molecules in a given volume, at a certain temperature and pressure, is something which is characteristic, not of a particular gas, but of all gases. It is most astonishing that the kinetic theory not only predicts the existence of such a universal number, but enables us to determine it. To this point we shall return very soon.

The kinetic theory of matter explains quantitatively as well as qualitatively the laws of gases as determined by experiment. Furthermore, the theory is not restricted to gases, although its greatest successes have been in this domain.

A gas can be liquefied by means of a decrease of temperature. A fall in the temperature of matter means a decrease in the average kinetic energy of its particles. It is therefore clear that the average kinetic energy of a liquid particle is smaller than that of a corresponding gas particle.

A striking manifestation of the motion of particles in liquids was given for the first time by the so-called *Brownian movement*, a remarkable phenomenon which would remain quite mysterious and incomprehensible without the kinetic theory of matter. It was first observed by the botanist Brown, and was explained eighty years later, at the beginning of this century. The only apparatus necessary for observing Brownian motion is a microscope, which need not even be a particularly good one.

Brown was working with grains of pollen of certain plants, that is:

> . . . particles or granules of unusually large size varying from one four-thousandth to about five-thousandth of an inch in length.

He reports further:

> While examining the form of these particles immersed in water, I observed many of them evidently in motion. . . . These motions were such as to satisfy me, after frequently repeated observation, that they arose neither from current in the fluid nor from its gradual evaporation, but belonged to the particle itself.

What Brown observed was the unceasing agitation of the granules when suspended in water and visible through the microscope. It is an impressive sight!

Is the choice of particular plants essential for the phenomenon? Brown answered this question by repeating the experiment with many different plants, and found that all the granules, if sufficiently small, showed such motion when suspended in water. Furthermore, he found the same kind of restless, irregular motion in very small particles of inorganic as well as organic substances. Even with a pulverized fragment of a sphinx he observed the same phenomenon!

How is this motion to be explained? It seems contradictory

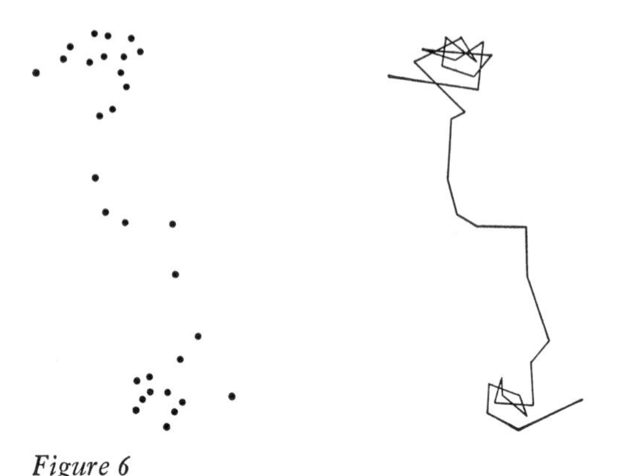

Figure 6

to all previous experience. Examination of the position of one suspended particle, say every thirty seconds, reveals the fantastic form of its path. The amazing thing is the apparently eternal character of the motion. A swinging pendulum placed in water soon comes to rest if not impelled by some external force. The existence of a never diminishing motion seems contrary to all experience. This difficulty was splendidly clarified by the kinetic theory of matter.

Looking at water through even our most powerful microscopes we cannot see molecules and their motion as pictured by the kinetic theory of matter. It must be concluded that if the theory of water as a congregation of particles is correct, the size of the particles must be beyond the limit of visibility of the best microscopes. Let us nevertheless stick to the theory and assume that it represents a consistent picture of reality. The Brownian particles visible through a microscope are bombarded by the smaller ones composing the water itself. The Brownian movement exists if the bombarded particles are sufficiently small. It exists because this bombardment is not uniform from all sides and cannot be averaged out, owing to its irregular and haphazard character. The observed motion is thus the result of the unobservable one. The behavior of the big particles reflects in some way that of the molecules, constituting, so to speak, a magnification so high that it becomes visible through the microscope. The irregular and haphazard character of the path of the Brownian particles reflects a similar irregularity in the path of the smaller particles which constitute matter. We can understand, therefore, that a quantitative study of Brownian movement can give us deeper insight into the kinetic theory of matter. It is apparent that the visible Brownian motion depends on the size of the invisible bombarding molecules. There would be no Brownian motion at all if the bombarding molecules did not possess a certain amount of energy or, in other words, if they did not have mass and velocity. That the study of Brownian motion can lead to a determination of the mass of a molecule is therefore not astonishing.

Through laborious research, both theoretical and experimental, the quantitative features of the kinetic theory were formed. The clew originating in the phenomenon of Brownian movement was one of those which led to the quantitative data. The same data can be obtained in different ways, starting from quite different clews. The fact that all these methods support the same view is most important, for it demonstrates the internal consistency of the kinetic theory of matter.

Only one of the many quantitative results reached by experiment and theory will be mentioned here. Suppose we have a gram of the lightest of all elements, hydrogen, and ask: how many particles are there in this one gram? The answer will characterize not only hydrogen but also all other gases, for we already know under what conditions two gases have the same number of particles.

The theory enables us to answer this question from certain measurements of the Brownian motion of a suspended particle. The answer is an astonishingly great number: a three followed by twenty-three other digits! The number of molecules in one gram of hydrogen is

303,000,000,000,000,000,000,000.

Imagine the molecules of a gram of hydrogen so increased in size that they are visible through a microscope, say that the diameter becomes one five-thousandth of an inch, such as that of a Brownian particle. Then, to pack them closely, we should have to use a box each side of which is about one-quarter of a mile long!

We can easily calculate the mass of one such hydrogen molecule by dividing 1 by the number quoted above. The answer is a fantastically small number:

$$0.000\,000\,000\,000\,000\,000\,000\,0033 \text{ grams,}$$

representing the mass of one molecule of hydrogen.

The experiments on Brownian motion are only some of the many independent experiments leading to the determination of this number which plays such an important part in physics.

In the kinetic theory of matter and in all its important achievements we see the realization of the general philosophical program: to reduce the explanation of all phenomena to the interaction between particles of matter.

We Summarize: In mechanics the future path of a moving body can be predicted and its past disclosed if its present condition and the forces acting upon it are known. Thus, for example, the future paths of all planets can be foreseen. The active forces are Newton's gravitational forces depending on the distance alone. The great results of classical mechanics suggest that the mechanical view can be consistently applied to all branches of physics, that all phenomena can be explained by the action of forces representing either attraction or repulsion, depending only upon distance and acting between unchangeable particles.

In the kinetic theory of matter we see how this view, arising from mechanical problems, embraces the phenomena of heat and how it leads to a successful picture of the structure of matter.

There are a great many events permitted by such conservation laws as those of energy, momentum, and electric charge, that nevertheless do not take place. Objects do not rise spontaneously into the air, for example, growing cooler as their thermal energy converts itself to potential energy. The reason this does not happen is the same as the reason that a ship cannot use the heat of the ocean to propel itself—the second law of thermodynamics. A master expositor of science, George Gamow, discusses the second law and some of its implications in the following selection, which is from his **Matter, Earth, and Sky** (Prentice-Hall, 1958). Gamow became famous in his early twenties, when he applied the then-new wave mechanics to explain the emission of alpha particles by radioactive nuclei. Like Joule, Niels Bohr, and other distinguished physicists, some of the support for his early research came from a brewery. Gamow came to the United States in 1934 and is now at the University of Colorado. He has done original work in cosmology and molecular biology as well as in nuclear physics and is noted for his popular books on science and mathematics.

George Gamow

ENTROPY

If we could transform one hundred per cent of a given amount of heat into mechanical energy, we would be almost as well-to-do as we were with the "perpetual motion" machines described in the chapter on mechanical energy. Instead of "producing energy from nothing," we could turn the heat content of any surrounding medium into mechanical energy. An ocean liner could pump in sea water, extract the heat energy from it to drive its propellers, and throw overboard the resulting blocks of ice. An airplane could take in air, turn its heat content into kinetic energy, and throw the ice-cold jet out through the nozzle in the rear. In fact, since the air, the water, and the ground are heated well above the temperature of absolute zero, these "perpetual motion machines of the second kind" would be just as effective as the "perpetual motion machines of the first kind." But, as we have seen before, such machines are also impossible. We cannot use the heat content of our surroundings to produce mechanical work any more than we can use the water in the oceans to run hydropower installations. The potential energy of the water in the oceans is useless because there is no lower water level to which this water can flow; the heat content of our surroundings is useless because there is no lower temperature region to which this heat can flow.

Summarizing the above facts, we may say that *the natural direction of heat flow is from hot regions to cold regions and the natural direction of energy transformation is from mechanical energy into heat energy.*

In the "natural" direction, both processes can proceed by themselves one hundred per cent, but if either of them is to run in the "unnatural" direction, there must always be an accompanying process running in the "natural" direction which is sufficient to compensate for the "unnatural" behavior of the first one. Thus, it is "unnatural" for heat to escape from the cool interior of a refrigerator into the warm kitchen air, but this process can take place because it is compensated for and even over-compensated for by the "natural" transformation of the electric energy driving the refrigerator's motor into heat. It is "unnatural" for the heat of the steam in a locomotive's boiler to go over into mechanical energy and drive the wheels, but, here again, the "unnaturality" of the process is over-compensated for by the "naturality" of the flow of a part of the heat from the hot boiler to the cool air outside.

In *thermodynamics*, i.e., the study of the relation between heat and mechanical motion, the degree of "naturality" of heat transformation is called *entropy*. We say that the entropy increases when the process goes in the "natural" direction and decreases when it goes in the opposite direction. When a hot object cools down upon being thrown into cold water or an automobile is stopped by application of its brakes, the total entropy of the system goes up. In the work of steam engines or refrigerators, the entropy of the working parts (cylinder and piston or the cooling unit) of the machine goes down, but it is compensated for (or over-compensated for) by an increase of entropy elsewhere. *But in the grand total, the entropy of the entire system cannot decrease and it either remains constant or, in most cases, goes up.* If this were not so, engineers would be able to construct the fabulous perpetual motion machines of the second kind, described in the beginning of this section, and we would have an unlimited supply of free energy for industrial and other uses. Technically, the change of entropy of a given body is measured by the amount of heat it gains or loses (a negative sign in the second case) divided by its (absolute) temperature. In the earlier example of the steam engine that operated between the temperatures T_1 and T_2, the change of entropy of the boiler when the amount of heat Q_1 is taken from it is $-Q_1/T_1$, and the corresponding change in the cooler is $+Q_2/T_2$. Since the total change of entropy must be equal to or larger than zero, we easily arrive at the rule first stated by the French engineer Sadi Carnot (1796–1832): *the largest fraction of original heat "descending" from the temperature T_1 to the temperature T_2 that can be turned into mechanical energy is, at best, equal to the ratio of the temperature difference to the higher temperature* $(T_1 - T_2)/T_1$, where the temperatures are counted from absolute zero. If, for example, a locomotive engine operates between a boiler temperature of 100°C and an outside temperature of, say, 40°C (373 and 313 in the absolute scale) the maximum fraction of heat from the boiler that can be transformed into mechanical work is:

$$\frac{373 - 313}{373} = \frac{40}{373} = 0.107, \quad \text{or about 11 per cent}$$

The reader must have noticed that both examples given above for the local decreases of entropy (a steam engine and a refrigerator) are man-made machines. Indeed, all, or almost all, processes in nature run in "natural" directions, with the entropy increasing more or less uniformly everywhere. The trick of producing local entropy decreases that are compensated for by an increase elsewhere is essentially the product of human ingenuity, the brain child of clever engineers. The notable exception is that of living organisms, which operate on principles very similar to those used in man-made machines. But in building his machines, of course, man simply imposes on inorganic matter the same ingenious principles that operate in his own body. We will return to this problem later.

Order vs. Disorder. The kinetic theory of heat leaves no doubt that what we usually call "heat" is the manifestation of the internal micromotion of the molecules that form all material bodies, and that "temperature" characterizes the intensity of the internal molecular agitation. But, in discussing the phenomenon of heat, we also spoke of *entropy*, which was interpreted as the "degree of naturality" of various thermal transformations. In all "natural" processes, such as the flow of heat from a hot body to a cooler one or the transformation of mechanical energy into heat (as, for example, in the case of friction), the entropy is increasing. The "unnatural" processes, such as the flow of heat from a cool body to a hot one or the transformation of heat into mechanical energy, never occur spontaneously and are possible only in conjunction with some "natural" processes which compensate for the "unnaturality" of the former ones. The decrease of entropy in an "unnatural" process is always compensated for (or over-compensated for) by the increase of entropy in the accompanying "natural" process, so that the total entropy of the entire system is always going up.

What is the interpretation of entropy from the point of view of the kinetic theory of heat, and what is the physical meaning of the statement that "the entropy can never decrease"? Let us consider a lead bullet flying towards a steel plate with a certain velocity v. In this case we can say that all the molecules forming the material of the bullet are moving towards the target with an equal and parallel velocity, v. (In this argument we disregard, for the sake of simplicity, the velocities of the thermal vibrations of the atoms forming the bullet, which are usually small as compared with a bullet's velocity.) When the bullet hits the steel plate it stops, and the mechanical energy of its motion is transformed into the internal kinetic energy of its molecules. (Again, for the sake of simplicity, we neglect the heating of the steel wall hit by the bullet and assume that the entire kinetic energy of the bullet is transformed into heat within its own body.) With these simplifying assumptions, made only for the purpose of making this discussion less complicated, we find that, while before the impact all the molecules of the bullet had identical velocities v in the same direction, after the impact their velocities are distributed equally in all directions, which is as it should be in random thermal motion. The "organized" motion of the molecules, when all of them were moving in the same direction, is transformed into a "disorganized" (or random) motion within the body of the bullet. The "mechanical energy" of motion is transformed into "heat." This example shows quite clearly that *the transformation of mechanical energy into heat is the same as the transformation of organized motion into disorganized motion.*

Speaking of the transformation of order into disorder, we can quote many authoritative opinions:

1. Every housewife knows that, while it takes a lot of work to keep the house spick and span, all she has to do to get it in disorder is just to sit pretty and do nothing.

2. Every highway commissioner knows that all he has to do to make the roads impassable is to lean back in his chair and discontinue maintenance and repairs.

3. Every army officer knows that to get his troops disorganized requires much less effort than to maintain discipline.

Messy houses, impassable roads, and disorganized groups of men are "natural" states of affairs. Well-kept houses, good roads, and organized teams of men are "unnatural" states and require a lot of organizing activity in order to be maintained.

Since molecules have no feeling of personal responsibility, we should expect that *the natural tendency of any physical system consisting of a large number of individual units is to go from a state of order into a state of disorder.* While the "orderly" translatory motion of the molecules in a bullet goes quite easily into "disorderly" thermal motion as the result of an impact, it is impossible to heat a bullet in a flame and then to arrange things in such a way that all the molecular velocities are turned in the same direction, thus forcing the bullet to take off and fly away at a high speed!

The fact that the "natural" way for heat to flow is from hotter places to cooler ones is explained in the same way. The hotter a body is, the higher is the commotion among its molecules.

Of course, with the anthropomorphic examples given above, we can always reverse the argument by referring to the human brain, consciousness, and initiative, but molecules "ain't human" and, obeying straight-forward "low brow" rules, they prefer disorder to order. In this sense, *"mysterious" entropy is simply a measure of the disorder of molecular motion*, and the statement that "the entropy always increases" is equivalent to the statement that "all the processes in nature proceed in the direction of increasing molecular disorder." Thus, the second law of thermodynamics is reduced to a statistical argument pertaining to the behavior of the multitude of individual molecules forming material bodies.

Thermodynamics of Life. At first sight it would seem that the second law of thermodynamics fails in the case of living organisms, since the word "organism" itself implies a high degree of order and organization of the molecules forming it. Consider a plant growing from a seed inside a glass box containing soil at the bottom and abundantly supplied by fresh water and air, which brings in the carbon dioxide necessary for building new material for the growing plant. Although both water and carbon dioxide gas possess a very low degree of order, the plant nevertheless manages to organize H, O, and C atoms and to form these simple substances into highly complex organic compounds such as sugars, proteins, etc. Don't we witness here a case where disorder goes spontaneously into order, with the entropy decreasing in contradiction to the basic rules of thermodynamics? The answer is: No. We have forgotten that, apart from water and a carbon dioxide supply (plus a small amount of some salts from the soil), the plant needs for its growth and development an abundance of sunshine. The sun's rays that are absorbed by the green leaves of the plant bring in the energy necessary for building up complex organic molecules from the simple molecules of H_2O and CO_2;

but this is not the point. We are not worried here about the first law of thermodynamics (i.e., conservation of energy), but about its second law, which prohibits any spontaneous decrease of entropy.

During the transformation of H_2O and CO_2 into complex organic molecules, the entropy of the system decreases,* and, according to the second law of thermodynamics, we have to look for some related process that results in an equal or larger entropy increase. In fact, we find that, apart from supplying a growing plant with necessary amounts of energy, the sun's rays also take care of the necessary entropy decrease. The point is that when solar radiation arrives at the surface of the earth, it is strongly "diluted" in the sense that, whereas its *prevailing wave length* still corresponds to the temperature of the solar surface (i.e., 6,000°K), its *intensity* is not more than that of the radiation emitted by a room-heating radiator. A thermodynamical study of radiant energy indicates that such a dilution of the radiation without a reduction of the prevailing wave length leads to a high entropy *deficiency* or, as we sometimes put it, to the presence of "negative entropy." It is the inflow of this "negative entropy" that permits a plant to grow by organizing the H_2O and CO_2 into more complex organic molecules. The processes of the growing of a plant under the action of the rays of the sun and the subsequent burning of the material so produced in the fireplace can best be described by the following two symbolic equations:

$$\underset{\text{from soil}}{H_2O} + \underset{\text{from air}}{CO_2} + \underset{\text{from the sun}}{(\text{energy} + \text{entropy deficiency})} \rightarrow \text{wood} + O_2$$

$$\text{wood} + \underset{\text{from air}}{O_2} \rightarrow (\text{energy} + \text{entropy excess}) + H_2O + CO_2$$

The energy, which *is to be conserved,* is absorbed in the first process and liberated in the second. The entropy, which *must*

* The fact that a piece of wood burns spontaneously when set afire proves that (wood) $\rightarrow H_2O + CO_2$ is the *natural* direction of the process.

always increase, increases in both processes, since, indeed, the "disappearance of a deficiency" is equivalent to the "appearance of an excess."

The high organization of molecules (negative entropy), obtained by plants from the sun's rays is then passed, along with accumulated energy, to animals, which in this case are entirely parasitic beings, at least from the point of view of the plants.

Gases and solids represent extremes in molecular behavior. Gas molecules move about freely in random paths, colliding frequently with one another and with the walls of their container. The molecules of a solid, however, are usually fixed in place and experience such strong mutual interactions that they lose certain aspects of their individuality. Ideally, then, gases represent total disorder and solids total order, and so it is not surprising that these states of matter can be understood fairly well on the bases of simplified models. Liquids, however, are another matter, and theories of the liquid state are still primitive compared with those of the gaseous and solid states. Especially disconcerting to the theorist are the peculiar effects liquids exhibit near absolute zero. The study of superfluid phenomena is an active branch of contemporary physics, and though they can hardly be said to be understood at the present time, at least the outlines of an explanation seem well along.

The following selection was written by K. Mendelssohn, a member of the physics department at Oxford University and a distinguished worker in the field. It originally appeared in the journal **Science** of the American Association for the Advancement of Science as one of a series of articles on current problems in research. It is not always easy reading, but the insights it offers make the effort worthwhile.

K. Mendelssohn

SUPERFLUIDS

For quite a long time experiments at low temperatures were aimed at reaching the absolute zero. Absolute zero, as such, is a rather old concept. Two hundred and fifty years ago Amontons had already visualized some state of matter at which all motion would come to rest, and which thereby would constitute a lower limit to our temperature scale. The concept of the ultimate cessation of molecular motion was maintained in this form for quite some time, until 50 years ago, when Nernst, by enunciating the third law of thermodynamics, somewhat modified it by substituting for the zero point of energy the zero point of entropy.

Entropy is a concept which many people consider "difficult." Even scientists dislike it sometimes, but, after all, it is not such an abstract thing. It simply measures the degree of disorder in any physical system. Thus, with the advent of the third law of thermodynamics, a change occurred in the approach to absolute zero as the approach to complete order, and not, as it was thought formerly, to complete rest. At the same time, the third law of thermodynamics contained the provision that absolute zero could not be reached by any physical process, and thereby the emphasis of research has been shifted to the question of approach rather than the question of attainment of a final point in the temperature scale.

Recent low-temperature research has therefore been directed toward better understanding of the state of ultimate order rather than that of ultimate rest in matter. As such, it has revealed aspects which are unique. These strange phenomena, which have now been classed under the general term *superfluids*, have no counterpart in the observational world of everyday physics. They stand entirely on their own and, possibly for this reason, have so far resisted theoretical explanation.

It seems quite clear that these phenomena must be related in some way to the amount of energy remaining at absolute zero in any substance—the zero-point energy—or rather to the ratio between zero-point energy and thermal energy. We can expect on the basis of first principles that the region in which the zero-point energy is large compared with the thermal energy will be distinguished as the region in which energy quantization assumes an ever larger part in the aspect of the physical world. In fact, in the phenomena of superfluidity, quantization of energy, which at normal temperatures is restricted to particles of interatomic or perhaps intermolecular size, now transcends into large-scale phenomena, and this is a condition which is alien to our normal observational experience.

Superconductivity. The first of the superfluid phenomena, superconductivity, was discovered by H. Kamerlingh Onnes in Leiden in 1911, three years after the first liquefaction of helium. What Kamerlingh Onnes did was to investigate the dependence of the resistance of a metal on the absolute temperature. At that time there were two different ideas about what the resistance of a metal might do at absolute zero. One school assumed that the resistance should gradually drop to the value zero as zero temperature was approached, whereas the other opinion held that it should rise to infinity. Kamerlingh Onnes used mercury as the first metal to be investigated for the simple reason that he could get it very pure. What he found was rather astonishing. It was so astonishing, in fact, that he had to do a second experiment in order to verify properly the first results. The results showed

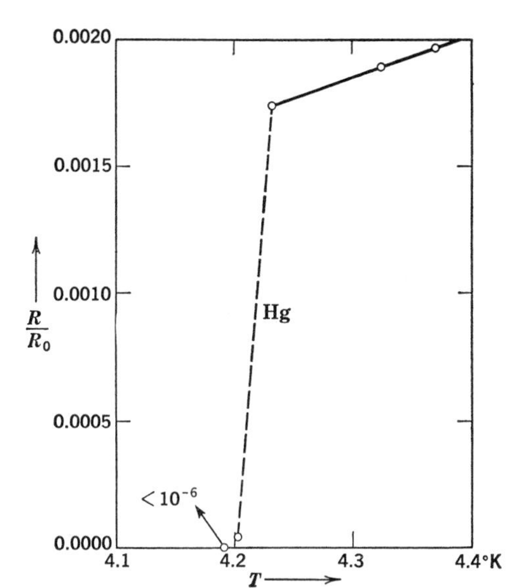

Figure 1 Kamerlingh Onnes' discovery of superconductivity in mercury.

that the resistance of mercury at first dropped constantly as the temperature was lowered until, at 4°K, it attained an unmeasurably small resistance. It was only in the second experiment, when he had made his method more sensitive, that he found the amazing fact that the resistance, at about 4 degrees, disappeared completely and discontinuously (Fig. 1). This was the first observation of superconductivity, a phenomenon which has since been found in a great number of metals and even in compounds.

If you take a closed ring of a superconductive metal such as lead and induce a current in it, then this current will run for seconds, minutes, days, weeks, months—as long as the ring is kept in liquid helium. Recently it has been shown that the current will run for years without any decrease in its strength. These so-called persistent currents are clearly something that do not occur in ordinary macroscopic physics. In a Dewar vessel containing liquid helium, such a current was induced in a set of rings, and a lead sphere was dropped into the system of rings. As the sphere approached the rings, the persistent currents in the rings induced a system of persistent currents on the surface of the sphere. These currents being mutually repellent, the sphere was slowed down in its fall until it came to rest at a position where the mutual repulsion of the currents just counterbalanced the weight of the sphere. There it hung suspended in space by this unusual and strange phenomenon. It does not require much imagination or detailed calculation to see that this is a phenomenon which has no counterpart in the other domains of physics.

Figure 2 shows the distribution of the superconductors in the periodic table. For a little while it looked as if they were grouped in two regions in the table, but now other superconductors have been discovered between these regions. One thing seems certain: the monovalent metals are not superconducting. Perhaps a more impressive and slightly more informative diagram can be made when we plot the atomic volume against the atomic number (Fig.

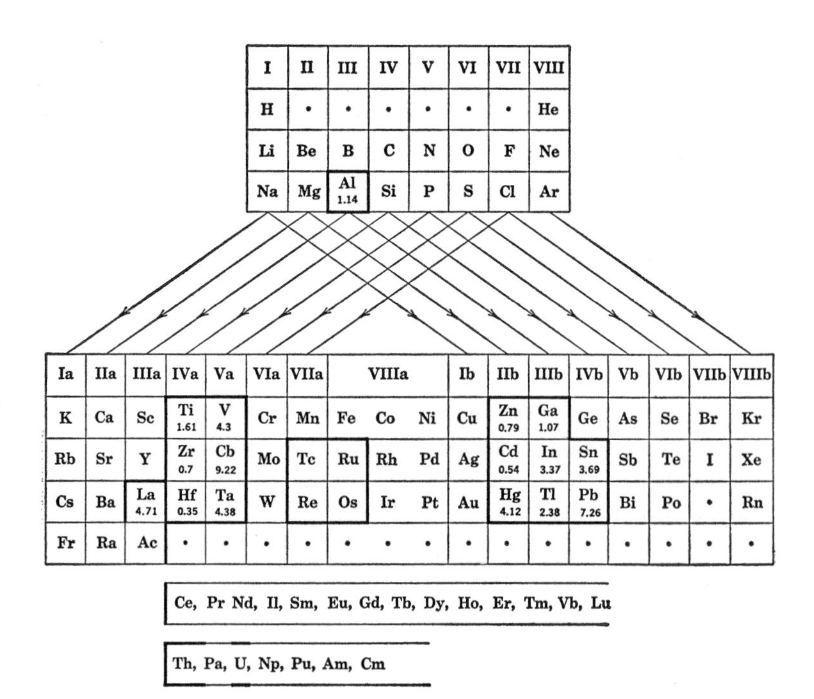

Figure 2 Superconductors in the periodic table.

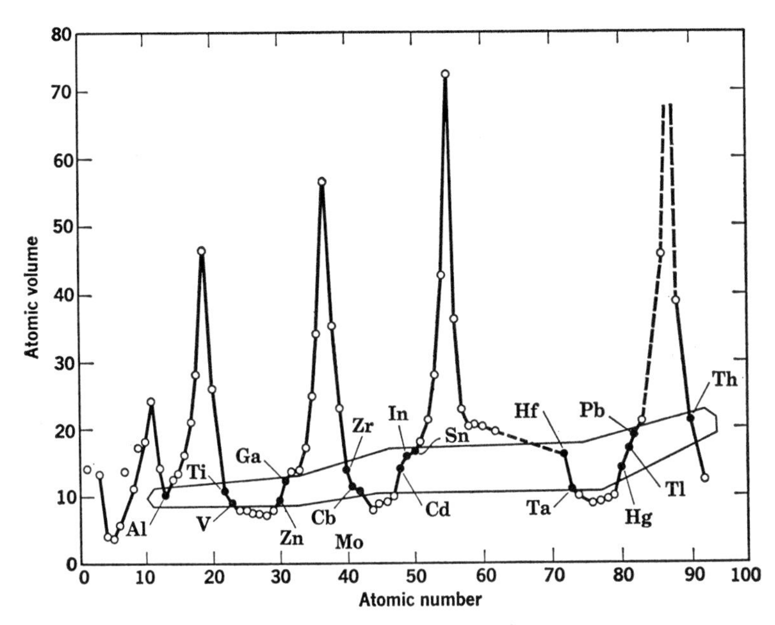

Figure 3 All superconductors have similar volume.

3). Then the superconductors are all contained in a belt which has intermediate atomic volumes. An interesting region of this diagram is the superconducting series, lead, thallium, and mercury. Bismuth is just a bit too large to be a superconductor, and gold is just a bit too small. But if an intermetallic compound of gold and bismuth (Au_2Bi) is made, then this compound will be a superconductor. The case is quite analogous to that of the Heusler alloys in ferromagnetism, where two nonferromagnetic elements will produce a ferromagnetic compound. Here you have two nonsuperconductive parent metals, gold and bismuth, producing a superconductor. This also indicates that superconduction cannot be a property of the atom, but must be due to some rearrangement of the free electrons in the energy spectrum of the metal. Superconductivity is confined to rather low temperatures, which means that the energy difference is of the order of 10^{-4} electron volts, and it would be difficult to find energy transitions of this order in an individual atom. Figure 4 shows that the transition is

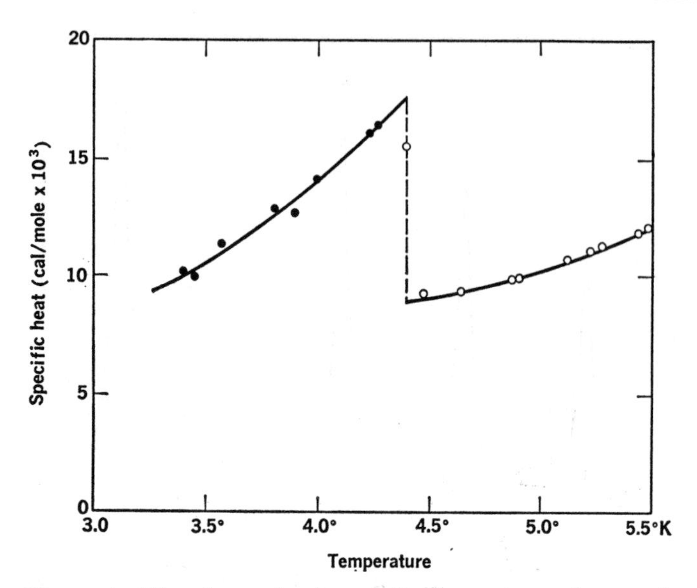

Figure 4 The change in the specific heat of tantalum at the occurrence of superconductivity.

connected with an anomaly in the specific heat which by its small absolute size clearly marks it out as an electronic phenomenon.

This very strange and unusual phenomenon of superconductivity has been known for 45 years, and quite a number of attempts have been made to explain it. On the whole, in the intervening years these attempts have averaged three in peacetime and two in wartime per year, but none of them have been very successful. This failure is not due to the fact that we know so little about superconductivity; actually, the trouble is that we know rather too much. Any theory now will have to contain a whole set of phenomena which must all find a consistent explanation. However, before we hazard any opinions on what kind of state the electrons in the metal pass into when the metal becomes superconducting, let us first have a look at the other superfluid, liquid helium itself.

Liquid Helium. Liquid helium was first produced in 1908 by Kamerlingh Onnes, but somehow the discovery of its unusual properties seemed to be dogged by misfortune, or perhaps rather by the fact that people did not quite believe their eyes. The first indication that there was a change in the liquid helium itself at a temperature well below its boiling point was obtained by Dana and Kamerlingh Onnes. They measured the heat of vaporization of helium and found that there was a sort of indentation in the curve for the heat of vaporization against temperature. They also carried out some preliminary specific heat measurements, which, if these had been pursued, would have shown that the difficulty experienced in reaching lower temperatures with helium was due to a large anomaly.

The next indication was found when the density of helium was investigated by Kamerlingh Onnes. The density, as for any ordinary liquid, first increases with falling temperature, but then, at about 2.2 degrees Kelvin, there is a change in the direction of the density curve, and the density decreases again. Helium thus has a density maximum at about 2.2 degrees Kelvin. There are, of course, other substances, among them water, which have density maxima in the liquid phase, because of some secondary effect. But this sort of explanation became quite untenable when the specific heat was measured by Keesom and Clusius, whose results

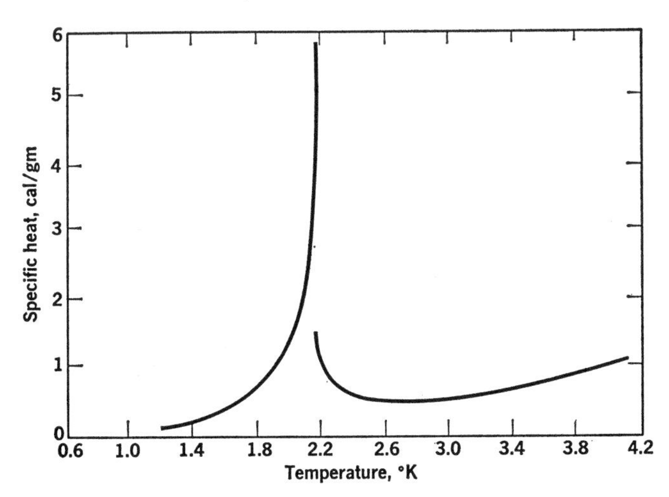

Figure 5 The lambda-point anomaly in the specific heat of liquid helium.

are shown by Fig. 5. These results led Keesom to the concept of the two states of liquid helium, which are separated from each other by this large anomaly known as the lambda-point. On the basis of these measurements, Keesom proposed to call the form of the liquid below this temperature, helium II, and the one above, helium I. One has to be careful in the term used because it would not be correct to use *phase* or *modification*, for with these terms, one always connects the separation of the forms in space. As is evident from the specific heat curve, there is never a coexistence of helium I and helium II, since there is no latent heat separating the two forms.

For a while the hope remained that there would be a conventional explanation—such as, perhaps, the appearance of liquid crystals—for helium II. Indeed, one has to remember that, owing to its high zero-point energy, helium remains a liquid down to absolute zero. As is clear from Fig. 6, external pressure is required to transform it into the solid phase. Therefore, for a little while the idea was entertained that the anomaly was after all the lost triple-point. Then the x-ray investigations made by Keesom and Taconis showed unmistakably that the form below the lambda-

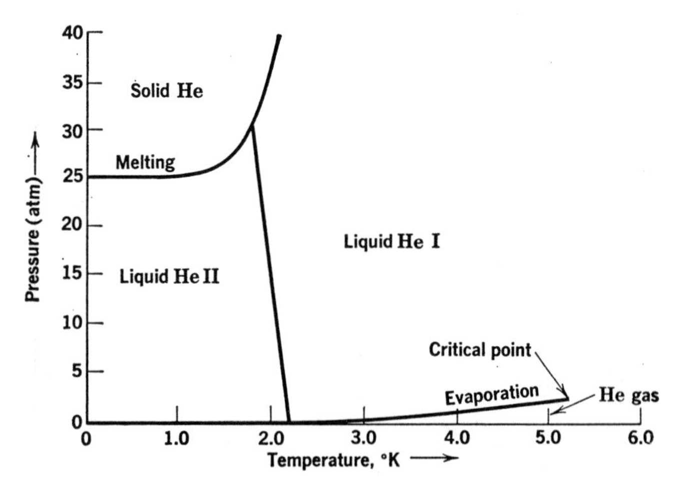

Figure 6 The phase diagram of helium showing the absence of a triple point.

point, helium II, was a liquid showing none of the ordered structure of a solid.

Whereas the helium I, admittedly somewhat gaslike owing to its high zero-point energy, still retains the properties of a liquid, or at least those of a reasonably classical aggregate, helium II is quite different. A long time elapsed before this was realized. In retrospect, it seems strange that so many people should have seen and talked about the phenomena in helium below this temperature without having hit upon the correct explanation.

As a bath of liquid helium is cooled by withdrawal of the vapor from above the liquid, the liquid boils vigorously until the lambda-point is reached, when the boiling suddenly stops abruptly. From then on, although one knows from the flow meter that liquid is evaporating, the meniscus stands sharp against the glass wall like the edge of a knife. This phenomenon was quite well known and, while the explanation of it is obvious, it must have appeared very far-fetched. Later on, when Keesom and Miss Keesom made accurate determinations of the heat conductivity, they found indeed that the heat conduction of this dielectric liquid was increasing at this temperature by a factor of about 1 million. This result explained the cessation of boiling immediately, but who would have postulated that a dielectric liquid should suddenly become a substance with the best heat conductivity known, more than a hundred times better than copper or silver. Moreover, it was soon discovered that the heat conductivity of helium II depended on the temperature gradient, on the size of the capillary in which it was measured, on the shape of the vessel, and on other factors. In fact, while there exists high heat flow in liquid helium, the concept of heat *conduction* seems to have lost its meaning.

The same kind of behavior was discovered when the viscosity was investigated. It turned out that the viscosity of liquid helium II also depends on the type of measurement which is used. A value of about 10^{-5} poise is obtained when an oscillating disk is used as the measuring instrument. If, on the other hand, one uses a Poiseuille method of outflow through narrow channels, the viscosity is less than 10^{-11} poise. Here again is a clear factor of a million between the measured values of the viscosity. Moreover, it was found in a great number of experiments that helium flows through quite narrow channels at a very high rate and largely independent of pressure. This was the discovery of superfluidity. In addition to these phenomena, there exist peculiar thermal effects.

Thermal Effects. If two vessels are connected by a capillary (Fig. 7), and the level of liquid is higher in one vessel than in the other, helium will flow through the capillary toward the lower level, but in doing so the helium below the dropping level will heat up, and the helium below the rising level will cool down. This effect has its exact opposite in that, when one starts with equal levels and supplies heat to one of the reservoirs, the level in the heated vessel will rise, and that in the other vessel will fall. We therefore have a flow of helium from the lower to the higher temperature. This effect can be demonstrated very strikingly, by substituting for the capillary a little vessel which is open to the helium bath and is filled with powder and which is heated by shining a light on it. The pressure generated by the liquid flow toward the heat will be so high that helium will squirt out in the form of a little fountain. This has become known as the "fountain effect," but it is less confusing to talk about the two thermal effects as the mechanocaloric effect and the thermomechanical effect.

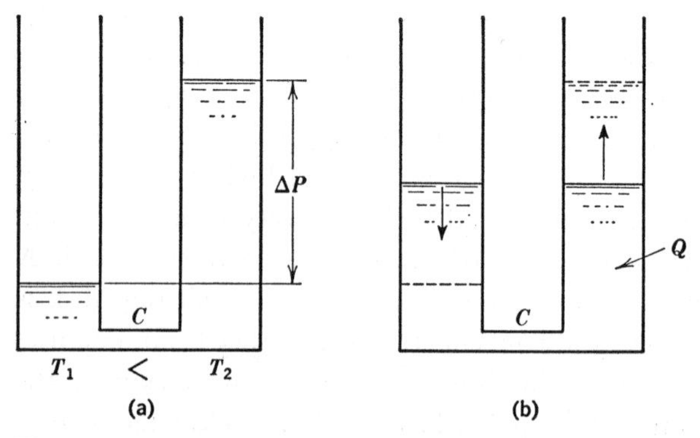

Figure 7 The (a) *mechanocaloric and* (b) *thermomechanical effects.*

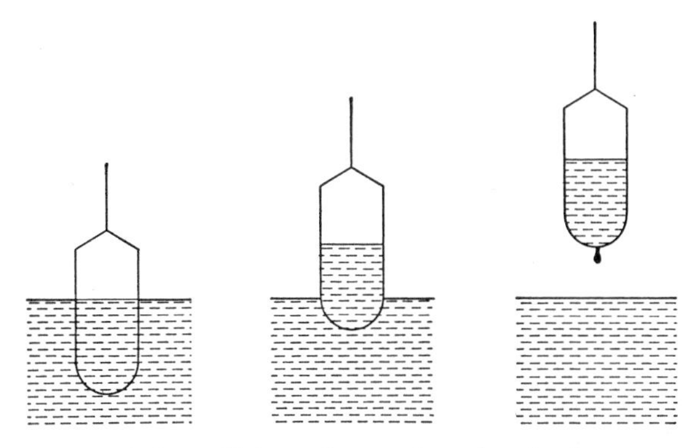

Figure 8 Film flow of helium II in and out of a glass beaker.

Film Flow. This is not all. All solid substances in contact with helium II are covered with a film of about 10^{-6} centimeter thick, and this film also acts as a vehicle for superflow. Figure 8 shows what happens in a very simple type of experiment. An empty glass beaker has been dipped partly into liquid helium. Helium is then seen to appear in the bottom of this beaker, and it slowly rises until the same level is attained on the inside as on the outside. If the beaker is now withdrawn from the bath, the level will drop until it has reached the level of the bath. If the beaker is pulled out completely, the level will still drop, and one can see little drops of helium forming at the bottom of the beaker and falling back into the bath. This is the sort of thing that makes one look twice and rub his eyes and wonder whether it is quite true. I remember well the night when we first observed this film transfer. It was well after dinner, and we looked round the building and finally found two nuclear physicists still at work. When they, too, saw the drops, we were happier.

Figure 9 shows the really striking aspect of the film flow—namely, that if one withdraws the filled beaker and now plots the drop of level against time, the outflow will be quite constant. As the level in the beaker falls, a number of conditions change. First of all, the difference in height, and with it, the pressure, varies. Second, the length of the path over which the helium has to travel changes. Third, the height of the barrier over which the

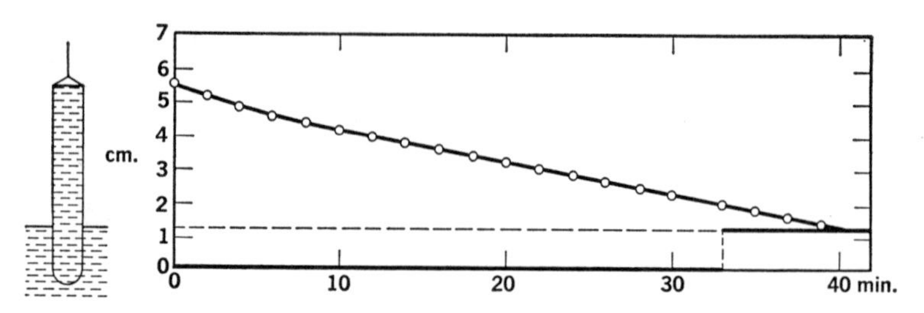

Figure 9 Superflow takes place at a steady rate.

film passes changes. However, all these variations leave the rate of outflow quite unaltered. If we look around for physical phenomena which have any similarity to this steady outflow, the best thing we can find is a lump of radium in which, uninfluenced by external conditions, the nuclei break up at a given rate, disgorging alpha particles. One is greatly tempted to look at superfluidity in the same way and to regard the outflow simply as the quantum statistical probability of finding a helium atom outside rather than inside the beaker. Whereas the uncertainty principle in the case of the radium atoms does not operate over very large distances, here, as a result of the disproportion between zero-point energy and thermal energy, it will transgress into these large-scale dimensions.

In the case of an individual nucleus of radium, one cannot of course say whether it will explode in the next millionth of a second or will not explode for a hundred million years. All one knows is that, of the large number of atoms in the lump, half will have decayed in 1600 years. I think the same consideration must be applied to the phenomena in helium. One should not try to look at one helium atom as a billiard ball running up one side of the wall and down the other. The helium atoms are wave packets which leak out over the beaker.

In a slight modification of this experiment, superfluidity can be even more clearly demonstrated. Figure 10 shows an arrangement which consists of two beakers placed concentrically into each other. To start with, the level of the helium is the same in

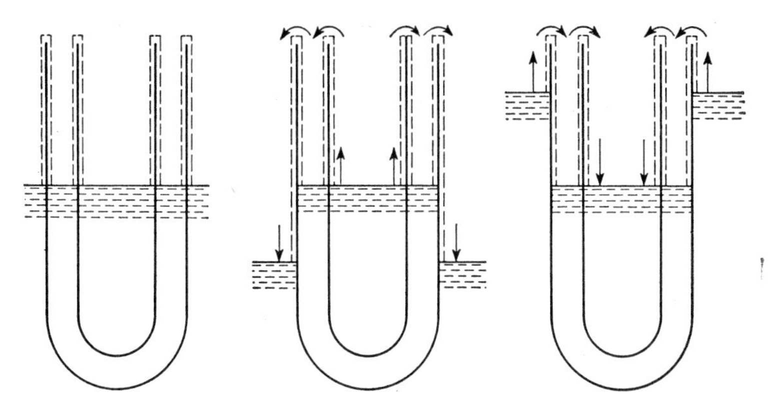

Figure 10 Experimental demonstration of zero friction.

both the inner and the outer beaker and in the bath. When the apparatus is lifted out, liquid helium will run from the inner into the outer beaker and from the outer beaker into the bath. What is significant is that there is *no difference in level* between the inner and the outer beakers. The wall of the outer beaker acts as a restricting perimeter to the outflow, and zero potential difference exists between the inner and outer levels. This means that the helium in the film flows completely without friction.

The experiment is the flow counterpart to a well-known electrical phenomenon, namely that of a super current. Figure 11 shows the circuit which is usually employed to find out whether a substance is a superconductor. There is a battery in the circuit with an ammeter, a superconductor, and a limiting resistance which will keep the current below the critical value. Then a

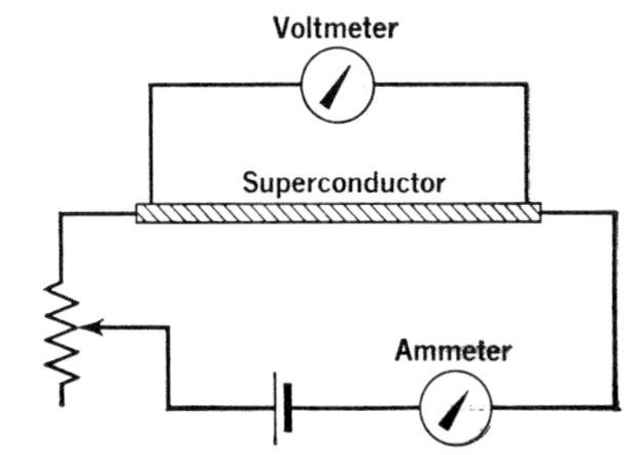

Figure 11 Superconductive analogy of the double beaker experiment.

voltmeter connected across the superconductor will show zero potential difference. In Fig. 10 the difference in levels between the bath and the inner level corresponds to the battery, the outflow rate is the ammeter, the wall of the outer beaker represents the limiting resistance, and the wall of the inner beaker is the superconductor, across which there is zero potential difference.

Entropy. Coming back to our starting point—namely, the postulate that as absolute zero is approached the order in the system increases—we can now ask whether the order is increased when these superfluid phenomena occur. The question can easily be answered by measuring the specific heats and deriving the entropy diagrams (Fig. 12). There is a linear drop toward absolute zero in the normal state—in the metal before it becomes a superconductor, or in the hellium I. This is followed by a much more rapid decrease in entropy as superfluidity sets in. It is tempting to connect this drop in entropy with the phenomenon of superfluidity; this can be done because superfluids seem to be mixtures of a curious kind. The so-called two-fluid model for superfluids has been used extensively, and in spite of certain shortcomings it is useful in explaining the properties. In this model the superfluid is considered as being made up of the same particles—that is, electrons diluted in electrons in the superconductor, and helium atoms diluted in helium atoms in the lambda phenomenon. As, on cooling, the transition temperature is passed, some of these particles pass into a state of lower energy, and finally, at 0 degrees Kelvin, the whole assembly is made up of these lower energy particles. So, as the temperature is decreased, the superfluid constituent in both cases increases all the time at the expense of the normal one. Such a mixture model will have exactly all the requisite properties. For instance, if one has an oscillating disk in helium, it will be impeded by the normal part of the fluid, but if one has a capillary, then the superfluid part will run through the capillary and give the impression of a much smaller viscosity.

As long as we just talk about the normal and the superfluid

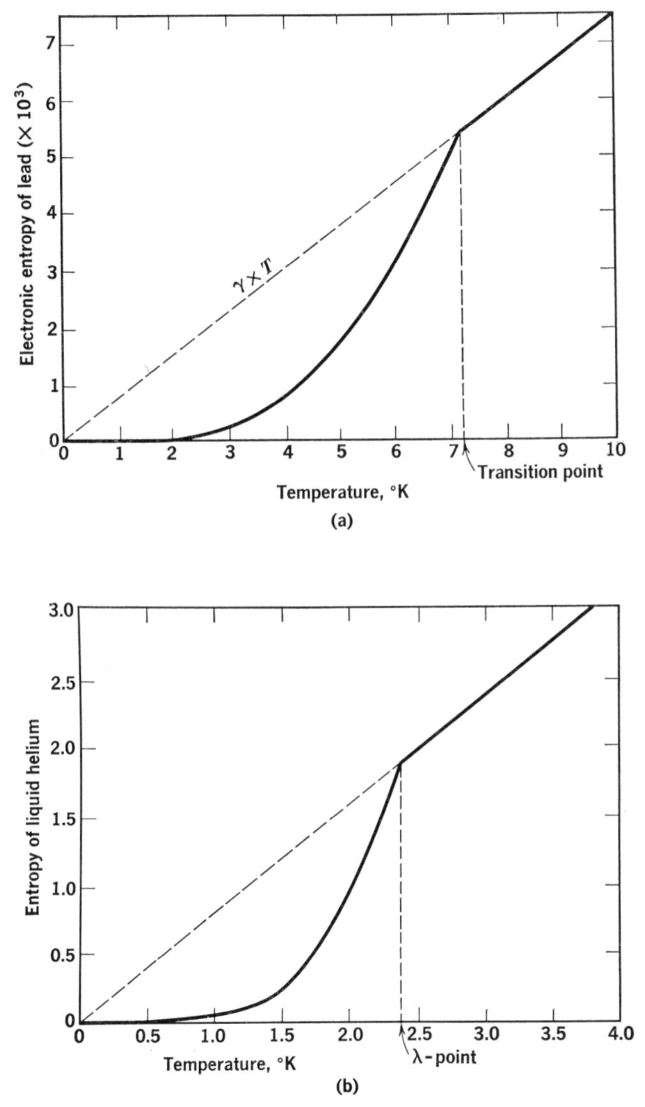

Figure 12 Entropy diagrams of the electrons (a) *in a superconductive metal and* (b) *of liquid helium.*

part without going into any atomistic explanation, the model is comparatively innocuous and we can use it as a working hypothesis. For instance, we can make experiments on the flow of the superfluid constituent, measuring its entropy separately. In a persistent current only the superconducting electrons take part in the motion, and in flow through a capillary only the superfluid part. By making a suitable type of measurement, we can determine the entropy of that part of the two-fluid model which moves without friction. It turns out that this entropy is zero in both cases. The drop in entropy is thus due to the growth of the superfluid phase at the expense of the other phase, and to the fact that the superfluid phase has zero entropy. This constitutes no violation of the third law of thermodynamics for the simple reason that we cannot separate these two phases without a change in temperature.

Whereas we can determine the amount by which order is increased, the concept of entropy is unfortunately so general that we cannot say anything about the way in which this order is increased. In order to get some idea, we have to start thinking afresh about the basic principles of defining order. In both these cases—that of the free electrons and that of the helium atoms—we deal with fluids and not with solids. There is, therefore, no crystallization, and all the aspects which we normally connect with the concept of order are missing. Therefore we have to ask ourselves: What is actually the concept of order?

For instance, the chairs in a lecture room are arranged in a definite predetermined pattern, which we consider as order. It seems to us quite natural that order involves position. We feel that we can only speak of order when we can talk about the relative position of one particle to another. But that is not quite true, because, as Gibbs showed long ago, in a description of a set of particles we do not deal only with the three dimensions of position-space; we must take into account all the six dimensions of phase-space—the three coordinates of position and the three coordinates of momentum.

Momentum and Position. The great strength of physics as a method is that it allows comparatively sure predictions. Modern technology is based on the combination of well-known principles, and these principles allow a fairly clear prediction of what will happen in the end. In order to make such a prediction, it is not sufficient to know the position of particles at one given time. We must also know their positions in the next instant. In other words, the momenta of the particles are as important as their positions. This complementarity is made clear by the fact that the uncertainty relation, the basic principle of quantum mechanics, does contain these two quantities, the position and the momentum, as complete equivalents. They are not similar; they are as different as lock and key. However, lock or key alone would not make sense; both must be considered together.

The idea of taking into account also the momentum coordinates immediately offers an entirely new aspect of the definition of order. Since the coordinates of momentum are quite equivalent to those of position, we must be able to conceive of order with respect to the momenta in the same way as we are accustomed to regard the chess-board pattern of position as a state of order. And it is perhaps significant that in the superfluids the striking features are provided by the transport phenomena. This means that the relevant phenomena are those which are connected with momentum, with the properties of motion, rather than with any static properties. The only difficulty appears to be that somehow our brains are so constructed that we cannot imagine happenings in momentum-space in the same way as we visualize happenings in position-space. On the other hand, if what we observe in the superfluids are momentum condensations, they do not occur in dimensions which are inaccessible to us. On the contrary, these are very striking phenomena which we can see. Perhaps we can make a model of velocity condensations conceivable even with our brains which are accustomed to position order.

In fact, a certain type of momentum condensation has been invented by all civilized governments—that is, those whose subjects own motor cars—by the introduction of a speed limit. Clearly if you have cars moving at all velocities from 5 to 100 miles per hour over the road and you then impose (and enforce) a speed limit of 30 miles per hour, then all the higher velocities will be compressed to 30 miles an hour. If you were to make a movie of this from a great height, then, although you would only observe positions at intervals, you would nevertheless see a pattern of order appear. Take a section of road somewhere where there are a bus, two cars, another bus, and a truck, and later look at the same string at quite a different part of the road. You will then note a degree of order if the relative positions of and distances between the vehicles have been maintained. This is clearly a condensation in momentum-space. I would like to make it clear straight away that this model has no other merit than to show that we can understand, conceive, and recognize momentum condensations in our imagination, but this is certainly not the model which can be applied to liquid helium and superconductors. In our example, recognition of the pattern depends on our ability to make a distinction between the different vehicles, and of course one must not make a distinction between atoms. This is a classical model, and it shows nothing more than that momentum condensations can be created and might therefore possibly exist in nature.

Aggregation of Momenta. If we go that far and assume that momentum condensations are the basis of the phenomena of superfluidity, then we must immediately go one further step in our speculations. That is to assume that this order pattern must be of a very fundamental nature, because in the two cases which we know, electrons in super-conductors and helium atoms in liquid helium, we deal with particles in very different settings and of a very different nature. In one case they are charged light particles in a metal matrix, which obey Fermi-Dirac statistics, and in the other case they are uncharged atoms which by themselves form a liquid and obey Bose-Einstein statistics. If the superfluid state occupies in momentum-space the same position as a crystal in coordinate space, then we can expect that, quite independently of the originating process, the model may be one of great generality. In the cohesion of a solid we may have exchange forces such as in a metal, or van der Waal's forces as in solid argon, or ionic forces as in sodium chloride. These are quite different processes, but they all result in a pattern with very much the same general properties—that is, they result in a crystal.

Last of all, one might ask whether helium and superconductivity are the only representatives of this new state of aggregation. We must call it a state of aggregation in the same way as we call a solid a state of aggregation, only here the aggregation is in momenta and not in positions. Probably on the crust of the earth, which is after all a very unrepresentative bit of the universe, these states may occur only in the laboratory. If, on the other hand, one considers the interior of astronomical bodies of not too high a temperature, it is quite conceivable that under those conditions of very high zero-point energy, the state of aggregation of this frictionless pattern may be more favored than that of position. In fact, we know that here position-order is quite impossible. It thus may turn out that the frictionless state of aggregation is the common form of aggregate matter in the universe, and that the solid state is a rather strange oddity reserved for our own odd corner of the universe.

That is one possibility, but there is another one. We can, of course, become bolder and, knowing the position condensates in the form of crystals, having postulated and almost believed in momentum condensates in the form of superfluids, we can look around in Gibbs space for further possibilities. There are regions in it where we must find other condensates, mixed condensates of position and momenta. We do not know what these mixed condensates can be, but we can say beforehand what properties they must have. They must have very low entropy, because you have here the chance of ordering to a very great extent. Second, they must have the properties of position-order—that is they must be tangible things with a given volume and shape. Third, they must have the characteristic properties of a condensation in momentum. One of the significant properties is that some essential feature is spread over the whole volume of the momentum condensate. Take, for instance, a superconducting ring. If there were no current in the ring and you cut it somewhere, not much harm would be done. There would be an array of atoms not much different from the atoms before cutting. It would not be generally noticed that the ring had been cut. But once a persistent current is flowing and you cut the ring, the whole current disappears from it. This means that the condensation or ordering in respect to the momentum vector, which you have destroyed locally, is now destroyed over the whole of the ring. Therefore, the properties of these velocity condensates are characteristic of the whole structure, and if you cut it in two, it has lost its meaning. If one tries to think where we might find structures like this, one sees that they are very improbable in the first place. They must have low entropy, they must be tangible structures, and they will lose their significance if they are cut in two. There are indeed structures which fulfill these conditions—the structures of living matter. However, this is just an amusing speculation.

We are accustomed to think of forces as "pushes" or "pulls" directly applied by one body on another, and so it is natural to interpret such forces as those of gravitation, electricity, and magnetism, which act despite the physical separation of the bodies involved, as being transmitted through the intervening space by some sort of mechanical process there. In the nineteenth century this idea took the form of a belief that space is pervaded by an invisible, weightless **ether** in which strains can be set up to carry forces from one place to another and which supports the oscillations that constitute light waves, a belief that replaced the once-popular doctrine of direct action at a distance. As it happens, the mathematical formulation of the ether theory makes no reference to the ether itself, and is indistinguishable from what we today call a field theory. The transition from describing electromagnetic phenomena in terms of action at a distance to describing them in terms of interacting fields was essential to the advance of physics, and Michael Faraday's part in bringing it about is one of the reasons he is so outstanding a figure in the history of this science. Faraday, an experimenter of genius but with no knowledge of mathematics, found it useful in understanding electromagnetic induction to take seriously the patterns that iron filings assume near magnets and electric currents. His **lines of force** have definite properties: they behave as though they are under tension and they exert a transverse repulsion on one another. To clinch the success of this description, he discovered that a piece of glass in a strong magnetic field rotates the plane of polarization of light passing through it parallel to the lines of force, something that could not possibly be understood in terms of a mechanical theory of light.

James Clerk Maxwell, an able mathematician with an intuitive grasp of physical phenomena, found in Faraday's lines of force just the clue he needed to formulate a field theory of electricity and magnetism. By associating a displacement current with a changing electric field, Maxwell was able to derive the existence of electromagnetic waves and to compute their velocity of propagation—which turned out to be exactly equal to the velocity of light. The electromagnetic theory of light, whose correctness is today assumed without question, was too remarkable a concept to find universal belief when first announced. Not until Hertz, some years later, actually produced indubitable electromagnetic waves in the laboratory and showed that their properties are identical with those of light was Maxwell's theory accepted. Although Maxwell replaced action at a distance with a field description, he still clung to the idea of an ether, an idea that finally met its downfall in Einstein's interpretation of the Michelson-Morley experiment (as we shall learn in the next selection). Action at a Distance is a talk that Maxwell gave before the Royal Institution of Great Britain in 1873. It is worth noting his reverence for Faraday, his continuing faith in some kind of ether, and his masterful prose style.

James Clerk Maxwell

ACTION AT A DISTANCE

I have no new discovery to bring before you this evening. I must ask you to go over very old ground, and to turn your attention to a question which has been raised again and again ever since men began to think.

The question is that of the transmission of force. We see that two bodies at a distance from each other exert a mutual influence on each other's motion. Does this mutual action depend on the existence of some third thing, some medium of communication, occupying the space between the bodies, or do the bodies act on each other immediately, without the intervention of anything else?

The mode in which Faraday was accustomed to look at phenomena of this kind differs from that adopted by many other modern inquirers, and my special aim will be to enable you to place yourselves at Faraday's point of view, and to point out the scientific value of that conception of *lines of force* which, in his hands, became the key to the science of electricity.

When we observe one body acting on another at a distance, before we assume that this action is direct and immediate, we generally inquire whether there is any material connection between the two bodies; and if we find strings, or rods, or mechanism of any kind, capable of accounting for the observed action between the bodies, we prefer to explain the action by means of these intermediate connections, rather than to admit the notion of direct action at a distance.

Thus, when we ring a bell by means of a wire, the successive parts of the wire are first tightened and then moved, till at last the bell is rung at a distance by a process in which all the intermediate particles of the wire have taken part one after the other. We may ring a bell at a distance in other ways, as by forcing air into a long tube, at the other end of which is a cylinder with a piston which is made to fly out and strike the bell. We may also use a wire; but instead of pulling it, we may connect it at one end with a voltaic battery, and at the other with an electromagnet, and thus ring the bell by electricity.

Here are three different ways of ringing a bell. They all agree, however, in the circumstance that between the ringer and the bell there is an unbroken line of communication, and that at every point of this line some physical process goes on by which the action is transmitted from one end to the other. The process of transmission is not instantaneous, but gradual; so that there is an interval of time after the impulse has been given to one extremity of the line of communication, during which the impulse is on its way, but has not reached the other end.

It is clear, therefore, that in many cases the action between bodies at a distance may be accounted for by a series of actions between each successive pair of a series of bodies which occupy the intermediate space; and it is asked, by the advocates of mediate action, whether, in those cases in which we cannot perceive the intermediate agency, it is not more philosophical to admit the existence of a medium which we cannot at present perceive, than to assert that a body can act at a place where it is not.

To a person ignorant of the properties of air, the transmission of force by means of that invisible medium would appear as unaccountable as any other example of action at a distance, and yet in this case we can explain the whole process, and determine the rate at which the action is passed on from one portion to another of the medium.

Why then should we not admit that the familiar mode of communicating motion by pushing and pulling with our hands is the type and exemplification of all action between bodies, even in cases in which we can observe nothing between the bodies which appears to take part in the action?

Here for instance is a kind of attraction with which Professor Guthrie has made us familiar. A disk is set in vibration, and is then brought near a light suspended body, which immediately begins to move towards the disk, as if drawn towards it by an invisible cord. What is this cord? Sir W. Thomson has pointed out that in a moving fluid the pressure is least where the velocity is greatest. The velocity of the vibratory motion of the air is greatest nearest the disk. Hence the pressure of the air on the suspended body is less on the side nearest the disk than on the opposite side, the body yields to the greater pressure, and moves toward the disk.

The disk, therefore, does not act where it is not. It sets the air next it in motion by pushing it, this motion is communicated to more and more distant portions of the air in turn, and thus the pressures on opposite sides of the suspended body are rendered unequal, and it moves towards the disk in consequence of the excess of pressure. The force is therefore a force of the old school—a case of *vis a tergo*—a shove from behind.

The advocates of the doctrine of action at a distance, however, have not been put to silence by such arguments. What right, say they, have we to assert that a body cannot act where it is not? Do we not see an instance of action at a distance in the case of a magnet, which acts on another magnet not only at a distance, but with the most complete indifference to the nature of the matter which occupies the intervening space? If the action depends on something occupying the space between the two magnets, it cannot surely be a matter of indifference whether this space is filled with air or not, or whether wood, glass, or copper, be placed between the magnets.

Besides this, Newton's law of gravitation, which every astronomical observation only tends to establish more firmly.

asserts not only that the heavenly bodies act on one another across immense intervals of space, but that two portions of matter, the one buried a thousand miles deep in the interior of the earth, and the other a hundred thousand miles deep in the body of the sun, act on one another with precisely the same force as if the strata beneath which each is buried had been non-existent. If any medium takes part in transmitting this action, it must surely make some difference whether the space between the bodies contains nothing but this medium, or whether it is occupied by the dense matter of the earth or of the sun.

But the advocates of direct action at a distance are not content with instances of this kind, in which the phenomena, even at first sight, appear to favour their doctrine. They push their operations into the enemy's camp, and maintain that even when the action is apparently the pressure of contiguous portions of matter, the contiguity is only apparent—that a space *always* intervenes between the bodies which act on each other. They assert, in short, that so far from action at a distance being impossible, it is the only kind of action which ever occurs, and that the favourite old *vis a tergo* of the schools has no existence in nature, and exists only in the imagination of schoolmen.

The best way to prove that when one body pushes another it does not touch it, is to measure the distance between them. Here are two glass lenses, one of which is pressed against the other by means of a weight. By means of the electric light we may obtain on the screen an image of the place where the one lens presses against the other. A series of coloured rings is formed on the screen. These rings were first observed and first explained by Newton. The particular colour of any ring depends on the distance between the surfaces of the pieces of glass. Newton formed a table of the colours corresponding to different distances, so that by comparing the colour of any ring with Newton's table, we may ascertain the distance between the surfaces at that ring. The colours are arranged in rings because the surfaces are spherical, and therefore the interval between the surfaces depends on the distance from the line joining the centres of the spheres. The central spot of the rings indicates the place where the lenses are nearest together, and each successive ring corresponds to an increase of about the 4000th part of a millimètre in the distance of the surfaces.

The lenses are now pressed together with a force equal to the weight of an ounce; but there is still a measurable interval between them, even at the place where they are nearest together. They are not in optical contact. To prove this, I apply a greater weight. A new colour appears at the central spot, and the diameters of all the rings increase. This shews that the surfaces are now nearer than at first, but they are not yet in optical contact, for if they were, the central spot would be black. I therefore increase the weights, so as to press the lenses into optical contact.

But what we call optical contact is not real contact. Optical contact indicates only that the distance between the surfaces is much less than a wavelength of light. To shew that the surfaces are not in real contact, I remove the weights. The rings contract, and several of them vanish at the centre. Now it is possible to bring two pieces of glass so close together, that they will not tend to separate at all, but adhere together so firmly, that when torn asunder the glass will break, not at the surface of contact, but at some other place. The glasses must then be many degrees nearer than when in mere optical contact.

Thus we have shewn that bodies begin to press against each other whilst still at a measurable distance, and that even when pressed together with great force they are not in absolute contact, but may be brought nearer still, and that by many degrees.

Why, then, say the advocates of direct action, should we continue to maintain the doctrine, founded only on the rough experience of a pre-scientific age, that matter cannot act where it is not, instead of admitting that all the facts from which our ancestors concluded that contact is essential to action were in reality cases of action at a distance, the distance being too small to be measured by their imperfect means of observation?

If we are ever to discover the laws of nature, we must do

so by obtaining the most accurate acquaintance with the facts of nature, and not by dressing up in philosophical language the loose opinions of men who had no knowledge of the facts which throw most light on these laws. And as for those who introduce ætherial, or other media, to account for these actions, without any direct evidence of the existence of such media, or any clear understanding of how the media do their work, and who fill all space three and four times over with æthers of different sorts, why the less these men talk about their philosophical scruples about admitting action at a distance the better.

If the progress of science were regulated by Newton's first law of motion, it would be easy to cultivate opinions in advance of the age. We should only have to compare the science of to-day with that of fifty years ago; and by producing, in the geometrical sense, the line of progress, we should obtain the science of fifty years hence.

The progress of science in Newton's time consisted in getting rid of the celestial machinery with which generations of astronomers had encumbered the heavens, and thus "sweeping cobwebs off the sky."

Though the planets had already got rid of their crystal spheres, they were still swimming in the vortices of Descartes. Magnets were surrounded by effluvia, and electrified bodies by atmospheres, the properties of which resembled in no respect those of ordinary effluvia and atmospheres.

When Newton demonstrated that the force which acts on each of the heavenly bodies depends on its relative position with respect to the other bodies, the new theory met with violent opposition from the advanced philosophers of the day, who described the doctrine of gravitation as a return to the exploded method of explaining everything by occult causes, attractive virtues, and the like.

Newton himself, with that wise moderation which is characteristic of all his speculations, answered that he made no pretence of explaining the mechanism by which the heavenly bodies act on each other. To determine the mode in which their mutual action depends on their relative position was a great step in science, and this step Newton asserted that he had made. To explain the process by which this action is effected was a quite distinct step, and this step Newton, in his *Principia*, does not attempt to make.

But so far was Newton from asserting that bodies really do act on one another at a distance, independently of anything between them, that in a letter to Bentley, which has been quoted by Faraday in this place, he says:

> It is inconceivable that inanimate brute matter should, without the mediation of something else, which is not material, operate upon and affect other matter without mutual contact, as it must do if gravitation, in the sense of Epicurus, be essential and inherent in it. . . . That gravity should be innate, inherent, and essential to matter, so that one body can act upon another at a distance, through a vacuum, without the mediation of anything else, by and through which their action and force may be conveyed from one to another, is to me so great an absurdity, that I believe no man who has in philosophical matters a competent faculty of thinking can ever fall into it.

Accordingly, we find in his *Optical Queries*, and in his letters to Boyle, that Newton had very early made the attempt to account for gravitation by means of the pressure of a medium, and that the reason he did not publish these investigations "proceeded from hence only, that he found he was not able, from experiment and observation, to give a satisfactory account of this medium, and the manner of its operation in producing the chief phenomena of nature."

The doctrine of direct action at a distance cannot claim for its author the discoverer of universal gravitation. It was first asserted by Roger Cotes, in his preface to the *Principia*, which he edited during Newton's life. According to Cotes, it is by experience that we learn that all bodies gravitate. We do not learn in any other way that they are extended, movable, or solid.

Gravitation, therefore, has as much right to be considered an essential property of matter as extension, mobility, or impenetrability.

And when the Newtonian philosophy gained ground in Europe, it was the opinion of Cotes rather than that of Newton that became most prevalent, till at last Boscovich propounded his theory, that matter is a congeries of mathematical points, each endowed with the power of attracting or repelling the others according to fixed laws. In his world, matter is unextended, and contact is impossible. He did not forget, however, to endow his mathematical points with inertia. In this some of the modern representatives of his school have thought that he "had not quite got so far as the strict modern view of 'matter' as being but an expression for modes or manifestations of 'force'."

But if we leave out of account for the present the development of the ideas of science, and confine our attention to the extension of its boundaries, we shall see that it was most essential that Newton's method should be extended to every branch of science to which it was applicable—that we should investigate the forces with which bodies act on each other in the first place, before attempting to explain *how* that force is transmitted. No men could be better fitted to apply themselves exclusively to the first part of the problem, than those who considered the second part quite unnecessary.

Accordingly Cavendish, Coulomb, and Poisson, the founders of the exact sciences of electricity and magnetism, paid no regard to those old notions of "magnetic effluvia" and "electric atmospheres," which had been put forth in the previous century, but turned their undivided attention to the determination of the law of force, according to which electrified and magnetized bodies attract or repel each other. In this way the true laws of these actions were discovered, and this was done by men who never doubted that the action took place at a distance, without the intervention of any medium, and who would have regarded the discovery of such a medium as complicating rather than as explaining the undoubted phenomena of attraction.

We have now arrived at the great discovery by Örsted of the connection between electricity and magnetism. Örsted found that an electric current acts on a magnetic pole, but that it neither attracts it nor repels it, but causes it to move round the current. He expressed this by saying that "the electric conflict acts in a revolving manner."

The most obvious deduction from this new fact was that the action of the current on the magnet is not a push-and-pull force, but a rotatory force, and accordingly many minds were set a-speculating on vortices and streams of æther whirling round the current.

But Ampère, by a combination of mathematical skill with experimental ingenuity, first proved that two electric currents act on one another, and then analysed this action into the resultant of a system of push-and-pull forces between the elementary parts of these currents.

The formula of Ampère, however, is of extreme complexity, as compared with Newton's law of gravitation, and many attempts have been made to resolve it into something of greater apparent simplicity.

I have no wish to lead you into a discussion of any of these attempts to improve a mathematical formula. Let us turn to the independent method of investigation employed by Faraday in those researches in electricity and magnetism which have made this Institution one of the most venerable shrines of science.

No man ever more conscientiously and systematically laboured to improve all his powers of mind than did Faraday from the very beginning of his scientific career. But whereas the general course of scientific method then consisted in the application of the ideas of mathematics and astronomy to each new investigation in turn, Faraday seems to have had no opportunity of acquiring a technical knowledge of mathematics, and his knowledge of astronomy was mainly derived from books.

Hence, though he had a profound respect for the great discovery of Newton, he regarded the attraction of gravitation as a sort of sacred mystery, which, as he was not an astronomer, he had no right to gainsay or to doubt, his duty being to believe it in the exact form in which it was delivered to him. Such a dead faith was not likely to lead him to explain new phenomena by means of direct attractions.

Besides this, the treatises of Poisson and Ampère are of so technical a form, that to derive any assistance from them the student must have been thoroughly trained in mathematics, and it is very doubtful if such a training can be begun with advantage in mature years.

Thus Faraday, with his penetrating intellect, his devotion to science, and his opportunities for experiments, was debarred from following the course of thought which had led to the achievements of the French philosophers, and was obliged to explain the phenomena to himself by means of a symbolism which he could understand, instead of adopting what had hitherto been the only tongue of the learned.

This new symbolism consisted of those lines of force extending themselves in every direction from electrified and magnetic bodies, which Faraday in his mind's eye saw as distinctly as the solid bodies from which they emanated.

The idea of lines of force and their exhibition by means of iron filings was nothing new. They had been observed repeatedly, and investigated mathematically as an interesting curiosity of science. But let us hear Faraday himself, as he introduces to his reader the method which in his hands became so powerful.

> It would be a voluntary and unnecessary abandonment of most valuable aid if an experimentalist, who chooses to consider magnetic power as represented by lines of magnetic force, were to deny himself the use of iron filings. By their employment he may make many conditions of the power, even in complicated cases, visible to the eye at once, may trace the varying direction of the lines of force and determine the relative polarity, may observe in which direction the power is increasing or diminishing, and in complex systems may determine the neutral points, or places where there is neither polarity nor power, even when they occur in the midst of powerful magnets. By their use probable results

may be seen at once, and many a valuable suggestion gained for future leading experiments.

Experiment on Lines of Force. In this experiment each filing becomes a little magnet. The poles of opposite names belonging to different filings attract each other and stick together, and more filings attach themselves to the exposed poles, that is, to the ends of the row of filings. In this way the filings, instead of forming a confused system of dots over the paper, draw together, filing to filing, till long fibres of filings are formed, which indicate by their direction the lines of force in every part of the field.

The mathematicians saw in this experiment nothing but a method of exhibiting at one view the direction in different places of the resultant of two forces, one directed to each pole of the magnet; a somewhat complicated result of the simple law of force.

But Faraday, by a series of steps as remarkable for their geometrical definiteness as for their speculative ingenuity, imparted to his conception of these lines of force a clearness and precision far in advance of that with which the mathematicians could then invest their own formulæ.

In the first place, Faraday's lines of force are not to be considered merely as individuals, but as forming a system, drawn in space in a definite manner so that the number of the lines which pass through an area, say of one square inch, indicates the intensity of the force acting through the area. Thus the lines of force become definite in number. The strength of a magnetic pole is measured by the number of lines which proceed from it; the electro-tonic state of a circuit is measured by the number of lines which pass through it.

In the second place, each individual line has a continuous existence in space and time. When a piece of steel becomes a magnet, or when an electric current begins to flow, the lines of force do not start into existence each in its own place, but as the strength increases new lines are developed within the magnet or current, and gradually grow outwards, so that the whole system expands from within, like Newton's rings in our former experiment. Thus every line of force preserves its identity during the whole course of its existence, though its shape and size may be altered to any extent.

I have no time to describe the methods by which every question relating to the forces acting on magnets or on currents, or to the induction of currents in conducting circuits, may be solved by the consideration of Faraday's lines of force. In this place they can never be forgotten. By means of this new symbolism, Faraday defined with mathematical precision the whole theory of electromagnetism, in language free from mathematical technicalities, and applicable to the most complicated as well as the simplest cases. But Faraday did not stop here. He went on from the conception of geometrical lines of force to that of physical lines of force. He observed that the motion which the magnetic or electric force tends to produce is invariably such as to shorten the lines of force and to allow them to spread out laterally from each other. He thus perceived in the medium a state of stress, consisting of a tension, like that of a rope, in the direction of the lines of force, combined with a pressure in all directions at right angles to them.

This is quite a new conception of action at a distance, reducing it to a phenomenon of the same kind as that action at a distance which is exerted by means of the tension of ropes and the pressure of rods. When the muscles of our bodies are excited by that stimulus which we are able in some unknown way to apply to them, the fibres tend to shorten themselves and at the same time to expand laterally. A state of stress is produced in the muscle, and the limb moves. This explanation of muscular action is by no means complete. It gives no account of the cause of the excitement of the state of stress, nor does it even investigate those forces of cohesion which enable the muscles to support this stress. Nevertheless, the simple fact, that it substitutes a kind of action which extends continuously along a material substance for one of which we know only a cause and an effect at a distance from each other, induces us to accept it as a real addition to our knowledge of animal mechanics.

For similar reasons we may regard Faraday's conception of a state of stress in the electro-magnetic field as a method of explaining action at a distance by means of the continuous transmission of force, even though we do not know how the state of stress is produced.

But one of Faraday's most pregnant discoveries, that of the magnetic rotation of polarised light, enables us to proceed a step farther. The phenomenon, when analysed into its simplest elements, may be described thus:—Of two circularly polarised rays of light, precisely similar in configuration, but rotating in opposite directions, that ray is propagated with the greater velocity which rotates in the same direction as the electricity of the magnetizing current.

It follows from this, as Sir W. Thomson has shewn by strict dynamical reasoning, that the medium when under the action of magnetic force must be in a state of rotation—that is to say, that small portions of the medium, which we may call molecular vortices, are rotating, each on its own axis, the direction of this axis being that of the magnetic force.

Here, then, we have an explanation of the tendency of the lines of magnetic force to spread out laterally and to shorten themselves. It arises from the centrifugal force of the molecular vortices.

The mode in which electromotive force acts in starting and stopping the vortices is more abstruse, though it is of course consistent with dynamical principles.

We have thus found that there are several different kinds of work to be done by the electro-magnetic medium if it exists. We have also seen that magnetism has an intimate relation to light, and we know that there is a theory of light which supposes it to consist of the vibrations of a medium. How is this luminiferous medium related to our electro-magnetic medium?

It fortunately happens that electro-magnetic measurements have been made from which we can calculate by dynamical principles the velocity of propagation of small magnetic disturbances in the supposed electro-magnetic medium.

This velocity is very great, from 288 to 314 millions of metres per second, according to different experiments. Now the velocity of light, according to Foucault's experiments, is 298 millions of metres per second. In fact, the different determinations of either velocity differ from each other more than the estimated velocity of light does from the estimated velocity of propagation of small electro-magnetic disturbance. But if the luminiferous and the electro-magnetic media occupy the same place, and transmit disturbances with the same velocity, what reason have we to distinguish the one from the other? By considering them as the same, we avoid at least the reproach of filling space twice over with different kinds of æther.

Besides this, the only kind of electro-magnetic disturbances which can be propagated through a non-conducting medium is a disturbance transverse to the direction of propagation, agreeing in this respect with what we know of that disturbance which we call light. Hence, for all we know, light also may be an electro-magnetic disturbance in a non-conducting medium. If we admit this, the electro-magnetic theory of light will agree in every respect with the undulatory theory, and the work of Thomas Young and Fresnel will be established on a firmer basis than ever, when joined with that of Cavendish and Coulomb by the key-stone of the combined sciences of light and electricity–Faraday's great discovery of the electro-magnetic rotation of light.

The vast interplanetary and interstellar regions will no longer be regarded as waste places in the universe, which the Creator has not seen fit to fill with the symbols of the manifold order of His kingdom. We shall find them to be already full of this wonderful medium; so full, that no human power can remove it from the smallest portion of space, or produce the slightest flaw in its infinite continuity. It extends unbroken from star to star; and when a molecule of hydrogen vibrates in the dog-star, the medium receives the impulses of these vibrations; and after carrying them in its immense bosom for three years, delivers them in due course, regular order, and full tale into the spectroscope of Mr. Huggins, at Tulse Hill.

But the medium has other functions and operations besides bearing light from man to man, and from world to world, and giving evidence of the absolute unity of the metric system of the universe. Its minute parts may have rotatory as well as vibratory motions, and the axes of rotation form those lines of magnetic force which extend in unbroken continuity into regions which no eye has seen, and which, by their action on our magnets, are telling us in language not yet interpreted, what is going on in the hidden underworld from minute to minute and from century to century.

And these lines must not be regarded as mere mathematical abstractions. They are the directions in which the medium is exerting a tension like that of a rope, or rather, like that of our own muscles. The tension of the medium in the direction of the earth's magnetic force is in this country one grain weight on eight square feet. In some of Dr. Joule's experiments, the medium has exerted a tension of 200 lbs. weight per square inch.

But the medium, in virtue of the very same elasticity by which it is able to transmit the undulations of light, is also able to act as a spring. When properly wound up, it exerts a tension, different from the magnetic tension, by which it draws oppositely electrified bodies together, produces effects through the length of telegraph wires, and when of sufficient intensity, leads to the rupture and explosion called lightning.

These are some of the already discovered properties of that which has often been called vacuum, or nothing at all. They enable us to resolve several kinds of action at a distance into actions between contiguous parts of a continuous substance. Whether this resolution is of the nature of explication or complication, I must leave to the metaphysicians.

It is impossible to overstate the importance of the special theory of relativity in our attempts at understanding the natural world. The fact that its influence pervades almost all aspects of physics is not surprising, for this theory is concerned with the meaning of such concepts as space, time, and mass. Remarkably enough, as we shall learn from the following selection, all the evidence Albert Einstein used in formulating the special theory had been known for two decades before he published his first paper on the subject in 1905. The qualities of imagination, insight, and analytical ability that led the youthful Einstein (he was twenty-six at the time) to special relativity also resulted in that year in remarkable papers on the photoelectric effect and on Brownian motion—the former firmly establishing the quantum theory of radiation and the latter doing the same for the molecular theory of matter. Had he accomplished nothing further, Einstein's name would still be immortal, but his creative output continued until his death. Most notable of his subsequent works, of course, is the general theory of relativity, published in 1915. The special theory is restricted to uniform relative motion, while the general theory considers accelerations as well. The general theory interprets gravitation as a distortion in space-time, a characteristically striking idea the implications of which are still being studied. In his later years Einstein was occupied with trying to formulate a unified field theory, uniting gravitation with electromagnetic phenomena in a single, all-embracing mathematical picture.

The selection that follows is devoted to special relativity. It was written by a layman, Lincoln Barnett, rather than by a physicist, and its careful, lucid discussion of rather difficult concepts is an example of popular science writing at its best. Scientists tend to unconsciously assume certain knowledge on the part of their readers. Barnett does not, and there is no better illustration of his talent than his ability to communicate so much of the background and meaning of special relativity without using mathematical arguments. Special Relativity is part of Barnett's **The Universe and Dr. Einstein** (Sloane, 1957, and Mentor Books).

Lincoln Barnett

SPECIAL RELATIVITY

In his great treatise On Human Understanding philosopher John Locke wrote three hundred years ago:

> A company of chessmen standing on the same squares of the chessboard where we left them, we say, are all in the same place or unmoved: though perhaps the chessboard has been in the meantime carried out of one room into another. . . . The chessboard, we also say, is in the same place if it remain in the same part of the cabin, though perhaps the ship which it is in sails all the while; and the ship is said to be in the same place supposing it kept the same distance with the neighboring land, though perhaps the earth has turned around; and so chessmen and board and ship have every one changed place in respect to remoter bodies.

Embodied in this little picture of the moving but unmoved chessmen is one principle of relativity—relativity of position. But this suggests another idea—relativity of motion. Anyone who has ever ridden on a railroad train knows how rapidly another train flashes by when it is traveling in the opposite direction, and conversely how it may look almost motionless when it is moving in the same direction. A variation of this effect can be very deceptive in an enclosed station like Grand Central Terminal in New York. Once in a while a train gets under way so gently that passengers feel no recoil whatever. Then if they happen to look out the window and see another train slide past on the next track, they have no way of knowing which train is in motion and which is at rest; nor can they tell how fast either one is moving or in what direction. The only way they can judge their situation is by looking out the other side of the car for some fixed body of reference like the station platform or a signal light. Sir Isaac Newton was aware of these tricks of motion, only he thought in terms of ships. He knew that on a calm day at sea a sailor can shave himself or drink soup as comfortably as when his ship is lying motionless in harbor. The water in his basin, the soup in his bowl, will remain unruffled whether the ship is making five knots, 15 knots, or 25 knots. So unless he peers out at the sea it will be impossible for him to know how fast his ship is moving or indeed if it is moving at all. Of course if the sea should get rough or the ship change course abruptly, then he will sense his state of motion. But granted the idealized conditions of a glass-calm sea and a silent ship, nothing that happens below decks—no amount of observation or mechanical experiment performed *inside* the ship—will disclose its velocity through the sea. The physical principle suggested by these considerations was formulated by Newton in 1687. "The motions of bodies included in a given space," he wrote, "are the same among themselves, whether that space is at rest or moves uniformly forward in a straight line." This is known as the Newtonian or Galilean Relativity Principle. It can also be phrased in more general terms: mechanical laws which are valid in one place are equally valid in any other place which moves uniformly relative to the first.

The philosophical importance of this principle lies in what it says about the universe. Since the aim of science is to explain the world we live in, as a whole and in all its parts, it is essential to the scientist that he have confidence in the harmony of nature. He must believe that physical laws revealed to him on earth are in truth universal laws. Thus in relating the fall of an apple to the wheeling of the planets around the sun Newton hit upon a universal law. And although he illustrated his principle of relative motion by a ship at sea, the ship he actually had in mind was the earth. For all ordinary purposes of science the earth can be regarded as a stationary system. We may say if we choose that mountains, trees, houses, are at rest, and animals, automobiles, and airplanes move. But to the astrophysicist, the earth, far from being at rest, is whirling through space in a giddy and highly complicated fashion. In addition to its daily rotation about its axis at the rate of 1000 miles an hour, and its annual revolution about the sun at the rate of 20 miles a second, the earth is also involved in a number of other less familiar gyrations. Contrary to popular belief the moon does not revolve around the earth; they revolve around each other—or more precisely, around a common center of gravity. The entire solar system, moreover, is moving within the local star system at the rate of 13 miles a second; the local star system is moving within the Milky Way at the rate of 200 miles a second; and the whole Milky Way is drifting with respect to the remote external galaxies at the rate of 100 miles a second—and all in different directions!

Although he could not then know the full complexity of the earth's movements, Newton was nevertheless troubled by the problem of distinguishing relative motion from true or "absolute" motion in a confusingly busy universe. He suggested that "in the remote regions of the fixed stars or perhaps far beyond them, there may be some body absolutely at rest," but admitted there was no way of proving this by any celestial object within man's view. On the other hand it seemed to Newton that space itself might serve as a fixed frame of reference to which the wheeling of the stars and galaxies could be related in terms of absolute motion. He regarded space as a physical reality, stationary and immovable; and while he could not support this conviction by any scientific argument, he nevertheless clung to it on theological grounds. For to Newton space represented the divine omnipresence of God in nature.

In the next two centuries it appeared probable that Newton's view would prevail. For with the development of the wave theory of light scientists found it necessary to endow empty space with certain mechanical properties—to assume, indeed, that space was some kind of substance. Even before Newton's time the French philosopher, Descartes, had argued that the mere separation of bodies by distance proved the existence of a medium between them. And to eighteenth and nineteenth century physicists it was obvious that if light consisted of waves, there must be some medium to support them, just as water propagates the waves of the sea and air transmits the vibrations we call sound. Hence when experiments showed that light can travel in a vacuum, scientists evolved a hypothetical substance called "ether" which they decided must pervade all space and matter. Later on Faraday propounded another kind of ether as the carrier of electric and magnetic forces. When Maxwell finally identified light as an electromagnetic disturbance the case for the ether seemed assured.

A universe permeated with an invisible medium in which the stars wandered and through which light traveled like vibrations in a bowl of jelly was the end product of Newtonian physics. It provided a mechanical model for all known phenomena of nature, and it provided the fixed frame of reference, the absolute and immovable space, which Newton's cosmology required. Yet the ether presented certain problems, not the least of which was that its actual existence had never been proved. To discover once and for all whether there really was any such thing as ether, two American physicists, A. A. Michelson and E. W. Morley, performed a classic experiment in Cleveland in the year 1881.

The principle underlying their experiment was quite simple. They reasoned that if all space is simply a motionless sea of ether, then the earth's motion through the ether should be detectable and measurable in the same way that sailors measure the velocity of a ship through the sea. As Newton pointed out, it is impossible to detect the movement of a ship through calm waters by any mechanical experiment performed *inside* the ship. Sailors ascertain a ship's speed by throwing a log overboard and watching the

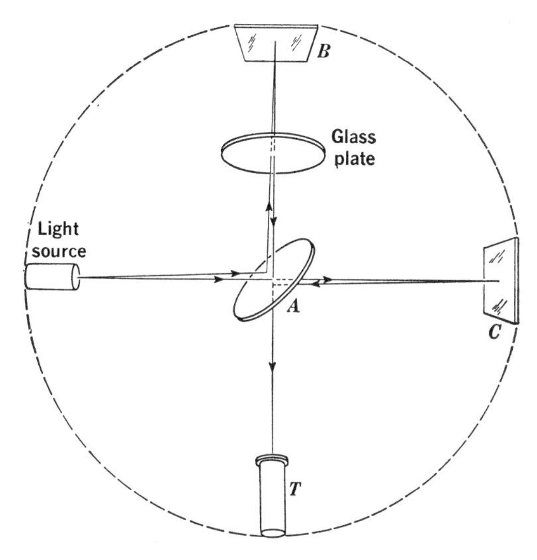

Figure 1 The Michelson-Morley interferometer consisted of an arrangement of mirrors, so designed that a beam transmitted from a light source (above left) was divided and sent in two directions at the same time. This was done by a mirror, A, the face *of which was only thinly silvered, so that part of the beam was permitted to pass through to mirror C (right) and the remainder reflected at right angles toward mirror B. Mirrors B and C then reflected the rays back to mirror A where, reunited, they proceeded to an observing telescope T. Since the beam ACT had to pass three times through the thickness of glass behind the reflecting face of mirror A, a clear glass plate of equal thickness was placed between A and B to intercept beam ABT and compensate for this retardation. The whole apparatus was rotated in different directions so that the beams ABT and ACT could be sent with, against, and at right angles to the postulated ether stream. At first it might appear that a trip "downstream," for example from B to A, should compensate in time for an "upstream" trip from A to B. But this is not so. To row a boat one mile upstream and another mile downstream takes longer than rowing two miles in still water or across current, even with allowance for drift. Had there been any acceleration or retardation of either beam by the ether stream, the optical apparatus at T would have detected it.*

unreeling of the knots on the log line. Hence to detect the earth's motion through the ether sea, Michelson and Morley threw a "log" overboard, and the log was a beam of light. For if light really is propagated through the ether, then its velocity should be affected by the ether stream arising from the earth's movement. Specifically a light ray projected in the direction of the earth's movement should be slightly retarded by the ether flow, just as a swimmer is retarded by a current when going upstream. The difference would be slight, for the velocity of light (which was accurately determined in 1849) is 186,284 miles a second, while the velocity of the earth in its orbit around the sun is only 20 miles a second. Hence a light ray sent *against* the ether stream should travel at the rate of 186,264 miles a second, while one sent *with* the ether stream should be clocked at 186,304 miles a second. With these ideas in mind Michelson and Morley constructed an instrument of such great delicacy that it could detect a variation of even a fraction of a mile per second in the enormous velocity of light. This instrument, which they called an "interferometer" consisted of a group of mirrors so arranged that a light beam could be split in two and flashed in different directions at the same time. The whole experiment was planned and executed with such painstaking precision that the result could not be doubted. And the result was simply this: there was no difference whatsoever in the velocity of the light beams regardless of their direction.

The Michelson-Morley experiment confronted scientists with an embarrassing alternative. On the one hand they could scrap the ether theory which had explained so many things about electricity, magnetism, and light. Or if they insisted on retaining the ether they had to abandon the still more venerable Copernican theory that the earth is in motion. To many physicists it seemed almost easier to believe that the earth stood still than that waves—light waves, electromagnetic waves—could exist without a medium to sustain them. It was a serious dilemma and one that split scientific thought for a quarter century. Many new hypotheses were advanced and rejected. The experiment was tried again by

Morley and by others, with the same conclusion; the apparent velocity of the earth through the ether was zero.

Among those who pondered the enigma of the Michelson-Morley experiment was a young patent office examiner in Berne, named Albert Einstein. In 1905, when he was just twenty-six years old, he published a short paper suggesting an answer to the riddle in terms that opened up a new world of physical thought. He began by rejecting the ether theory and with it the whole idea of space as a fixed system or framework, absolutely at rest, within which it is possible to distinguish absolute from relative motion. The one indisputable fact established by the Michelson-Morley experiment was that the velocity of light is unaffected by the motion of the earth. Einstein seized on this as a revelation of universal law. If the velocity of light is constant regardless of the earth's motion, he reasoned, it must be constant regardless of the motion of any sun, moon, star, meteor, or other system moving anywhere in the universe. From this he drew a broader generalization, and asserted that the laws of nature are the same for all uniformly moving systems. This simple statement is the essence of Einstein's Special Theory of Relativity. It incorporates the Galilean Relativity Principle which stated that mechanical laws are the same for all uniformly moving systems. But its phrasing is more comprehensive; for Einstein was thinking not only of mechanical laws but of the laws governing light and other electromagnetic phenomena. So he lumped them together in one fundamental postulate: all the phenomena of nature, all the laws of nature, are the same for all systems that move uniformly relative to one another.

On the surface there is nothing very startling in this declaration. It simply reiterates the scientist's faith in the universal harmony of natural law. It also advises the scientist to stop looking for any absolute, stationary frame of reference in the universe. The universe is a restless place: stars, nebulae, galaxies, and all the vast gravitational systems of outer space are incessantly in motion. But their movements can be described only with respect to each other, for in space there are no directions and no boundaries. It is futile moreover for the scientist to try to discover the "true" velocity of any system by using light as a measuring rod, for the velocity of light is constant throughout the universe and is unaffected either by the motion of its source or the motion of the receiver. Nature offers no absolute standards of comparison; and space is—as another great German mathematician, Leibnitz, clearly saw two centuries before Einstein—simply "the order or relation of things among themselves." Without things occupying it, it is nothing.

Along with absolute space, Einstein discarded the concept of absolute time—of a steady, unvarying, inexorable universal time flow, streaming from the infinite past to the infinite future. Much of the obscurity that has surrounded the Theory of Relativity stems from man's reluctance to recognize that sense of time, like sense of color, is a form of perception. Just as there is no such thing as color without an eye to discern it, so an instant or an hour or a day is nothing without an event to mark it. And just as space is simply a possible order of material objects, so time is simply a possible order of events. The subjectivity of time is best explained in Einstein's own words.

> The experiences of an individual appear to us arranged in a series of events; in this series the single events which we remember appear to be ordered according to the criterion of 'earlier' and 'later.' There exists, therefore, for the individual, an I-time, or subjective time. This in itself is not measurable. I can, indeed, associate numbers with the events, in such a way that a greater number is associated with the later event than with an earlier one. This association I can define by means of a clock by comparing the order of events furnished by the clock with the order of the given series of events. We understand by a clock something which provides a series of events which can be counted.

By referring our own experiences to a clock (or a calendar) we make time an objective concept. Yet the time intervals provided by a clock or a calendar are by no means absolute quantities imposed on the entire universe by divine edict. All the clocks ever used by man have been geared to our solar system. What we call an hour is actually a measurement in space—an arc of 15 degrees in the apparent daily rotation of the celestial sphere. And what we call a year is simply a measure of the earth's progress in its orbit around the sun. An inhabitant of Mercury, however, would have very different notions of time. For Mercury makes its trip around the sun in 88 of our days, and in that same period rotates just once on its axis. So on Mercury a year and a day amount to the same thing. But it is when science ranges beyond the neighborhood of the sun that all our terrestrial ideas of time become meaningless. For Relativity tells us there is no such thing as a fixed interval of time independent of the system to which it is referred. There is indeed no such thing as simultaneity, there is no such thing as "now," independent of a system of reference. For example a man in New York may telephone a friend in London, and although it is 7:00 P.M. in New York and midnight in London, we may say that they are talking "at the same time." But that is because they are both residents of the same planet, and their clocks are geared to the same astronomical system. A more complicated situation arises if we try to ascertain, for example, what is happening on the star Arcturus "right now." Arcturus is 38 light years away. A light year is the distance light travels in one year, or roughly six trillion miles. If we should try to communicate with Arcturus by radio "right now" it would take 38 years for our message to reach its destination and another 38 years for us to receive a reply. [Radio waves travel at the same speed as light waves.] And when we look at Arcturus and say that we see it "now," in 1957, we are actually seeing a ghost—an image projected on our optic nerves by light rays that left their source in 1919. Whether Arcturus even exists "now" nature forbids us to know until 1995.

Despite such reflections it is difficult for earthbound man to accept the idea that *this very instant* which he calls "now" cannot reply to the universe as a whole. Yet in the Special Theory of Relativity Einstein proves by an unanswerable sequence of example and deduction that it is nonsense to think of events taking place simultaneously in unrelated systems. His argument unfolds along the following lines.

To begin with one must realize that the scientist, whose task it is to describe physical events in objective terms, cannot use subjective words like "this," "here," and "now." For him concepts of space and time take on physical significance only when the relations between events and systems are defined. And it is constantly necessary for him, in dealing with matters involving complex forms of motion (as in celestial mechanics, electrodynamics, etc.) to relate the magnitudes found in one system with those occurring in another. The mathematical laws which define these relationships are known as laws of transformation. The simplest transformation may be illustrated by a man promenading on the deck of a ship: if he walks forward along the deck at the rate of 3 miles an hour and the ship moves through the sea at the rate of 12 miles an hour, then the man's velocity with respect to the sea is 15 miles an hour; if he walks aft this velocity relative to the sea is of course 9 miles an hour. Or as a variation one may imagine an alarm bell ringing at a railway crossing. The sound waves produced by the bell spread away through the surrounding air at the rate of 400 yards a second. A railroad train speeds toward the crossing at the rate of 20 yards a second. Hence the velocity of the sound relative to the train is 420 yards a second so long as the train is approaching the alarm bell and 380 yards a second as soon as the train passes the bell. This simple addition of velocities rests on obvious common sense, and has indeed been applied to problems of compound motion since the time of Galileo. Serious difficulties arise, however, when it is used in connection with light.

In his original paper on Relativity, Einstein emphasized these difficulties with another railway incident. Again there is a crossing, marked this time by a signal light which flashes its beam down the track at 186,284 miles a second—the constant velocity of light, denoted in physics by the symbol c. A train steams toward the signal light at a given velocity v. So by the addition of velocities one concludes that the velocity of the light beam relative to the train is c plus v when the train moves toward the signal light, and c minus v as soon as the train passes the light. But this result conflicts with the findings of the Michelson-Morley experiment which demonstrated that the velocity of light is unaffected either by the motion of the source or the motion of the receiver. This curious fact has also been confirmed by studies of double stars which revolve around a common center of gravity. Careful analysis of these moving systems has shown that the light from the approaching star in each pair reaches earth at precisely the same velocity as the light from the receding star. Since the velocity of light is a universal constant it cannot in Einstein's railway problem be affected by the velocity of the train. Even if we imagine that the train is racing toward the signal light at a speed of 10,000 miles a second, the principle of the constancy of the velocity of light tells us that an observer aboard the train will still clock the speed of the oncoming light beam at precisely 186,284 miles a second, no more, no less.

The dilemma presented by this situation involves much more than a Sunday morning newspaper puzzle. On the contrary it poses a deep enigma of nature. Einstein saw that the problem lay in the irreconcilable conflict between his belief in (1) the constancy of the velocity of light, and (2) the principle of the addition of velocities. Although the latter appears to rest on the stern logic of mathematics (i.e., that two plus two makes four), Einstein recognized in the former a fundamental law of nature. He concluded, therefore, that a new transformation rule must be found to enable the scientist to describe the relations between moving systems in such a way that the results satisfy the known facts about light.

Einstein found what he wanted in a series of equations developed by the great Dutch physicist, H. A. Lorentz, in connection with a specific theory of his own. Although its original application is of interest now chiefly to scientific historians, the Lorentz transformation lives on as part of the mathematical framework of Relativity. To understand what it says, however, it is first neces-

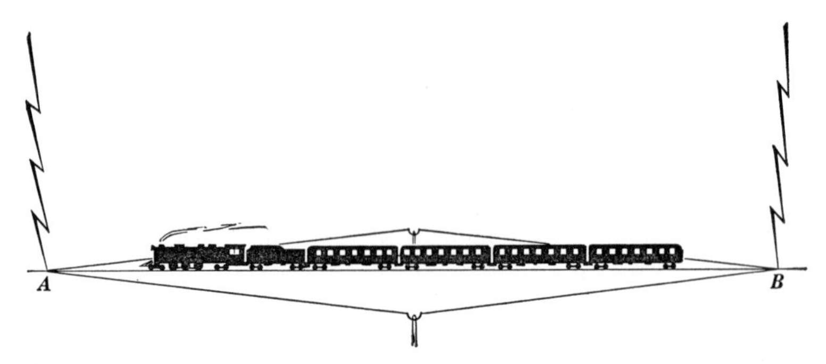

Figure 2

sary to perceive the flaws in the old principle of the addition of velocities. These flaws Einstein pointed out by means of still another railway anecdote. Once again he envisaged a straight length of track, this time with an observer sitting on an embankment beside it. A thunderstorm breaks, and two bolts of lightning strike the track simultaneously at separate points, *A* and *B*. Now, asks Einstein, what do we mean by "simultaneously"? To pin down this definition he assumes that the observer is sitting precisely half way between *A* and *B*, and that he is equipped with an arrangement of mirrors which enable him to see *A* and *B* at the same time without moving his eyes. Then if the lightning flashes are reflected in the observer's mirrors at precisely the same instant, the two flashes may be regarded as simultaneous. Now a train roars down the track, and a second observer is sitting precariously perched atop one of the cars with a mirror apparatus just like the one on the embankment. It happens that this moving observer finds himself directly opposite the observer on the embankment at the precise instant the lightning bolts hit *A* and *B*. The question is: will the lightning flashes appear simultaneous to him? The answer is: they will not. For if his train is moving away from lightning bolt *B* and toward lightning bolt *A*, then it is obvious that *B* will be reflected in his mirrors a fraction of a second later than *A*. Lest there be any doubt about this, one may imagine temporarily that the train is moving at the impossible rate of 186,284 miles a second, the velocity of light. In that event flash B, traveling at precisely the same velocity as flash A, will never be reflected in the mirrors at all because it will never be able to overtake the train. So the observer on the train will assert that only one lightning bolt struck the track. And whatever the speed of the train may be the moving observer will always insist that the lightning flash ahead of him has struck the track first. Hence the lightning flashes which are simultaneous relative to the stationary observer are *not* simultaneous relative to the observer on the train.

The paradox of the lightning flashes thus dramatizes one of the subtlest and most difficult concepts in Einstein's philosophy: the relativity of simultaneity. It shows that man cannot assume that his subjective sense of "now" applies to all parts of the universe. For, Einstein points out, "every reference body (or coordinate system) has its own particular time; unless we are told the reference body to which the statement of time refers, there is no meaning in a statement of the time of an event." The fallacy in the old principle of the addition of velocities lies therefore in its tacit assumption that the duration of an event is independent of the state of motion of the system of reference. In the case of the man pacing the deck of a ship, for example, it was assumed that if he walked three miles in one hour as timed by a clock on the moving ship, his rate would be just the same timed by a stationary clock anchored somehow in the sea. It was further assumed that the distance he traversed in one hour would have the same value whether it was measured relative to the deck of the ship (the moving system) or relative to the sea (the stationary system). This constitutes a second fallacy in the addition of velocities—for distance, like time, is a relative concept, and there is no such thing as a space interval independent of the state of motion of the system of reference.

Einstein asserted, therefore, that the scientist who wishes to describe the phenomena of nature in terms that are consistent for all systems throughout the universe must regard measurements of time and distance as variable quantities. The equations comprising the Lorentz transformation do just that. They preserve the velocity of light as a universal constant, but modify all measurements of time and distance according to the velocity of each system of reference.

The Lorentz transformation relates distances and times observed on moving systems with those observed on systems relatively at rest. Suppose, for example, that a system, or reference body, is moving in a certain direction, then according to the old principle of the addition of velocities, a distance or length x', measured with respect to the moving system along the direction of motion, is related to length x, measured with respect to a relatively stationary system, by the equation $x' = x \pm vt$, where v is the velocity of the moving system and t is the time. Dimensions y' and z', measured with respect to the moving system at right angles to x' and at right angles to each other (i.e., height and breadth), are related to dimensions y and z on the relatively stationary system by $y' = y$, and $z' = z$. And finally a time interval t', clocked with respect to the moving system, is related to time interval t, clocked with respect to the relatively stationary system, by $t' = t$. In other words, distances and times are not affected, in classical physics, by the velocity of the system in question. But it is this presupposition which leads to the paradox of the lightning flashes. The Lorentz transformation reduces the distances and times observed on moving systems to the conditions of the stationary observer, keeping the velocity of light c a constant for all observers. Here are the equations of the Lorentz transformation which have supplanted the older and evidently inadequate relationships cited above:

$$x' = \frac{x - vt}{\sqrt{1 - (v^2/c^2)}}$$

$$y' = y$$

$$z' = z$$

$$t' = \frac{t - (v/c^2)x}{\sqrt{1 - (v^2/c^2)}}$$

It will be noted that, as in the old transformation law, dimensions y' and z' are unaffected by motion. It will also be seen that if the velocity of the moving system v is small relative to the velocity of light c, then the equations of the Lorentz transformation reduce themselves to the relations of the old principle of the addition of velocities. But as the magnitude of v approaches that of c, then the values of x' and t' are radically changed.

So although Lorentz had originally developed his equations to meet a specific problem, Einstein made them the basis of a tremendous generalization, and to the edifice of Relativity another axiom: the laws of nature preserve their uniformity in all systems when related by the Lorentz transformation. Stated thus, in the abstract language of mathematics the significance of this axiom can scarcely be apparent to the layman. But in physics an equation is never a pure abstraction; it is simply a kind of shorthand expression which the scientist finds convenient to describe the phenomena of nature. Sometimes it is also a Rosetta Stone in which the theoretical physicist can decipher secret realms of knowledge. And so by deduction from the message written in the equations of the Lorentz transformation, Einstein discovered a number of new and extraordinary truths about the physical universe.

These truths can be described in very concrete terms. For once he had evolved the philosophical and mathematical bases of Relativity, Einstein had to bring them into the laboratory, where abstractions like time and space are harnessed by means of clocks and measuring rods. And so translating his basic ideas about time and space into the language of the laboratory, he pointed out some hitherto unsuspected properties of clocks and rods. For example: a clock attached to any moving system runs at a different rhythm from a stationary clock; and a measuring rod attached to any moving system changes its length according to the velocity of the system. Specifically the clock slows down as its velocity increases, and the measuring rod shrinks in the direction of its motion. These peculiar changes have nothing to do with the construction of the clock or the composition of the rod. The clock can be a pendulum clock, a spring clock, or an hour glass. The measuring rod can be a wooden ruler, a metal yardstick, or a ten-mile cable. The slowing of the clock and the contraction of the rod are not mechanical phenomena; an observer riding along with the clock and the measuring rod would not notice these changes. But a stationary observer, i.e., stationary relative to the moving system, would find that the moving clock has slowed down with respect to his stationary clock, and that the moving rod has contracted with respect to his stationary units of measurement.

This singular behavior of moving clocks and yardsticks accounts for the constant velocity of light. It explains why all observers in all systems everywhere, regardless of their state of motion, will always find that light strikes their instruments and departs from their instruments at precisely the same velocity. For as their own velocity approaches that of light, their clocks slow down, their yardsticks contract, and all their measurements are reduced to the values obtained by a relatively stationary observer. The laws governing these contractions are defined by the Lorentz transformation and they are very simple: the greater the speed, the greater the contraction. A yardstick moving with 90 per cent the velocity of light would shrink to about half its length; thereafter the rate of contraction becomes more rapid; and if the stick should attain the velocity of light, it would shrink away to nothing at all. Similarly a clock traveling with the velocity of light would stop completely. From this it follows that nothing can ever move faster than light, no matter what forces are applied. Thus Relativity reveals another fundamental law of nature: *the velocity of light is the top limiting velocity in the universe.*

At first meeting these facts are difficult to digest but that is simply because classical physics assumed, unjustifiably, that an object preserves the same dimensions whether it is in motion or at rest and that a clock keeps the same rhythm in motion and at rest. Common sense dictates that this must be so. But as Einstein has pointed out, common sense is actually nothing more than a deposit of prejudices laid down in the mind prior to the age of eighteen. Every new idea one encounters in later years must combat this accretion of "self-evident" concepts. And it is because of Einstein's unwillingness ever to accept any unproven principle as self-evident that he was able to penetrate closer to the underlying realities of nature than any scientist before him. Why, he asked, is it any more strange to assume that moving clocks slow down and moving rods contract, than to assume that they don't? The reason classical physics took the latter view for granted is that man, in his everyday experience, never encounters velocities great enough to make these changes manifest. In an automobile, an airplane, even in a V-2 rocket, the slowing down of a watch is immeasurable. It is only when velocities approximate that of light that relativistic effects can be detected. The equations of the Lorentz transformation show very plainly that at ordinary speeds the modification of time and space intervals amounts practically to zero. Relativity does not therefore contradict classical physics. It simply regards the old concepts as limiting cases that apply solely to the familiar experiences of man.

Einstein thus surmounts the barrier reared by man's impulse to define reality solely as he perceives it through the screen of his senses. Just as the Quantum Theory demonstrated that elementary particles of matter do not behave like the larger particles we discern in the coarse-grained world of our perceptions, so Relativity shows that we cannot foretell the phenomena accompanying great velocities from the sluggish behavior of objects visible to man's indolent eye. Nor may we assume that the laws of Relativity deal with exceptional occurrences; on the contrary they provide a comprehensive picture of an incredibly complex universe in which the simple mechanical events of our earthly experience are the exceptions. The present-day scientist, coping with the tremendous velocities that prevail in the fast universe of the atom or with the immensities of sidereal space and time, finds the old Newtonian laws inadequate. But Relativity provides him in every instance with a complete and accurate description of nature.

Whenever Einstein's postulates have been put to test, their validity has been amply confirmed. Remarkable proof of the relativistic retardation of time intervals came out of an experiment performed by H. E. Ives of the Bell Telephone Laboratories in 1936. A radiating atom may be regarded as a kind of clock in that it emits light of a definite frequency and wave-length which can be measured with great precision by means of a spectroscope. Ives compared the light emitted by hydrogen atoms moving at high velocities with that emitted by hydrogen atoms at rest, and found that the frequency of vibration of the moving atoms was reduced in exact accordance with the predictions of Einstein's equations. Someday science may devise a far more interesting test of the same principle. Since any periodic motion serves to measure time, the human heart, Einstein has pointed out, is also a kind of clock. Hence, according to Relativity, the heartbeat of a person traveling with a velocity close to that of light would be relatively slowed, along with his respiration and all other physiological processes. He would not notice this retardation because his watch would slow down in the same degree. But judged by a stationary timekeeper he would "grow old" less rapidly.

In order to describe the mechanics of the physical universe, three quantities are required: time, distance, and mass. Since time and distance are relative quantities one might guess that the mass of a body also varies with its state of motion. And indeed the most important practical results of Relativity have arisen from this principle—the relativity of mass.

In its popular sense, "mass" is just another word for "weight." But as used by the physicist, it denotes a rather different and more fundamental property of matter: namely, resistance to a change of motion. A greater force is necessary to move or stop a freight car than a velocipede; the freight car resists a change in its motion more stubbornly than the velocipede because it has greater mass. In classical physics the mass of any body is a fixed and unchanging property. Thus the mass of a freight car should remain the same whether it is at rest on a siding, rolling across country at 60 miles an hour, or hurtling through outer space at 60,000 miles a second. But Relativity asserts that the mass of a moving body is by no means constant, but increases with its velocity relative to an observer. The old physics failed to discover this fact simply because man's senses and instruments are too crude to note the infinitesimal increases of mass produced by the feeble accelerations of ordinary experience. They become perceptible only when bodies attain velocities relatively close to that of light. (This phenomenon, incidentally, does not conflict with the relativistic contraction of length. One is tempted to ask: how can an object become smaller and at the same time get heavier? The contraction, it should be noted, is only in the direction of motion; width and breadth are unaffected. Moreover mass is not merely "heaviness" but resistance to a change in motion.)

Einstein's equation giving the increase of mass with velocity is similar in form to the other equations of Relativity but vastly more important in its consequences:

$$m = \frac{m_0}{\sqrt{1 - v^2/c^2}}$$

Here m stands for the mass of a body moving with velocity v, m_0 for its mass when at rest, and c for the velocity of light. Anyone who has ever studied elementary algebra can readily see that if v is small, as are all the velocities of ordinary experience, then the difference between m_0 and m is practically zero. But when v approaches the value of c then the increase of mass becomes very great, reaching infinity when the velocity of the moving body reaches the velocity of light. Since a body of infinite mass would offer infinite resistance to motion the conclusion is once again reached that no material body can travel with the speed of light.

Of all aspects of Relativity the principle of increase of mass has been most often verified and most fruitfully applied by experimental physicists. Electrons moving in powerful electrical fields and beta particles ejected from the nuclei of radioactive substances attain velocities ranging up to 99 per cent that of light. For atomic physicists concerned with these great speeds, the increase of mass predicted by Relativity is no arguable theory but an empirical fact their calculations cannot ignore. In fact the mechanics of the proton-synchroton and other new super-energy machines must be designed to allow for the increasing mass of particles as their speed approaches the velocity of light, in order to make them operate at all.

By further deduction from his principle of Relativity of mass, Einstein arrived at a conclusion of incalculable importance to the world. His train of reasoning ran somewhat as follows: since the mass of a moving body increases as its motion increases, and since motion is a form of energy (kinetic energy), then the increased mass of a moving body comes from its increased energy. In short, energy has mass! By a few comparatively simple mathematical steps, Einstein found the value of the equivalent mass m in any unit of energy E and expressed it by the equation $m = E/c^2$. Given this relation a high school freshman can take the remaining algebraic step necessary to write the most important and certainly the most famous equation in history: $E = mc^2$.

The part played by this equation in the development of the atomic bomb is familiar to most newspaper readers. It states in the shorthand of physics that the energy contained in any particle of matter is equal to the mass of that body multiplied by the square of the velocity of light, the proper units being chosen in each case. This extraordinary relationship becomes more vivid when its terms are translated into concrete values: i.e., one kilogram of coal (about two pounds), if converted *entirely* into energy, would yield 25 billion kilowatt hours of electricity or as much as all the power plants in the U.S. could generate by running steadily for two months.

$E = mc^2$ provides the answer to many of the long-standing mysteries of physics. It explains how radioactive substances like radium and uranium are able to eject particles at enormous velocities and to go on doing so for millions of years. It explains how the sun and all the stars can go on radiating light and heat for billions of years; for if our sun were being consumed by ordinary processes of combustion, the earth would have died in frozen darkness eons ago. It reveals the magnitude of the energy that slumbers in the nuclei of atoms, and forecasts how many grams of uranium must go into a bomb in order to destroy a city. Finally it discloses some fundamental truths about physical reality. Prior to Relativity scientists had pictured the universe as a vessel containing two distinct elements, matter and energy—the former inert, tangible, and characterized by a property called mass, and the latter active, invisible, and without mass. But Einstein showed that mass and energy are equivalent: the property called mass is simply concentrated energy. In other words matter is energy and energy is matter, and the distinction is simply one of temporary state.

In the light of this broad principle many puzzles of nature are resolved. The baffling interplay of matter and radiation which appears sometimes to be a concourse of particles and sometimes a meeting of waves, becomes more understandable. The dual role of the electron as a unit of matter and a unit of electricity, the wave electron, the photon, waves of matter, waves of probability, a universe of waves—all these seem less paradoxical. For all these concepts simply describe different manifestations of the same underlying reality, and it no longer makes sense to ask what any one of them "really" is. Matter and energy are interchangeable. If matter sheds its mass and travels with the speed of light we call it radiation or energy. And conversely if energy congeals and takes on a different form we call it matter. Heretofore science could only note their ephemeral properties and relations as they touched the perceptions of earth-bound man. But since July 16, 1945 man has been able to transform one into the other. For on that night at Alamogordo, New Mexico, man for the first time transmuted a substantial quantity of matter into the light, heat, sound, and motion which we call energy.

Yet the fundamental mystery remains. The whole march of science toward the unification of concepts—the reduction of all matter to elements and then to a few types of particles, the reduction of "forces" to the single concept "energy," and then the reduction of matter *and* energy to a single basic quantity—leads still to the unknown. The many questions merge into one, to which there may never be an answer: what is the essence of this mass-energy substance, what is the underlying stratum of physical reality which science seeks to explore?

Thus Relativity, like the Quantum Theory, draws man's intellect still farther away from the Newtonian universe, firmly rooted in space and time and functioning like some great, unerring, and manageable machine. Einstein's laws of motion, his basic principles of the relativity of distance, time, and mass, and his deductions from these principles comprise what is known as the Special Theory of Relativity. In the decade following the publication of this original work, he expanded his scientific and philosophical system into the General Theory of Relativity, through which he examined the mysterious force that guides the whirling of the stars, comets, meteors, and galaxies, and all the moving systems of iron, stone, vapor, and flame in the immense inscrutable void. Newton called this force "universal gravitation." From his own concept of gravitation Einstein attained a view of the vast architecture and anatomy of the universe as a whole.

The story of the Curies is one of the great legends of science—the young Polish girl, Marie Sklodowska, arriving in Paris in 1891 to study at the Sorbonne and living frugally in a garret; a casual meeting with Pierre Curie, "a tall young man with auburn hair and large, limpid eyes," already a physicist of note; marriage to Pierre in 1895 and their joint work on radioactivity, culminating in the discovery of radium; the Nobel prize; the tragic accidental death of Pierre in 1906; and the continuation of their researches by Marie, who became a popular symbol of the modest, brilliant, dedicated scientist. The passage that follows, by Mme. Curie herself, begins with her marriage and continues past the death of her husband to the outbreak of war in 1914. It is from the Autobiographical Notes that accompany her **Pierre Curie** (Macmillan, 1923). A more dramatic account of her life may be found in her daughter Eve's biography, **Madame Curie** (Doubleday, 1943, and Pocket Books).

Marie Curie

THE DISCOVERY OF RADIUM

With my marriage there began for me a new existence entirely different from the solitary life that I had known during the preceding years. My husband and I were so closely united by our affection and our common work that we passed nearly all of our time together. I have only a few letters from him, for we were so little apart. My husband spent all the time he could spare from his teaching at his research work in the laboratory of the school in which he was professor and I obtained authorization to work with him.

Our living apartment was near the school, so we lost little time in going and coming. As our material resources were limited, I was obliged to attend to most of the housekeeping myself, particularly the preparation of meals. It was not easy to reconcile these household duties with my scientific work, yet, with good will, I managed it. The great thing was that we were alone together in the little home which gave us a peace and intimacy that were very enjoyable for us.

At the same time that I was working in the laboratory, I still had to take a few study courses, for I had decided to take part in the examination for a certificate that would allow me to teach young girls. If I succeeded in this, I would be entitled to be named professor. In August, 1896, after having devoted several months to preparation, I came out first in the examination.

Our principal distraction from the close work of the laboratory consisted in walks or bicycle rides in the country. My husband greatly enjoyed the out-of-doors and took great interest in the plants and animals of woods and meadows. Hardly a corner in the vicinity of Paris was unknown to him. I also loved the country and these excursions were a great joy for me as well as to him, relieving our mind from the tension of the scientific work. We used to bring home bunches of flowers. Sometimes we forgot all about the time and got back late at night. We visited regularly my husband's parents where our room was always ready.

In the vacation we went on longer outings by means of our bicycles. In this way we covered much ground in Auvergne and in the Cevennes and visited several regions at the seashore. We took a great delight in these long all-day excursions, arriving at night always in a new place. If we stayed in one place too long, my husband began to wish to get back to the laboratory. It is also in vacation time that we visited once my family in the Carpathian mountains. My husband learned some Polish in view of this journey to Poland.

But first of all in our life was our scientific work. My husband gave much care to the preparation of his courses, and I gave him some assistance in this, which, at the time, helped me in my education. However, most of our time was devoted to our laboratory researches.

My husband did not then have a private laboratory. He could, to some extent, use the laboratory of the school for his own work, but found more freedom by installing himself in some unused corner of the Physics School building. I thus learned from his example that one could work happily even in very insufficient quarters. At this time my husband was occupied with researches on crystals, while I undertook an investigation of the magnetic properties of steel. This work was completed and published in 1897.

In that same year the birth of our first daughter brought a

great change in our life. A few weeks later my husband's mother died and his father came to live with us. We took a small house with a garden at the border of Paris and continued to occupy this house as long as my husband lived.

It became a serious problem how to take care of our little Irene and of our home without giving up my scientific work. Such a renunciation would have been very painful to me, and my husband would not even think of it; he used to say that he had got a wife made expressly for him to share all his preoccupations. Neither of us would contemplate abandoning what was so precious to both.

Of course we had to have a servant, but I personally saw to all the details of the child's care. While I was in the laboratory, she was in the care of her grandfather, who loved her tenderly and whose own life was made brighter by her. So the close union of our family enabled me to meet my obligations. Things were particularly difficult only in case of more exceptional events, such as a child's illness, when sleepless nights interrupted the normal course of life.

It can be easily understood that there was no place in our life for worldly relations. We saw but a few friends, scientific workers, like ourselves, with whom we talked in our home or in our garden, while I did some sewing for my little girl. We also maintained affectionate relations with my husband's brother and his family. But I was separated from all my relatives, as my sister had left Paris with her husband to live in Poland.

It was under this mode of quiet living, organized according to our desires, that we achieved the great work of our lives, work begun about the end of 1897 and lasting for many years.

I had decided on a theme for my doctorate. My attention had been drawn to the interesting experiments of Henri Becquerel on the salts of the rare metal uranium. Becquerel had shown that by placing some uranium salt on a photographic plate, covered with black paper, the plate would be affected as if light had fallen on it. The effect is produced by special rays which are emitted by the uranium salt and are different from ordinary luminous rays as they can pass through black paper. Becquerel also showed that these rays can discharge an electroscope. He at first thought that the uranium rays were produced as a result of exposing the uranium salt to light, but experiment showed that salts kept for several months in the dark continued the peculiar rays.

My husband and I were much excited by this new phenomenon, and I resolved to undertake the special study of it. It seemed to me that the first thing to do was to measure the phenomenon with precision. In this I decided to use that property of the rays which enabled them to discharge an electroscope. However, instead of the usual electroscope, I used a more perfect apparatus. One of the models of the apparatus used by me for these first measurements is now in the College of Physicians and Surgeons in Philadelphia.

I was not long in obtaining interesting results. My determinations showed that the emission of the rays is an atomic property of the uranium, whatever the physical or chemical conditions of the salt were. Any substance containing uranium is as much more active in emitting rays, as it contains more of this element.

I then thought to find out if there were other substances possessing this remarkable property of uranium, and soon found that substances containing thorium behaved in a similar way, and that this behavior depended similarly on an atomic property of thorium. I was now about to undertake a detailed study of the uranium and thorium rays when I discovered a new interesting fact.

I had occasion to examine a certain number of minerals. A few of them showed activity; they were those containing either uranium or thorium. The activity of these minerals would have had nothing astonishing about it, if it had been in proportion to the quantities of uranium or thorium contained in them. But it was not so. Some of these minerals revealed an activity three or four times greater than that of uranium. I verified this surprising fact carefully, and could not doubt its truth. Speculating about the reason for this, there seemed to be but one explanation. There must be, I thought, some unknown substance, very active, in these minerals. My husband agreed with me and I urged that we search at once for this hypothetical substance, thinking that, with joined efforts, a result would be quickly obtained. Neither of us could foresee that in beginning this work we were to enter the path of a new science which we should follow for all our future.

Of course, I did not expect, even at the beginning, to find a new element in any large quantity, as the minerals had already been analyzed with some precision. At least, I thought there might be as much as one per cent of the unknown substance in the minerals. But the more we worked, the clearer we realized that the new radioactive element could exist only in quite minute proportion and that, in consequence, its activity must be very great. Would we have insisted, despite the scarcity of our means of research, if we had known the true proportion of what we were searching for, no one can tell; all that can be said now is that the constant progress of our work held us absorbed in a passionate research, while the difficulties were ever increasing. As a matter of fact, it was only after several years of most arduous labor that we finally succeeded in completely separating the new substance, now known to everybody as radium. Here is, briefly, the story of the search and discovery.

As we did not know, at the beginning, any of the chemical properties of the unknown substance, but only that it emits rays, it was by these rays that we had to search. We first undertook the analysis of a pitchblende from St. Joachimsthal. Analyzing this ore by the usual chemical methods, we added an examination of its different parts for radioactivity, by the use of our delicate electrical apparatus. This was the foundation of a new method of chemical analysis which, following our work, has been extended, with the result that a large number of radioactive elements have been discovered.

In a few weeks we could be convinced that our prevision had been right, for the activity was concentrating in a regular way. And, in a few months, we could separate from the pitchblende a substance accompanying the bismuth, much more active than uranium, and having well defined chemical properties. In July, 1898, we announced the existence of this new substance, to which I gave the name of polonium, in memory of my native country.

While engaged in this work on polonium, we had also discovered that, accompanying the barium separated from the pitchblende, there was another new element. After several months more of close work we were able to separate this second new substance, which was afterwards shown to be much more important than polonium. In December, 1898, we could announce the discovery of this new and now famous element, to which we gave the name of radium.

However, the greatest part of the material work had yet to be done. We had, to be sure, discovered the existence of the remarkable new elements, but it was chiefly by their radiant properties that these new substances were distinguished from the bismuth and barium with which they were mixed in minute quantities. We had still to separate them as pure elements. On this work we now started.

We were very poorly equipped with facilities for this purpose. It was necessary to subject large quantities of ore to careful chemical treatment. We had no money, no suitable laboratory, no personal help for our great and difficult undertaking. It was like creating something out of nothing, and if my earlier studying years had once been called by my brother-in-law the heroic period of my life, I can say without exaggeration that the period on which my husband and I now entered was truly the heroic one of our common life.

We knew by our experiments that in the treatment of pitchblende at the uranium plant of St. Joachimsthal, radium must have been left in the residues, and, with the permission of the Austrian government, which owned the plant, we succeeded in securing a certain quantity of these residues, then quite valueless, —and used them for extraction of radium. How glad I was when the sacks arrived, with the brown dust mixed with pine needles, and when the activity proved even greater than that of the primitive ore! It was a stroke of luck that the residues had not been thrown far away or disposed of in some way, but left in a heap in the pine wood near the plant. Some time later, the Austrian government, on the proposition of the Academy of Science of Vienna, let us have several tons of similar residues at a low price. With this material was prepared all the radium I had in my laboratory up to the date when I received the precious gift from the American women.

The School of Physics could give us no suitable premises, but for lack of anything better, the Director permitted us to use an abandoned shed which had been in service as a dissecting room of the School of Medicine. Its glass roof did not afford complete shelter against rain; the heat was suffocating in summer, and the bitter cold of winter was only a little lessened by the iron stove, except in its immediate vicinity. There was no question of obtaining the needed proper apparatus in common use by chemists. We simply had some old pine-wood tables with furnaces and gas burners. We had to use the adjoining yard for those of our chemical operations that involved producing irritating gases; even then the gas often filled our shed. With this equipment we entered on our exhausting work.

Yet it was in this miserable old shed that we passed the best and happiest years of our life, devoting our entire days to our work. Often I had to prepare our lunch in the shed, so as not to interrupt some particularly important operation. Sometimes I had to spend a whole day mixing a boiling mass with a heavy iron rod nearly as large as myself. I would be broken with fatigue at the day's end. Other days, on the contrary, the work would be a most minute and delicate fractional crystallization, in the effort to concentrate the radium. I was then annoyed by the floating dust of iron and coal from which I could not protect my precious products. But I shall never be able to express the joy of the untroubled quietness of this atmosphere of research and the excitement of actual progress with the confident hope of still better results. The feeling of discouragement that sometimes came after some unsuccessful toil did not last long and gave way to renewed activity. We had happy moments devoted to a quiet discussion of our work, walking around our shed.

One of our joys was to go into our workroom at night; we then perceived on all sides the feebly luminous silhouettes of the bottles or capsules containing our products. It was really a lovely sight and one always new to us. The glowing tubes looked like faint, fairy lights.

Thus the months passed, and our efforts, hardly interrupted by short vacations, brought forth more and more complete evidence. Our faith grew ever stronger, and our work being more and more known, we found means to get new quantities of raw material and to carry on some of our crude processes in a factory, allowing me to give more time to the delicate finishing treatment.

At this stage I devoted myself especially to the purification of the radium, my husband being absorbed by the study of the physical properties of the rays emitted by the new substances. It was only after treating one ton of pitchblende residues that I could get definite results. Indeed we know to-day that even in the best minerals there are not more than a few decigrammes of radium in a ton of raw material.

At last the time came when the isolated substances showed all the characters of a pure chemical body. This body, the radium, gives a characteristic spectrum, and I was able to determine for it an atomic weight much higher than that of the barium. This was achieved in 1902. I then possessed one decigramme of very pure radium chloride. It had taken me almost four years to produce the kind of evidence which chemical science demands, that radium is truly a new element. One year would probably have been enough for the same purpose, if reasonable means had been at my disposal. The demonstration that cost so much effort was the basis of the new science of radioactivity.

In later years I was able to prepare several decigrammes of pure radium salt, to make a more accurate determination of the atomic weight and even to isolate the pure radium metal. However, 1902 was the year in which the existence and character of radium were definitely established.

We had been able to live for several years entirely engrossed in the work of research, but gradually circumstances changed. In 1900 my husband was offered a professorship in the University of Geneva, but almost simultaneously he obtained a position of assistant professor at the Sorbonne, and I was made professor at the Normal Superior School for young girls at Sèvres. So we remained in Paris.

I became much interested in my work in the Normal School, and endeavored to develop more fully the practical laboratory exercises of the pupils. These pupils were girls of about twenty years who had entered the school after severe examination and had still to work very seriously to meet the requirements that would enable them to be named professors in the lycées. All these young women worked with great eagerness, and it was a pleasure for me to direct their studies in physics.

But a growing notoriety, because of the announcement of our discoveries, began to trouble our quiet work in the laboratory, and, little by little, life became more difficult. In 1903 I finished my doctor's thesis and obtained the degree. At the end of the same year the Nobel prize was awarded jointly to Becquerel, my husband and me for the discovery of radioactivity and new radioactive elements.

This event greatly increased the publicity of our work. For some time there was no more peace. Visitors and demands for lectures and articles interrupted every day.

The award of the Nobel prize was a great honor. It is also known that the material means provided by this prize was much greater than is usual in prizes for science. This was a great help in the continuation of our researches. Unhappily, we were overtired and had a succession of failures of health for the one or the other of us, so that it was not until 1905 that we were able to go to Stockholm, where my husband gave his Nobel lecture and where we were well received.

The fatigue resulting from the effort exceeding our forces, imposed by the unsatisfactory conditions of our labor, was augmented by the invasion of publicity. The overturn of our voluntary isolation was a cause of real suffering for us and had all the effect of disaster. It was serious trouble brought into the organization of our life, and I have already explained how indispensable was our freedom from external distraction, in order to maintain our family life and our scientific activity. Of course, people who contribute to that kind of trouble generally mean it kindly. It is only that they do not realize the conditions of the problem.

In 1904 our second daughter, Eve Denise, came to us. I had, of course, to interrupt my work in the laboratory for a while. In the same year, because of the awarding of the Nobel prize and the general public recognition, a new chair of physics was created in Sorbonne, and my husband was named as its occupant. At the same time I was named chief of work in the laboratory that was to be created for him. But in reality the laboratory was not constructed then, and only a few rooms taken from other uses were available to us.

In 1906 just as we were definitely giving up the old shed laboratory where we had been so happy, there came the dreadful catastrophe which took my husband away from me and left me alone to bring up our children and, at the same time, to continue our work of research.

It is impossible for me to express the profoundness and importance of the crisis brought into my life by the loss of the one who had been my closest companion and best friend. Crushed by the blow, I did not feel able to face the future. I could not forget, however, what my husband used sometimes to say, that, even deprived of him, I ought to continue my work.

The death of my husband, coming immediately after the general knowledge of the discoveries with which his name is associated, was felt by the public, and especially by the scientific circles, to be a national misfortune. It was largely under the influence of this emotion that the Faculty of Sciences of Paris decided to offer me the chair, as professor, which my husband had occupied only one year and a half in the Sorbonne. It was an exceptional decision, as up to then no woman had held such a position. The University by doing this offered me a precious mark of esteem and gave me opportunity to pursue the researches which otherwise might have had to be abandoned. I had not expected a gift of this kind; I never had any other ambition than to be able to work freely for science. The honor that now came to me was deeply painful under the cruel circumstances of its coming. Besides I wondered whether I would be able to face such a grave responsibility. After much hesitation, I decided that I ought at least to try to meet the task, and so I began in 1906 my teaching in the Sorbonne, as assistant professor, and two years later I was named titular professor.

In my new situation the difficulties of my life were considerably augmented, as I alone had now to carry the burden formerly weighing on my husband and me together. The cares of my young children required close vigilance; in this, my husband's father, who continued to live with us, willingly took his share. He was happy to be occupied with the little girls, whose company was his chief consolation after his son's death. By his effort and mine, the children had a bright home, even if we lived with our inner grief, which they were too young to realize. The strong desire of my father-in-law being to live in the country, we took a house with a garden in Sceaux, a suburb of Paris, from which I could reach the city in half an hour.

This country life had great advantages, not only for my father-in-law, who enjoyed his new surroundings, and especially his garden, but also for my girls, who had the benefit of walks in the open country. But they were more separated from me, and it became necessary to have a governess for them. This position was filled first by one of my cousins, and then by a devoted woman who had already brought up the daughter of one of my sisters. Both of them were Polish, and in this way my daughters learned my native tongue. From time to time, some one of my Polish family came to see me in my grief, and we managed to meet in vacation time, at the seashore in France, and once in the mountains of Poland.

In 1910 we suffered the loss of my very dear father-in-law, after a long illness, which brought me many sorrowful days. I used to spend at his bedside as much time as I could, listening to his remembrances of passed years. His death affected deeply my elder daughter, who, at twelve, knew the value of the cheerful hours spent in his company.

There were few resources for the education of my daughters in Sceaux. The youngest one, a small child, needed principally a hygienic life, outdoor walks and quite elementary schooling. She had already shown a vivid intelligence and an unusual disposition for music. Her elder sister resembled her father in the form of her intelligence. She was not quick, but one could already see that she had a gift of reasoning power and that she would like science. She had some training in a private school in Paris, but I had not wanted to keep her in a lycée, as I have always found the class hours in these schools too long for the health of the children.

My view is that in the education of children the requirement of their growth and physical evolution should be respected, and that some time should be left for their artistic culture. In most schools, as they exist to-day, the time spent in various reading and writing exercises is too great, and the study required to be done at home too much. I also find these schools lacking, in general, in practical exercises to accompany the scientific studies.

With a few friends in the university circle who shared these views, we organized, therefore, a coöperative group for the education of our children, each of us taking charge of the teaching of a particular subject to all of the young people. We were all very busy with other things, and the children varied in age. Nevertheless, the little experiment thus made was very interesting. With a small number of classes we yet succeeded in reuniting the scientific and literary elements of a desirable culture. The courses in science were accompanied by practical exercises in which the children took great interest.

This arrangement, which lasted two years, proved to be very beneficial for most of the children; it was certainly so for my elder daughter. Following this preparation, she was able to enter a higher class in one of the *collèges* of Paris, and had no difficulty in passing her bachelor's examination before the usual age, after which she continued her scientific studies in the Sorbonne.

My second daughter, although not benefiting by a similar arrangement for her earlier studies, at first followed the classes of a *collège* only partially, and later completely. She showed herself a good pupil, doing satisfactory work in all directions.

I wanted very much to assure for my children a rational physical education. Next to outdoor walks, I attach a great importance to gymnastics and sports. This side of a girl's education is still rather neglected in France. I took care that my children did gymnastics regularly. I was also careful to have them spend vacations either in the mountains or at the seashore. They can canoe and swim very well and are not afraid of a long walk or a bicycle ride.

But of course the care of my children's education was only a part of my duties, my professional occupations taking most of my time. I have been frequently questioned, especially by women, how I could reconcile family life with a scientific career. Well, it has not been easy; it required a great deal of decision and of self-sacrifice. However, the family bond has been preserved between me and my now grown-up daughters, and life is made brighter by the mutual affection and understanding in our home, where I could not suffer a harsh word or selfish behavior.

In 1906, when I succeeded my husband at the Sorbonne, I had only a provisional laboratory with little space and most limited equipment. A few scientists and students had already been admitted to work there with my husband and me. With their help, I was able to continue the course of research with good success.

In 1907, I received a precious mark of sympathy from Mr. Andrew Carnegie, who donated to my laboratory an annual income for research fellowships which enabled some advanced students or scientists to devote their whole time to investigation. Such foundations are very encouraging to those whose inclinations and talents are such as to warrant their entire devotion to research work. They ought to be multiplied in the interest of science.

As for myself, I had to devote again a great deal of time to the preparation of several decigrammes of very pure radium chloride. With this I achieved, in 1907, a new determination of the atomic weight of radium, and in 1910 I was able to isolate the metal. The operation, an extremely delicate one, was performed with the assistance of a distinguished chemist belonging to the laboratory staff. It has never been repeated since that time, because it involves a serious danger of loss of radium, which can be avoided only with utmost care. So I saw at last the mysterious white metal, but could not keep it in this state, for it was required for further experiments.

As for the polonium, I have not been able to isolate it, its quantity in the mineral being even much less than the quantity of radium. However, very concentrated polonium has been prepared in my laboratory, and important experiments have been performed with this substance, concerning especially the production of helium by radiation of polonium.

I had to devote special care to the improvement of the measuring methods in the laboratory. I have told how important precise measurements were in the discovery of radium. It is still to be hoped that efficient methods of quantitative determination may lead to new discoveries.

I devised a very satisfactory method for determining the quantity of radium by the means of a radioactive gas produced by it and called "emanation." This method, frequently used in my laboratory, permits of the measurement of very small quantities of radium (less than a thousandth of a milligramme), with a fair precision. More important quantities are often measured by their penetrating radiation, named Gamma-rays. For this we also possess in my laboratory a suitable equipment. It is easier and more satisfactory to measure the radium by the emitted rays, than to weigh it in a balance. However, these measurements require the disposition of reliable standards. So the question of a radium standard had to be taken into careful consideration.

The measurements of radium had to be established on a solid basis, for the benefit of laboratories and scientific research, which, of course, is in itself an important reason, and moreover, the growing medical utilization of this substance made it necessary to control the relative purity of commercially produced radium.

The first experiments on the biological properties of radium were successfully made in France with samples from our laboratory, while my husband was living. The results were, at once, encouraging, so that the new branch of medical science, called radiumtherapy (in France, *Curietherapy*), developed rapidly, first in France and later in other countries. To supply the radium wanted for this purpose, a radium-producing industry was established. The first plant was created in France and worked very successfully, but afterwards manufactures were founded in other countries, the most important of which are now in America, where great quantities of radium ore, named "carnotite," are available. The radiumtherapy and the radium production developed conjointly, and the results were more and more important, for the treatment of several diseases, and particularly of cancer. As a consequence of this, several institutes have been founded, in the large cities, for the application of the new therapy. Some of these institutes own several grammes of radium, the commercial price of the gramme being now about $70,000, the cost of production depending on the very small proportion of radium in the ore.

It may be easily understood how deeply I appreciated the privilege of realizing that our discovery had become a benefit to mankind, not only through its great scientific importance, but also by its power of efficient action against human suffering and terrible disease. This was indeed a splendid reward for our years of hard toil.

The success of the therapy depends, of course, on the precise knowledge of the quantity of radium which is used, so that the measurements of radium are as important for industry and for medicine as for physicochemical research.

Considering all these needs, a commission of scientific men of different countries was formed who agreed to take as a base an international standard, formed of a carefully weighed quantity of pure radium salt. Secondary standards were then to be prepared for each country, and compared to the basic standard by means of their radiation. I was appointed to prepare the primary standard.

This was a very delicate operation, as the weight of the standard sample, quite small (about 21 milligrammes of chloride), had to be determined with great precision. I performed the preparation in 1911. The standard is a thin glass tube, of a few centimeters in length, containing the pure salt which was used for the determination of atomic weight. It was accepted by the Commission and is deposited in the International Bureau of Weights and Measures at Sèvres, near Paris. Several secondary standards, compared with the primary one, have been put into service by the Commission. In France the control of radium tubes, by the measurement of their radiation, takes place in my laboratory, where any one may bring the radium to be tested; in the United States this is done in the Bureau of Standards.

Near the end of the year 1910, I was proposed for the decoration of the Legion of Honor. A similar proposal was made earlier in favor of my husband, who, however, being opposed to all honorary distinctions, did not accept the nomination. As my husband and I were too united in all things for me to act differently from him in this matter, I did not accept the decoration, in spite of the insistence of the Ministry. At that time also, several colleagues persuaded me to be a candidate for election to the Academy of Sciences of Paris, of which my husband was a member during the last months of his life. I hesitated very much, as such a candidacy requires, by custom, a great number of personal visits to Academy members. However, I consented to offer myself a candidate, because of the advantages an election would have for my laboratory. My candidacy provoked a vivid public interest, especially because it involved the question of the admission of women to the Academy. Many of the Academicians were opposed to this in principle, and when the scrutiny was made, I had a few votes less than was necessary. I do not ever wish to renew my candidacy, because of my strong distaste for the personal solicitation required. I believe that all such elections should be based wholly on a spontaneous decision, without any personal efforts involved, as was the case for several Academies and Societies which made me a member without any demand or initiative on my part.

As a result of all the cares devolving on me, I fell seriously ill at the end of 1911, when, for the second time, I received, this time alone, the award of the Nobel prize. This was a very exceptional honor, a high recognition of the discovery of the new elements and of the preparation of pure radium. Suffering though I was, I went to Stockholm to receive the prize. The journey was extremely painful for me. I was accompanied by my eldest sister and my young daughter Irene. The ceremony of delivery of the Nobel prizes is very impressive, having the features of a national solemnity. A most generous reception was accorded me, specially by the women of Sweden. This was a great comfort to me, but I was suffering so much that when I returned I had to stay in bed for several months. This grave illness, as well as the necessities of my children's education, obliged me to move my home from Sceaux to Paris.

During the year 1912 I had the opportunity of collaborating in the creation of a laboratory of radium at Warsaw. This laboratory was founded by the Scientific Society of Warsaw which offered me its direction. I could not leave France to go back to my native country, but I willingly agreed to occupy myself with the organization of the studies in the new laboratory. In 1913, having improved my health, I was able to attend an inauguration fête in Warsaw, where a touching reception was given, leaving me an unforgettable memory of national sentiment which succeeded in creating useful work under particularly difficult political conditions.

While still only partially recovered from my illness, I renewed my efforts for the construction of a suitable laboratory in

Paris. Finally it was arranged for, and work began in 1912. The Pasteur Institute wished to be associated with this laboratory, and, in accord with the University, it was decided to create an Institute of Radium, with two laboratories, one of physics and one of biology, the first to be devoted to studies of the physical and chemical properties of the radioactive elements, the second to the study of their biological and medical applications. But, because of the lack of financial means, the construction work proceeded very slowly, and was not yet entirely finished when the war broke out in 1914.

Few specialized research instruments have captured the popular imagination to the extent that the cyclotron has. And no wonder: it and its giant successors are marvelously impressive affairs to look at in addition to being among the most productive devices in the history of science. In the course of probing the atomic nucleus to ascertain its structure, accelerator-bred particles have outdone even cosmic rays in the information they have yielded on the elementary particles and fundamental interactions that underlie the macroscopic world. Until the current fad for rockets and satellites as scientific status symbols developed, giant accelerators played a similar role. Nations as well as universities were graded by the cognoscenti on the basis of the particle energies their machines could produce. As in space research, this size comparison has a certain validity as a measure of scientific leadership.

The word cyclotron and the name Ernest Orlando Lawrence are inseparable. This remarkable man conceived the cyclotron and guided it to success. At the Berkeley campus of the University of California he established the world-famous Radiation Laboratory, now named after him, and attracted a staff so gifted and enthusiastic that a total of five Nobel Prizes have been awarded to its members, including, of course, the one that Lawrence received for his invention. The Radiation Laboratory has, from its start, been the leader in high-energy laboratory research. From it has come the first artificially produced mesons and the first artificially produced antiprotons and antineutrons. Lawrence was in charge of the entire operation until his death in 1958 at the age of fifty-seven.

The following selection was originally read by M. Stanley Livingston of the Massachusetts Institute of Technology as a memorial to Lawrence at the American Physical Society meeting in Washington, in the Spring of 1959; it has since been published in **Physics Today.** Livingston constructed the first cyclotron for his Ph.D. thesis under Lawrence and has subsequently been associated with a number of significant developments in accelerator technology. He currently heads the Cambridge Electron Accelerator project, which is jointly sponsored by Harvard University and the Massachusetts Institute of Technology.

M. Stanley Livingston

HISTORY OF THE CYCLOTRON

The principle of the magnetic resonance accelerator, now known as the cyclotron, was proposed by Professor Ernest O. Lawrence of the University of California in 1930, in a short article in *Science* by Lawrence and N. E. Edlefsen. It was suggested by the experiment of Wideröe in 1928, in which ions of Na and K were accelerated to twice the applied voltage while traversing two tubular electrodes in line between which an oscillatory electric field was applied—an elementary linear accelerator. In 1953 Professor Lawrence described to the writer the origin of the idea, as he then remembered it.

The conception of the idea occurred in the library of the University of California in the early summer of 1929, when Lawrence was browsing through the current journals and read Wideröe's paper in the *Archiv für Elektrotechnik.* Lawrence speculated on possible variations of this resonance principle, including the use of a magnetic field to deflect particles in circular paths so they would return to the first electrode, and thus reuse the electric field in the gap. He discovered that the equations of motion predicted a constant period of revolution, so that particles could be accelerated indefinitely in resonance with an oscillatory electric field—the "cyclotron resonance" principle.

Lawrence seems to have discussed the idea with others during this early formative period. For example, Thomas H. Johnson has told the writer that Lawrence discussed it with himself and Jesse W. Beams during a conference at the Bartol Institute in Philadelphia during that summer, and that further details grew out of the discussion.

The first opportunity to test the idea came during the spring of 1930, when Lawrence asked Edlefsen, then a graduate student at Berkeley who had completed his thesis and was awaiting the June degree date, to set up an experimental system. Edlefsen used an existing small magnet in the laboratory and built a glass vacuum chamber with two hollow internal electrodes to which radiofrequency voltage could be applied, with an unshielded probe electrode at the periphery. The current to the probe varied with magnetic field, and a broad resonance peak was observed which was interpreted as due to the resonant acceleration of hydrogen ions.

However, Lawrence and Edlefsen had not in fact observed true cyclotron resonance; this came a little later. Nevertheless, this first paper was the initial announcement of a principle of acceleration which was soon found to be valid and which became the basis for all future cyclotron development.

Doctoral Thesis. In the summer of 1930 Professor Lawrence suggested the problem of resonance acceleration to the author, then a graduate student at Berkeley, as an experimental research investigation. In my early efforts to confirm Edlefsen's results I found that the broad peak observed by him was probably due to single acceleration of N and O ions from the residual gas, which curved in the magnetic field and struck the unshielded electrode at the edge of the chamber.

It was my opportunity and responsibility to continue the study and to demonstrate true cyclotron resonance. A Doctoral Thesis by the author dated April 14, 1931, reported the results of the study. It was not published but is on file at the University of California library. The electromagnet available was of 4-inch pole diameter. The vacuum chamber was made of brass and copper. Only one "D" was used, on this and several subsequent models; the need for a more efficient electrical circuit for the radiofrequency electrodes came later with the effort to increase energy. A vacuum tube oscillator provided up to 1,000 volts on the electrode, at a frequency which could be varied by adjusting the number of turns in a resonant inductance. Hydrogen ions (H_2^+ and later H^+) were produced through ionization of hydrogen gas in the chamber, by electrons emitted from a tungsten-wire cathode at the center. Resonant ions which reached the edge of the chamber were observed in a shielded collector cup and had to traverse a deflecting electric field. Sharp peaks were observed in the collected current at the magnetic field for resonance with H_2^+ ions. Also present were 3/2 and 5/2 resonance peaks at proportionately lower magnetic fields, due to harmonic resonances of H_2^+ ions. By varying the frequency of the applied electric field, resonance was observed over a wide range of frequency and magnetic field, proving conclusively the validity of the resonance principle.

The small magnet used in these resonance studies had a maximum field of 5,200 gauss, for which resonance with H_2^+ ions occurred at 76 meters wavelength or 4.0 megacycles frequency. In this small chamber the final ion energy was 13,000 electron volts, obtained with the application of a minimum of 160 volts peak on the D. This corresponds to about 40 turns or 80 accelerations. A stronger magnet was borrowed for a short time, capable of producing 13,000 gauss, with which it was possible to extend the resonance curve and to produce hydrogen ions of 80,000 ev energy. This goal was reached on January 2, 1931.

The First 1-Mev Cyclotron. Lawrence moved promply to exploit this breakthrough. In the spring of 1931 he applied for and was awarded a grant by the National Research Council (about $1,000) for a machine which could give useful energies for nuclear research. The writer was appointed as an instructor at the University of California on completion of the doctorate in order to continue the research. During the summer and fall of 1931, the writer, under the supervision of Lawrence, designed and built a 9-inch diameter magnet and brought it into operation, first with H_2^+ ions of 0.5-Mev energy. Then the poles were enlarged to 11 inches and protons were accelerated to 1.2 Mev. This was the first time in scientific history that artificially accelerated ions of this energy had been produced. The beam intensity available at a target was about 0.01 microampere. The progress and results were reported in a series of three abstracts and papers by Lawrence and Livingston in *The Physical Review.*

Of course, Lawrence had other interests and other students in the laboratory. Milton White continued research with the first cyclotron. David Sloan developed a series of linear accelerators for heavy ions, limited by the radio power tubes and techniques available at that time, for Hg ions and later for Li ions. With Wesley Coates, Robert Thornton, and Bernard Kinsey, Sloan also invented and developed a resonance transformer using a radio-frequency coil in a vacuum chamber which developed 1 million volts. With Jack Livingood and Frank Exner he tried for a time to make this into an electron accelerator. I must again thank Dave Sloan for the many times that he assisted me in solving problems of the cyclotron oscillator.

The Race for High Voltage. To understand the meaning of this achievement we must look at it from the perspective of the status of science throughout the world. When Rutherford demonstrated in 1919 that the nitrogen nucleus could be disintegrated by the naturally occurring alpha particles from radium and thorium, a new era was opened in physics. For the first time man was able to modify the structure of the atomic nucleus, but in submicroscopic quantities and only by borrowing the enormous energies (5 to 8 Mev) of radioactive matter. During the 1920's x-ray techniques were developed so machines could be built for 100 to 200 kilovolts. Development to still higher voltages was limited by corona discharge and insulation breakdown, and the multimillion volt range seemed out of reach.

Physicists recognized the potential value of artificial sources of accelerated particles. In a speech before the Royal Society in 1927 Rutherford expressed his hope that accelerators of sufficient energy to disintegrate nuclei could be built. Then in 1928 Gamow and also Condon and Gurney showed how the new wave mechanics, which was to be so successful in atomic science, could be used to describe the penetration of nuclear potential barriers by charged particles. Their theories made it seem probable that energies of 500 kilovolts or less would be sufficient to cause the disintegration of light nuclei. This more modest goal seemed feasible. Experimentation started around 1929 in several laboratories to develop the necessary accelerating devices.

This race for high voltage started on several fronts. Cockcroft and Walton in the Cavendish Laboratory of Cambridge University, urged on by Rutherford, chose to extend the known engineering techniques of the voltage-multiplier, which had already been successful in some x-ray installations. Van de Graaff chose the long-known phenomena of electrostatics and developed a new type of belt-charged static generator to obtain high voltages. Others explored the Tesla coil transformer with an oil-insulated high-voltage coil, or the "surge-generator" in which capacitors are charged in parallel and discharged in series, and still others used transformers stacked in cascade on insulated platforms.

The first to succeed were Cockcroft and Walton. They reported the disintegration of lithium by protons of about 400 kilovolts energy, in 1932. I like to consider this as the first significant date in accelerator history and the practical start of experimental nuclear physics.

All the schemes and techniques described above have the same basic limitation in energy; the breakdown of dielectrics or gases sets a practical limit to the voltages which can be successfully used. This limit has been raised by improved technology, especially in the pressure-insulated electrostatic generator, but it still remains as a technological limit. The cyclotron avoids this voltage-breakdown limitation by the principle of resonance acceleration. It provides a method of obtaining high particle energies without the use of high voltage.

The Cyclotron Splits Its First Atoms. The above digression into the story of the state of the art shows why the 1.2-Mev protons from the 11-inch Berkeley cyclotron were so important. This small and relatively inexpensive machine could split atoms! This was Lawrence's goal. This was why Lawrence literally danced with glee when, watching over my shoulder as I tuned the magnet through resonance, the galvanometer spot swung across the scale indicating that 1,000,000-volt ions were reaching the collector. The story quickly spread around the laboratory and we were busy all that day demonstrating million-volt protons to eager viewers.

We had barely confirmed our results and I was busy with revisions to increase beam intensity when we received the issue of the *Proceedings of the Royal Society* describing the results of Cockcroft and Walton in disintegrating lithium with protons of only 400 000 electron volts. We were unprepared at that time to observe disintegrations with adequate instruments. Lawrence sent an emergency call to his friend and former colleague, Donald Cooksey at Yale, who came out to Berkeley for the summer with Franz Kurie; they helped develop the necessary counters and instruments for disintegration measurements. Within a few months after hearing the news from Cambridge we were ready to try for ourselves. Targets of various elements were mounted on removable stems which could be swung into the beam of ions. The counters clicked, and we were observing disintegrations! These first early results were published on October 1, 1932, as confirmation of the work of Cockcroft and Walton, by Lawrence, Livingston, and White.

The "27-inch" Cyclotron. Long before I had completed the 11-inch machine as a working accelerator, Lawrence was planning the next step. His aims were ambitious, but supporting funds were small and slow in arriving. He was forced to use many economies.

and substitutes to reach his goals. He located a magnet core from an obsolete Poulsen arc magnet with a 45-inch core, which was donated by the Federal Telegraph Company. Two pole cores were used and machined to form the symmetrical, flat pole faces for a cyclotron. In the initial arrangement the pole faces were tapered to a 27½-inch diameter pole face; in later years this was expanded to 34 inches and still higher energies were obtained. The windings were layer-wound of strip copper and immersed in oil tanks for cooling. (The oil tanks leaked! We all wore paper hats when working between coils to keep oil out of our hair.) The magnet was installed in the "old radiation lab" in December 1931; this was an old frame warehouse building near the University of California Physics Building which was for years the center of cyclotron and other accelerator activities.

Other dodges were necessary to meet the mounting bills for materials and parts. The Physics Department shops were kept filled with orders for machining. Willing graduate students worked with the mechanics installing the components. My appointment as instructor terminated, and for the following year Lawrence arranged for me an appointment as research assistant in which I not only continued development on the cyclotron but also supervised the design and installation of a 1-Mev resonance transformer x-ray installation of the Sloan design in the University Hospital in San Francisco.

The vacuum chamber for the 27-inch machine was a brass ring with many radial spouts, fitted with "lids" of iron plate on top and bottom which were extensions of the pole faces. Sealing wax and a special soft mixture of beeswax and rosin were first used for vacuum seals, but were ultimately replaced by gasket seals. In the initial model only one insulated D-shaped electrode was used, facing a slotted bar at ground potential which was called a "dummy D." In the space behind the bar the collector could be mounted at any chosen radius. The beam was first observed at a small radius, and the magnet was "shimmed" and other adjustments made to give maximum beam intensity. Then the chamber was opened, the collector moved to a larger radius, and the tuning and shimming extended. Thus we learned, the hard way, of the necessity of a radially decreasing magnetic field for focusing. If our optimism persuaded us to install the collector at too large a radius, we made a "strategic retreat" to a smaller radius and recovered the beam. Eventually we reached a practical maximum radius of 10 inches and installed two symmetrical D's with which higher energies could be attained. Technical improvements and new gadgets were added day by day as we gained experience. The progress during this period of development from 1-Mev protons to 5-Mev deuterons was reported in *The Physical Review* by Livingston in 1932 and by Lawrence and Livingston in 1934.

I am indebted to Edwin M. McMillan for a brief chronological account of these early developments on the 27-inch cyclotron. (It seems that earlier laboratory notebooks were lost.) These records show, for example:

June 13, 1932. 16-cm radius, 28-meter wavelength, beam of 1.24-Mev H_2^+ ions.

August 20, 1932. 18-cm radius, 29 meters, 1.58-Mev H_2^+ ions.

August 24, 1932. Sylphon bellows put on filament for adjustment.

September 28, 1932. 25.4-cm radius, 25.8 meters, 2.6-Mev H_2^+ ions.

October 20, 1932. Installed two D's in tank, radius fixed at 10 in.

November 16, 1932. 4.8-Mev H_2^+ ions, ion current 10^{-9} amps.

December 2–5, 1932. Installed target chamber for studies of disintegrations with Geiger counter. Start of long series of experiments.

March 20, 1933. 5 Mev of H_2^+; 1.5 Mev of He^+; 2 Mev of $(HD)^+$. Deuterium ions accelerated for first time.

September 27, 1933. Observed neutrons from targets bombarded by D^+.

December 3, 1933. Automatic magnet current control circuit installed.

February 24, 1934. Observed induced radioactivity in C by deuteron bombardment. 3-Mev D^+ ions, beam current 0.1 microampere.

March 16, 1934. 1.6-Mev H^+ ions, beam current 0.8 microampere.

April–May, 1934. 5.0-Mev D^+ ions, beam current 0.3 microampere.

Those were busy and exciting times. Other young scientists joined the group, some to assist in the continuing development of the cyclotron and others to develop the instruments for research instrumentation. Malcolm Henderson came in 1933 and developed counting instruments and magnet control circuits, and also spent long hours repairing leaks and helping with the development of the cyclotron. Franz Kurie joined the team, and Jack Livingood and Dave Sloan continued with their linear accelerators and resonance transformers, but were always available to help with problems on the cyclotron. Edwin McMillan was a major thinker in the planning and design of research experiments. And we all had a fond regard for Commander Telesio Lucci, retired from the Italian Navy, who became our self-appointed laboratory assistant. As the experiments began to show results we depended heavily on Robert Oppenheimer for discussions and theoretical interpretation.

One of the exciting periods was our first use of deuterons in the cyclotron. Professor G. N. Lewis of the Chemistry Department had succeeded in concentrating "heavy water" with about 20% deuterium from battery acid residues, and we electrolyzed it to obtain gas for our ion source. Soon after we tuned in the first beam we observed alpha particles from a Li target with longer range and higher energy than any previously found in natural radioactivities–14.5-cm range, coming from the Li (d,p) reaction. These results were reported in 1933 by Lewis, Livingston, and Lawrence and led to an extensive program of research in deuteron reactions. Neutrons were also observed, in much higher intensities when deuterons were used as bombarding particles, and were put to use in a variety of ways.

We had frustrations–repairing vacuum leaks in the wax seals of the chamber or "tank" was a continuing problem. The ion source filament was another weak point, and required continuous development. And sometimes Lawrence could be *very* enthusiastic. I recall working till midnight one night to replace a filament and to reseal the tank. The next morning I cautiously warmed up and tuned the cyclotron to a new beam intensity record. Lawrence was so pleased and excited when he came into the laboratory that morning that he jubilantly ran the filament current higher and higher, exclaiming each time at the new high beam intensity, until he pushed too high and burned out the filament!

We made mistakes too, due to inexperience in research and the general feeling of urgency in the laboratory. The neutron had been identified by Chadwick in 1932. By 1933 we were producing and observing neutrons from every target bombarded by deuterons. They showed a striking similarity in energy, independent of the target, and each target also gave a proton group of constant energy. This led to the now forgotten mistake in which the neutron mass was calculated on the assumption that the deuteron was breaking up into a proton and a neutron in the nuclear field. The neutron mass was computed from the energy of the common proton group, and was much lower than the value determined by Chadwick. Shortly afterward, Tuve, Hafstad, and Dahl in Washington, D.C., using the first electrostatic generator to be completed and used for research, showed that these protons and neutrons came from the D(d,p) and D(d,n) reactions, in which the target was deuterium gas deposited in all targets by the beam. We were chagrined, and vowed to be more careful in the future.

We also had many successful and exciting moments. I recall the day early in 1934 (February 24) when Lawrence came racing into the lab waving a copy of the *Comptes Rendus* and excitedly told us of the discovery of induced radioactivity by Curie and Joliot in Paris, using natural alpha particles on boron and other light elements. They predicted that the same activities could be produced by deuterons on other targets, such as carbon. Now it just so happened that we had a wheel of targets inside the cyclotron which could be turned into the beam by a greased joint, and a thin mica window on a re-entrant seal through which we had been observing the long-range alpha particles from deuteron bombardment. We also had a Geiger point counter and counting circuits at hand. We had been making 1-minute runs on alpha

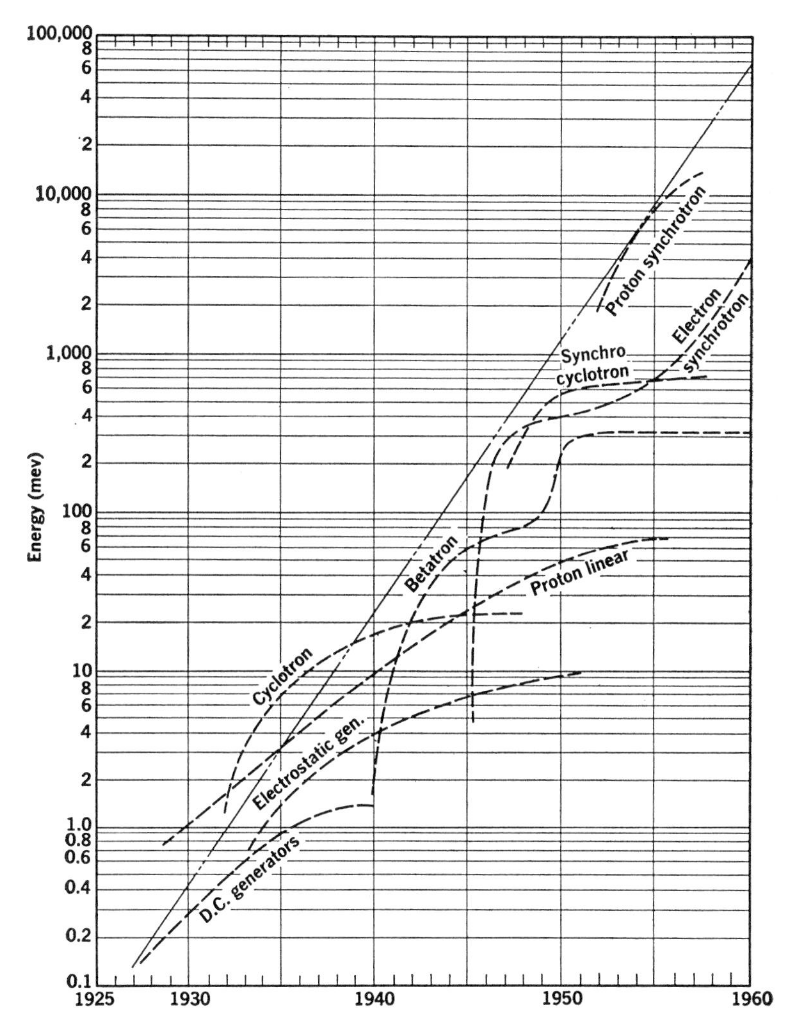

Figure 1 Energies attained with accelerators as a function of time.

particles, with the counter switch connected to one terminal of a double-pole knife-switch used to turn the oscillator on and off. We quickly disconnected this counter switch, turned the target wheel to carbon, adjusted the counter circuits, and then bombarded the target for 5 minutes. When the oscillator switch was opened this time, the counter was turned on, and click-click--click---click----click. We were observing induced radioactivity within less than a half-hour after hearing of the Curie-Joliot results. This result was first reported by Henderson, Livingston, and Lawrence in March, 1934.

I left the laboratory in July, 1934, to go to Cornell (and later to MIT) as the first missionary from the Lawrence cyclotron group. Edwin McMillan overlapped my term of apprenticeship by a few months, and stayed on to win the Nobel Prize and ultimately to succeed Professor Lawrence as director of the laboratory which he founded.

It would be unfair to the spirit of Professor Lawrence if I failed to indicate some gleam of great things to come, some vision of the future. Recently I prepared a graph of the growth of particle energies obtained with accelerators with time, shown in Fig. 1. To keep this rapidly rising curve on the plot, the energies are plotted on a logarithmic scale. The curves show the growth of accelerator energy for each type of accelerator plotted at the dates when new voltage records were achieved. The cyclotron was the first resonance accelerator to be successful, and it led to the much more sophisticated synchronous accelerators which are still in the process of growth. The over-all envelope to the curve of log E vs time is almost linear, which means an exponential rise in energy, with a 10-fold increase occurring every 6 years and with a total increase in particle energy of over 10,000 since the days of the first practical accelerators. The end is not yet in sight. If you are tempted to extrapolate this curve to 1960, or even to 1970, then you are truly sensing the exponentially rising spirit of the Berkeley Radiation Laboratory in those early days, stimulated by our unique leader, Professor Lawrence.

No announcement of a scientific achievement was more dramatic than the detonation of an atomic bomb over Hiroshima on August 6, 1945, and no scientific achievement has had a greater immediate impact upon the world at large. Since 1905, when Einstein discovered that mass and energy are equivalent, the possibility of releasing atomic energy at will had been realized, but not until early in 1939 did any means for accomplishing such a release become known. In that year it appeared from the work of several physicists that uranium, when bombarded with neutrons, splits into two fragments with the evolution of a large amount of energy—and also of several additional neutrons. The potentialities of fission and the chain reaction as an energy source were not overlooked by the scientific community in this country. After one or two abortive attempts at interesting the government, Einstein himself, Leo Szilard, and Eugene Wigner discussed the matter with Alexander Sachs of New York, who established the contact with President Roosevelt that ultimately led to the Manhattan District and the bomb. The history of the bomb project is, but for its dreadful result, one of the most romantic of all time. Great secrecy, high adventure, isolation on a remote mesa, the nation's life perhaps at stake, the low comedy of draft-board interference—not a touch is missing, not even the ironic fate of the director of the bomb laboratory, J. R. Oppenheimer.

The selection that follows is from the British Information Service statement, **Britain and the Atomic Bomb,** issued August 12, 1945. It is, of course, somewhat biased in favor of British accomplishments, but it is also a clear, succinct account of those findings in nuclear physics that led to the birth of atomic energy. Many books and articles have been published that take up the story of atomic energy where we leave it; most have something to say and are worth reading, but none has quite the flavor of Henry D. Smyth's **Atomic Energy for Military Purposes** (Princeton, 1945), the official report on the project.

The British Information Service

THE BIRTH OF ATOMIC ENERGY

The discovery of the fission of uranium and its application in the atomic bomb is no isolated event but follows a series of discoveries which, since the end of the last century, have been the basis of the modern science of physics. This work has been done in many countries and is the result of full and free collaboration between scientists, among whom those working in Britain have played a most important part.

Classical ideas on the nature and properties of matter culminated in the atomic theory of the nineteenth century. It was accepted that all matter was made up of discrete, indestructible particles or atoms which were classified into 92 different species or elements. From the atoms of one or more of these elements all the different chemical compounds that exist in nature are built up. But it was regarded as a cardinal point that the atoms of any one element could in no way be changed or converted into those of another.

Radioactivity. The fundamental break with this theory occurred when the French physicist H. Becquerel, in 1896, discovered that one of the elements—uranium—was continuously emitting radiation of an unknown type which could penetrate matter and affect a photographic plate. Further study of this new-found property of uranium led to the isolation of another element—radium—from the uranium mineral deposits in Joachimstal by Pierre and Marie Curie in 1898. Radium showed, to a much greater degree, this same property of emitting radiation and it was clear that the phenomenon of "radio-activity," as it was called, was altogether different from those associated with normal chemical reactions between atoms. In 1902 Rutherford and Soddy, who were then working at McGill University, Montreal, suggested that it could only be explained by the assumption that the atoms of uranium, radium, and of other radioactive elements which had by then been discovered were unstable and were continuously breaking up at rates which were characteristic for each element.

This suggestion was conclusively proved by detailed experimental work in the course of which the nature and properties of the radiation from radioactive elements were discovered. Part of this radiation, the so-called "alpha rays," consists of helium atoms, carrying a positive charge of electricity, and these were found to be of the greatest value as a tool for further exploration of the structure of atoms.

It was, in fact, research on the penetration of matter by alpha rays which led Rutherford, at Manchester University in 1911, to the fundamental discovery that the whole mass of each atom was concentrated in a minute central nucleus which carried a positive electric charge. Round this nucleus, but at relatively very great distances, revolved elementary negative electric charges—the electrons—in numbers sufficient to neutralize exactly the positive charge of the nucleus. The mass of these electrons was negligible compared with that of the nucleus. In terms of classical electromagnetic theory, however, such a system would be unstable and the energy of the revolving electrons would, in a very short time, be lost as radiation. Niels Bohr, of Copenhagen, put forward a theory in 1913 which combined Rutherford's model of the "nuclear atom" with the quantum theory of energy which had been enunciated by Planck to explain limitations of the classical electromagnetic theory.

The resulting Rutherford-Bohr model of the atom proved to be of the greatest value in explaining the results of experimental work in every branch of physics and, in particular, the relationship between the different elements as regards their ordinary physical and chemical properties. These are determined entirely by the electrons revolving round the nucleus and are therefore practically independent of the mass of the nucleus. It was, therefore, immediately understood that any element, with a given charge on the nucleus, could exist in more than one modification with different atomic masses but almost identical physical and chemical properties.

The existence of such modifications of any element, which were known as "isotopes," had first been suggested by Soddy in 1910 as a result of studies of the decay products of the natural radioactive elements.

Aston, at Cambridge, followed up work which had been started by J. J. Thomson and developed the so-called "mass-spectograph," which subjected a stream of electrically charged atoms—or ions—to a crossed electric and magnetic field and brought those of different mass to a focus at different points. It was proved, with the help of this instrument, that the great majority of elements consisted of a mixture of two or more isotopes and that the relative weight of the atom of any given isotope of any element was very nearly a simple multiple of the weight of a hydrogen nucleus, or proton.

Because the isotopes of an element have almost identical chemical properties it is in general extremely difficult to separate them or even to change appreciably their relative concentration. We must take recourse to processes which depend on the nuclear mass of the atoms, making use of the difference in mass between isotopes. This difference is usually only a small fraction of the total mass. Moreover, while some of these methods, such as that used in the mass-spectrograph, are not difficult to apply, they can ordinarily deal only with very small quantities of material, too small to be of much practical use.

In 1932 Urey and Brickwedde of Columbia University, New York, showed that hydrogen itself is not a simple element but contains a small amount (about 1/5000) of an isotope known as "heavy hydrogen" or deuterium which has almost double the mass of a proton. Because, in this case, the ratio of the masses of the isotopes is as two to one the physical and chemical properties of hydrogen and deuterium are sensibly different and it was found possible to separate them, in a pure state, in large amounts by normal technical methods.

The atoms of nearly all the elements are stable and there are only a few heavy elements which are radioactive and disintegrate spontaneously. It was one of the more obvious facts of radioactivity that the disintegration is accompanied by a release of energy. The amount of energy released in a single event, that is in the disintegration of a single radioactive nucleus, is incomparably greater than the amount obtained from a single event in a chemical reaction, say the burning of one atom of carbon. On the other hand, the amount of energy which can be obtained from radioactive elements is of no practical use, because the number of disintegrating atoms is small, only a minute fraction of the atoms present, and because the rate of disintegration cannot be influenced in any way. The phenomena of radioactivity thus indicated that there was an enormous reserve of energy in the atomic nuclei but gave no clue to methods of influencing its release. It was obvious that any hope of understanding the conditions under which the energy could be released would depend on an understanding of the structure of the atomic nucleus.

Artificial Disintegration of Atoms. The first decisive step in the solution of this problem was taken by Rutherford who, in 1919, showed experimentally that the charged alpha particles from radium-C could, in rare instances, collide with the nucleus of an atom of the common element nitrogen in such a way that it broke up, forming a nucleus of an oxygen atom and a hydrogen nucleus or proton.

While the discovery of radioactivity had shown that some of the elements could, spontaneously, break up to form other elements, Rutherford had now shown that the particles emitted in this process could be used to break up, or transmute, the atoms of other elements which were normally stable.

This development was pursued in the following years by Rutherford and Chadwick, who found that many other light elements could be transmuted in a similar way. In each case a proton was ejected, and generally the process of transmutation was accompanied by the release of a considerable amount of energy. It thus appeared that the proton was a common constituent of atomic nuclei and one of the fundamental particles of which matter is built up. Moreover, the release of energy in these processes was a further indication of the store of energy resident in atomic nuclei.

In parallel with this development, Rutherford with Chadwick and other colleagues and students of the Cavendish Laboratory attacked many other questions concerning the properties of atomic nuclei and their structure, laying the experimental foundations of a whole new branch of physics, now known as nuclear physics, arising from Rutherford's discoveries, first of the nature of the phenomenon of natural radioactivity, secondly, of the existence of the atomic nucleus, and thirdly, that some nuclei could be transmuted by bombardment with alpha particles.

A further very important step was taken in U.K. in 1932 when Cockcroft and Walton carried out an experiment in which hydrogen nuclei, produced artificially in an electric discharge and accelerated to a high velocity by means of an applied voltage, were used to bombard another stable element, lithium. The atoms of this element were found to disintegrate, and transmutation, the dream of the alchemists, had been achieved in a completely controlled laboratory experiment.

In this transmutation, and in others which followed this new discovery, the release of energy was enormous for such a minute event as a reaction involving a single nucleus. Nevertheless, the number of nuclear reactions was so small that the amount of energy generated by the reaction was extremely small compared with the total input of energy used to produce the bombarding particles. The practical value of these nuclear reactions as a source of energy was still completely negligible.

The reason is not far to seek; not only are the nuclear reactions very rare events, but the reactions are not self-propagating. This is quite different from the chemical reactions with which we are familiar in our daily life, such as the combustion of coal or oil. Once started, these propagate themselves and the reactions develop and spread, involving the whole bulk of material; thus the lighting of a fire releases enough heat to ignite the neighboring fuel, which in turn releases more heat to ignite more fuel, and so on. This is not the case for the nuclear reactions which have so far been mentioned; the particles which are formed in them are insufficient to affect neighboring nuclei so as to maintain the reaction and propagate it. It is clear that if we wish to tap the hidden reserves of energy in atomic nuclei and put them to practical use we must find a reaction which can propagate itself; for example, a reaction in which particles are emitted of the same kind that initiated it and in sufficient numbers to affect neighboring nuclei, which in their turn emit new particles to react with other nuclei, so beginning a chain-reaction which spreads through the whole mass.

It is convenient at this point to consider the form of this reserve of energy in atomic nuclei. As long ago as 1905 Einstein showed that, according to the theory of relativity, there is no essential difference between mass and energy, but that energy has mass and mass represents energy. For many years the proof that energy and mass were equivalent depended on indirect, although conclusive, evidence. The reason for this lack of immediate evidence is the extreme size of the ratio between mass and energy. A very small mass corresponds to a very large amount of energy. For example, a mass of one ounce transformed entirely into heat energy would be sufficient to convert nearly a million tons of water into steam. The fantastic size of the figure for conversion of mass to energy explains why a loss of mass has never been observed in ordinary chemical processes; the heat given off in combustion has, we believe, mass associated with it, but its amount is so small that it cannot be detected by the most sensitive balance.

Very striking and direct evidence for the equivalence of mass and energy was furnished by the experiments on the artificial transmutation of atoms. It was shown that in these nuclear reactions a release of energy was always accompanied by a decrease of mass and that the equivalence between mass and energy was exactly as predicted by Einstein. It thus appears that in these nuclear reactions matter is being partially converted into energy and that the reserve of energy of the atomic nucleus is hidden in the most obvious place, its own mass. There is therefore a store of energy resident in matter which is enormously greater than that available to us from any known chemical process. It is clear that since no such extraordinary sources are known on this earth there can be no appreciable conversion of matter into energy. On the other hand, it is now generally accepted that it is this store of energy in matter itself which maintains the heat of the sun and of other stars, through a cycle of nuclear changes in which matter is converted into energy.

Discovery of the Neutron. In 1932 Chadwick, working in the Cavendish Laboratory, made a discovery of fundamental importance. Some years earlier Bothe and Becker in Germany made the observation that the element beryllium, when bombarded with the alpha particles emitted by polonium, emitted a very penetrating radiation. Joliot and his wife Irene Curie-Joliot, in Paris, found that this radiation exhibited some quite extraordinary properties. From a close study of these properties and by detailed measurements Chadwick was able to prove that this radiation consisted of fundamental particles which had a mass almost the same as that of a proton, but had no electric charge. These new-found particles were called "neutrons" and it was at once realized that they, together with protons, were likely to be the ultimate constituents of the nuclei of atoms of all elements. The nucleus of any atom could be built up from the number of protons required to give the observed positive electric charge together with the additional number of neutrons to bring the nuclear mass up to the observed value.

The discovery of the neutron was, however, of even greater practical importance in that its lack of electric charge made it an ideal projectile for carrying out nuclear transformations.

The use of neutrons as a means of exploring the structure and reactions of atomic nuclei was taken up vigorously in physics laboratories throughout the world. Neutron sources could be made either by mixing radium or polonium with beryllium so as to take advantage of the nuclear reaction already mentioned or by the use of an instrument, known as the "cyclotron," which had been developed by E. O. Lawrence of the University of California, Berkeley. This instrument has been of great value in the production of high-energy beams of charged atoms or nuclei and many nuclear reactions, which could be carried out with such beams, were found to produce neutrons.

In the meantime an important contribution to the rapid advance in the new science of nuclear physics was made by Joliot and Mme Irene Curie-Joliot who, in 1933, showed that certain elements, which are normally stable, undergo nuclear reactions when bombarded by alpha rays and yield new atomic nuclei which are isotopes of known elements but which are not stable and decay in the way characteristic of the natural radioactive elements.

In 1934 E. Fermi, and the school of physicists then working with him at Rome, began an intensive study of the reactions produced when the nuclei of all atomic species were subjected to neutron bombardment. In the course of this work the heaviest known elements were examined and, in particular, uranium—with the atomic number 92—was subjected to neutron bombardment. The results of this work showed that new isotopes were formed which were unstable and were subject to radioactive decay.

It therefore seemed that, by bombardment of the heaviest known atom with neutrons, it was possible to produce in the laboratory atoms of higher atomic number, 93 and upwards, than were found in nature.

Further experimental work, however, led to certain difficulties in this explanation and it was found to be impossible to account for the existence, in the normal arrangement of atomic species, of the very large number of so-called "transuranic" elements that were discovered. At this time it was generally accepted that these new elements were all, in fact, of higher atomic number than uranium, and elaborate chemical tests had proved that they certainly could not be identified with any of the elements immediately below uranium in atomic number or weight.

Discovery of Fission. Professor O. Hahn and Dr. Strassmann in Berlin became interested in this problem at the end of 1938 and, from the particular point of view of their chemical nature, carefully reexamined the new elements.

In January 1939 they published a most important paper in which they reported positive chemical evidence to show that one, at least, of the new isotopes which were believed to be of higher atomic number and mass than uranium was, in fact, an isotope of the element barium which has an atomic number and mass not very different from half that of uranium.

Immediately afterwards Dr. O. Frisch and Professor Lise Meitner pointed out that this discovery could only mean that, when uranium was bombarded by neutrons, a nuclear reaction took place of a kind utterly different from any so far studied and that the uranium nucleus split into two parts of roughly equal mass. This phenomenon, for which they proposed the name "nuclear fission," could be explained in terms of the theory of nuclear reactions which had been developed by Professor Bohr in the preceding years. They also pointed out that the fragments of the uranium nucleus would fly apart with great energy and this prediction was given a direct proof by experiments carried out by Dr. Frisch in Copenhagen.

Confirmation of the reality of the fission process with uranium, and of the greatest energy release which accompanied it, was obtained by Professor Joliot in Paris independently (and at nearly the same time) and by other physicists throughout the world as soon as the original work was known to them.

Very shortly afterwards, in the spring of 1939, Professor Joliot and his collaborators Drs. Halban and Kowarski gave an experimental proof of the additional fact, which was expected on theoretical grounds, that when the fission of uranium takes place a number of free neutrons is also produced. Their first experiments showed this number to be about 3.

Experiments of the same type were carried out by Drs. Anderson, Fermi, Hanstein, Szilard and Zinn in the U.S.A. and independent confirmation was obtained of the fact that more than one free neutron is produced for each fission of a uranium nucleus. It was immediately recognized that this discovery was of the very greatest significance and that, for the first time, there was an experimental basis for the hope that the useful realization of the enormous store of atomic energy in matter could be achieved.

This hope depended on the facts that the fission process was initiated by a neutron and that more than one neutron appeared to be released during the process. The latter fact opened up the possibility of a chain reaction. If one atom in a block of uranium were to undergo fission, the neutrons emitted in this fission would be available to initiate fission in neighboring atoms of uranium; these fissions in turn provide further neutrons to affect more atoms of uranium, and so on. Thus conditions might be found in which whole chains of fissions would be produced, each fission being caused by a neutron released in a previous fission. In this way the process might become self-propagating and self-increasing, so that what started as an action affecting only one or two atoms might, in a short time, affect a large proportion of the atoms in the uranium block. In other words, a chain reaction would be set up. If these conditions could be realized, the energy released in the fission process could be made available on a large scale and the store of energy resident in matter put to practical use.

It was therefore only natural that there should be an outburst of activity in most of the physics laboratories of the world with a spate of publications in the scientific press. This continued until the outbreak of war, when an increasing sense of the great potential value of this work imposed restrictions.

Certain important facts emerged from the work that was published during this period and theoretical conclusions and expectations were announced but it is hardly possible to give any strictly chronological account of them. The work was done in so many laboratories and the results, sometimes in a very preliminary form, were communicated to so many journals and published at such varying intervals after communication that details of priority cannot be clearly settled.

But reference should be made to the visit which Professor Bohr paid to the U.S.A. from January to May 1939. He was able to report directly to American physicists the experiments carried out by Hahn, Frisch and Meitner and their suggested interpretation of the results. In addition, while in the U.S.A. Bohr developed and published, in collaboration with Professor J. A. Wheeler of Princeton University, New Jersey, a theory of the fission process.

One important prediction which was made from this theory related to the different behavior of the various isotopes of uranium. This element consists, for much the greater part (99.3 per cent) of atoms of mass number 238, but there is also an isotope (0.7 per cent) of mass 235 and a very small proportion (0.008 per cent) of an isotope of mass 234. U-238 and U-235 are the most important in connection with the uranium fission project. Bohr predicted in February 1939 that the common isotope, U-238, would be expected to undergo fission only when the bombarding neutrons had a high energy, but that the rarer U-235 isotope would behave differently in that it would not only show this reaction with high energy neutrons but in addition would be particularly liable to undergo fission when the energy, and therefore the velocity, of the bombarding neutrons was very low.

This prediction was, in fact, confirmed in March 1940 by experiments carried out by Nier of Minnesota and Booth, Dunning and Grosse of Columbia University, New York. They used a sample of uranium in which the content of U-235 had been increased above the normal value by means of Nier's mass-spectrograph.

It is relevant, at this point, to refer to a different phenomenon shown by the U-238 isotope when bombarded by neutrons of one rather narrowly defined energy value which is intermediate between the very high energy required to cause fission of this isotope and the very low energy which is most effective in causing fission of U-235.

Neutrons which have this so-called "resonance" energy are very strongly absorbed by the U-238 nucleus but fission does not follow. Instead the new nucleus, which now has a mass number 239, emits two electrons in successive steps and is thereby converted first to an isotope of an element with atomic number 93 (for which the name "neptunium" has been suggested) and then to one of an element with atomic number 94. This latter has, provisionally, been named "plutonium" and the isotope formed from U-238 after resonance capture of a neutron may be represented by the symbol Pu-239. Neptunium and plutonium are true "transuranic" elements, of the type suggested by Fermi, and are not found in nature.

Of the two, Pu-239 is of particular interest in connection with the general problem of fission and the release of atomic energy because it could be expected, from the Bohr-Wheeler theory, to show the same sort of properties as U-235 and to be capable of undergoing fission with the greatest ease when bombarded by neutrons of very low energy.

Reference must also be made to the fact that the three nuclear species U-235, U-238 and Pu-239 are not the only ones that can undergo fission. The two elements next below uranium in the atomic series were also shown to have this same property.

Thorium, with atomic number 90 and consisting of one isotope only of atomic mass 232, behaves in the same way as U-238, and fission can only be brought about when the bombarding neutrons have very high energy. The very rare radioactive element protoactinium, with atomic number 91 and atomic mass 231, behaves, as regards fission, in a manner intermediate between U-235 and U-238. These facts, again, are all explicable in terms of the Bohr-Wheeler theory which enumerates certain general rules covering the behavior to be expected with regard to fission of any heavy nucleus, known or unknown.

Chain Reaction and the Atomic Bomb. The foregoing survey of the development of atomic and nuclear physics, though necessarily brief and incomplete, has traced the growth of the idea that there are enormous reserves of energy in all matter; that these are of a nature quite different from those involved in chemical processes, such as the burning of coal or oil or the detonation of TNT or other explosives, and that the nuclear reactions by which they are released are more comparable to those occurring in the sun or stars or in the natural radioactive elements found on the earth.

While this idea has been formed and steadily strengthened since the discovery of the phenomenon of radioactivity at the end of the last century it is only since the discovery, reported at the beginning of 1939, of the special phenomenon of fission that a way has been clearly seen by which this atomic or nuclear energy in matter would be released, controlled and put to use by man.

In recent years the enormous effort expended on the solution of this problem, practically all of which has been borne by the U.S.A., has been concentrated on the development of an atomic bomb. Considerations of security make it impossible to disclose many of the details of this work but, in what follows, some indication is given of the share in it which has been carried out in Britain. Before doing this, however, it may be worth summarizing the nature of the problems relating to the use of fission, either to produce a violent explosion or to liberate atomic energy under controlled conditions, as they appeared when the work was organized, with a new sense of its urgency and importance, at the beginning of the war.

It was generally accepted that a chain reaction might be obtained in uranium which would yield enormous amounts of energy. This, on a basis of equal weights, would be millions of times greater than that produced by the combustion of coal or oil. But it was realized that, if this chain reaction was to be divergent and self-sustaining, certain critical conditions must be satisfied. In the first place the system as a whole must be of such a size that there was not too great a probability that neutrons, produced in the fission process, would escape from the system and so be unable to take any further part in the chain process.

Secondly, the system must not contain more than a limited amount of material that would absorb neutrons and, in this way again, remove their chance of contributing to the divergent fission chain reaction.

Thirdly, the fact was appreciated that, if the reaction was not to "run away," it was essential to make use of neutrons of very low energy in the individual steps of the chain process. Only then would it be possible to introduce methods which would allow the rate of development of the process to be controlled. The neutrons produced when fission occurs have very high energies but this is dissipated as a result of elastic collisions with the nuclei of other atoms that may be present.

Professor Joliot and his co-workers in Paris, Professor Fermi and other physicists in the U.S.A., and Professor Sir George Thomson and his colleagues in London were giving thought to the possibility of using a mixture of uranium and some suitable "slowing-down" medium arranged in such a way that the fast neutrons produced by fission would lose their energy by elastic collisions before initiating further fission in the uranium. A suitable "slowing-down" medium must, above all, not have any large probability of capturing a neutron and its atoms should be of as small mass as possible in order to get the maximum rate of loss of energy in the neutrons through elastic collisions. The most suitable materials to fulfill both these conditions were "heavy hydrogen" or its compound "heavy water," helium, beryllium and carbon.

At the beginning of 1940 Dr. Frisch and Professor Peierls, of Birmingham University, and Professor Sir James Chadwick, of Liverpool University, independently called attention to the possibility of producing a military weapon of unprecedented power. They pointed out that the slow neutron chain reaction would not produce explosive effects much greater than those obtained with ordinary explosives but that if a chain reaction with fast neutrons could be realized the explosive effects might be enormous. It was realized that ordinary uranium would not be suitable, for even if a fast chain reaction could be realized with it a very large quantity of metal would be required. On the other hand, the isotope U-235, if it could be separated, offered great possibilities. It seemed that the amount required to make a bomb would not be very large, certainly between one and one hundred kilograms, and rough calculations of the energy released showed that the explosion of such a bomb might be equivalent to many thousands of tons of TNT.

The explosion of an atomic bomb is very different in its mechanism from the ordinary chemical explosion for it can occur only if the quantity of U-235 is greater than a certain critical amount. This is because the reaction depends on the conservation of the neutrons produced in the fissions. In a block of pure, or nearly pure, U-235 the neutrons will either be absorbed in the mass of metal, producing new fissions, or they will escape into the outer air, thus being wasted and useless for propagating the reaction. The proportion of neutrons which escape can be reduced by increasing the size of the block of metal, since the production of neutrons is a volume effect and will therefore increase more rapidly with size than the loss by escape, which is a surface effect. It follows that if the explosion is possible it will require a certain minimum amount of material, which is called the critical size. The chain reaction will develop so fully that an explosion occurs only if the quantity of U-235 is greater than this critical amount. Quantities less than this are quite stable and perfectly safe. On the other hand, if the amount of material exceeds the critical size it is unstable and a reaction will develop and multiply itself with enormous rapidity, resulting in an explosion of unprecedented violence. Thus all that is necessary to detonate a bomb of U-235 is to bring together two pieces each less than the critical size but which when in contact form an amount exceeding it.

If an appreciable fraction of the atoms in a mass of U-235 undergo fission within a very short time the amount of energy liberated will be so great that the mass will attain a temperature of many million degrees and a pressure of many millions of atmospheres. It will consequently expand with very great rapidity. As the density of the mass decreases the neutrons can escape more easily from it, and the chain reaction will come to an end. In order to release an appreciable fraction of the available energy, it is therefore necessary that the reaction should develop so rapidly that a substantial part of the material can react before the system has time to fly apart. The neutrons produced in the fission process are fast enough to fulfill this condition (but not if they are slowed down by artificial means as mentioned in the paragraphs above). The interval of time between the beginning and end of the nuclear reaction is exceedingly brief. In this interval the mass will have expanded so much that the nuclear reaction breaks off, owing to the escape of neutrons. During this interval a substantial part of the mass of U-235 should undergo fission, releasing a large amount of energy. If only one pound of U-235 is affected this release of energy will be as much as from 8,000 tons of TNT.

Quantum theory has dominated the physics of this century. Reluctantly brought into being in 1900 by Max Planck, its implications were first realized by Einstein in 1905 and brilliantly applied to the atom by Bohr in 1913. Finally, in the brief period from 1925 to 1927, the complete structure of quantum mechanics materialized all at once. Reviewing the history of science, we might expect a revolution of this magnitude to have taken decades, perhaps centuries to be conceived, developed, and accepted—but all it took was a few years. In this selection the growth of quantum physics is recounted in an informal way by one of the active contributors to it. In his twenties Edward U. Condon, together with Ronald Gurney, achieved distinction by formulating the quantum mechanical theory of alpha radioactivity (which was also discovered simultaneously by George Gamow). Since then Condon has bulked large in American physics, both as a creator and as an administrator. He is currently at Washington University in St. Louis. Quantum Physics is from his presidential address before the American Association for the Advancement of Science in 1954.

Edward U. Condon

QUANTUM PHYSICS

Practically all the important progress in physics in this century is bound up with quantum ideas. Moreover, it has been a half-century in which physics has developed at a revolutionary pace that is totally unprecedented in the world's history. Therefore all that I can do here is to pass the main ideas in rapid review, perhaps lightening the story with an anecdote here and there, and hope to stimulate a wider interest in this exciting subject.

Quantum Ideas. By quantum physics we mean all parts of the science that involve a peculiar universal constant, known as Planck's constant, h, where

$$h = 6.63 \times 10^{-27} \text{ erg sec.}$$

So defined, quantum physics involves nearly all of physics and chemistry. It also involves a good share of astrophysics. Moreover, quantum ideas have required a good deal of searching into the philosophic foundations of physics.

The quantum idea was first introduced into physics in 1900 and 1901 by Max Planck in connection with the study of the radiations emitted by hot solid bodies. Throughout most of the 19th century, such radiation, including visible light, had been regarded as a wave motion. But, in developing the theory of radiation from hot bodies, Planck found it necessary to assume that light energy is not emitted and absorbed continuously by atoms. Rather he supposed that it was emitted and absorbed in definite little bundles of energy, or quanta.

Many experimental properties of light pointed to its being propagated as a wave motion. There is nothing remote or esoteric about these experiments. Take a silk umbrella and look through the fabric at a distant street light. In addition to a central white image, you will see a series of colored images extending out from the central image in two mutually perpendicular series in directions related to the warp and woof of the fabric. These are caused by interference of light waves which go through different interstices between the evenly spaced threads of the fabric.

A diffraction grating is an accurately made device for observing these spectra more accurately. By measuring the angle of spread between them and the central image, one can find the wavelength of the waves, and, by knowing the velocity of the waves, one can find the frequency or number of oscillations per second that occur as the wave passes a fixed point.

In this way, one finds that the wavelength for violet light is about 3×10^{-5} cm and that the wavelength for red light is about twice as great, or 6×10^{-5} cm. Thousands upon thousands of these wavelengths have been measured to at least 6 decimal places. These form the largest and most precise body of experimental data in all physics. Since the velocity of light is 3×10^{10} cm/sec, it turns out that the frequency of violet light is about 10^{15} cy/sec.

On Planck's view, light of frequency n cy/sec is emitted and absorbed in quanta of energy equal to hn, which is therefore about 6.6×10^{-12} erg for violet light. For x-rays the frequencies are some 10,000 times greater, and the quanta are therefore some 10,000 times greater.

The reasoning that led to this result was so complicated that Planck himself was not fully convinced of its validity. Physicists are all an extremely conservative group of people, at least in matters having to do with their own science, and they were reluctant to accept the radical quantum idea on such slender evidence.

In 1905 Einstein showed how clearly and neatly the main facts regarding the photoelectric effect could be understood if the quantum view of light were favored over the wave view. In the photoelectric effect, electrons are emitted from a metal when light shines on it.

Early experiments showed that increasing the brightness of the light caused more electrons to be emitted but did not increase the energy of motion with which the emitted electrons came out. On the wave view, one would think that a bigger wave would shake the electrons harder and make them come out with more energy.

Experiment also showed that the energy with which the electrons were emitted increased linearly as the frequency of the light was increased. This result was not at all understood in terms of the wave theory of light.

Einstein pointed out that on the quantum view, if 1 light quantum goes to 1 electron, then greater brightness means more quanta and therefore more emitted electrons. Planck had already found it necessary to suppose the energy content of a quantum to be proportional to the frequency of the light wave, and thus a natural explanation is provided of why the energy of the emitted electrons increases linearly with the frequency.

Wave-particle Duality. Thus was born the wave-particle duality or dilemma of modern physics. Light, on going through a series of closely spaced slits, behaves in ways that have found only quantitative explanation on the wave theory. Light, on falling on a metal, liberates electrons in ways that have found satisfactory explanation only in terms of the quantum or corpuscular theory. From here on, the subject began to develop at an ever-increasing rate.

When atoms are excited in a gaseous discharge tube, such as is used for advertising signs, the kinds of light emitted consist of sharply defined frequencies characteristic of the gas atoms in the discharge tube. If light is emitted in quanta of definite amounts, this must mean that the atoms are capable of existing only in states of definite energy values. The differences in these allowed, or quantized, energy values are the energies of the light quanta emitted by an atom in passing from a state of higher total energy to one of lower total energy. In 1913 Niels Bohr built his successful theory of the hydrogen atom on a combination of this quantum idea with the general picture of the nuclear atom that had been developed experimentally by Ernest Rutherford. Soon afterward, James Franck and Gustav Hertz performed experiments in which they showed the reality of these quantized energy levels in atoms by finding that electrons can give up quantized amounts of energy to atoms only on colliding with them, and that these quantized amounts are closely correlated with the sizes of the emitted light quanta.

In 1912 another discovery of major importance was made. Since the discovery of x-rays in 1896 by Wilhelm Roentgen, there had been speculation on whether these were a wave motion or a stream of corpuscles. Attempts at diffraction experiments gave negative results with a sensitivity indicating that, if they are a wave motion, the wavelength cannot be more than about 10^{-8} cm. This is just about the distance apart of layers of atoms in a crystal, which gave Max von Laue the idea that perhaps the regular arrangement of atoms in a crystal would diffract x-rays in the way that the rulings of a diffraction grating diffract light. The experiment was successful. Thus two new branches of physics were born. By use of a crystal of known structure, it was now possible to measure the wavelengths of the characteristic x-rays emitted by various atoms, so spectroscopy was extended to the x-ray region. By use of x-rays of known wavelength, it was possible to infer from the nature of the diffraction pattern how the atoms are arranged in crystals of unknown structure. Thus a powerful tool was provided for the study of the structure of solid matter.

All this served to point up the disturbing puzzle of the dilemma on whether x-rays and light were really a wave motion or really a stream of corpuscles, for it seemed to be something like both and yet no one could see how it was possible for it to be both in any sense. Only W. H. Bragg, writing in *Nature* in late 1912, hinted at a combined outlook. He wrote: "The problem then becomes, it seems to me, not to decide between the two theories of x-rays, but to find . . . one theory which possesses the capacities of both."

On Bohr's model of the atom, the electrons revolve around the nucleus like planets going around the sun in the solar system. Although the theory was immensely successful in correlating spectroscopic facts, it threw no light on the fundamental nature of the valence forces that hold atoms together in molecules. In Berkeley, G. N. Lewis developed a rival theory based on a static model of the atom in which electrons had favored locations at the corners of a series of cubes surrounding the nucleus, the eight corners corresponding to the length of the short periods in the periodic system of the elements.

When I entered the University of California as a freshman in 1921, the Bohr atom was being taught in the physics department and the Lewis atom was orthodox doctrine in the chemistry department. Now both departments are preaching the same kind of atom, which resembles neither of its forerunners and combines the best features of both. The things I am talking about are so old that if they are mentioned anywhere it is probably in the history department.

The early 1920's were an exciting time to be studying physics. We had these rival atomic theories, each with its inadequacies and uncertainties. Some things were lacking. In Livermore, California, there was only the rodeo and on Charter Hill nothing but the Big C and a few grazing cows.

In 1923 the wave-particle dilemma became even more acute. Arthur Compton, in St. Louis, discovered that x-ray quanta have momentum as well as energy. When x-rays are scattered by means of light atoms, it is found that some of them are scattered, but that the scattered x-rays consist of smaller quanta than those which struck, and the shift toward smaller quanta is greater, the larger the angle of deflection through which the x-rays are scattered. All this was exactly in accord with the idea that the x-ray quanta were scattered by colliding with electrons by exactly the same rules of conservation of energy and momentum that are applicable to the collision of two material particles, such as billiard balls.

In that same year, 1923, Louis de Broglie in Paris published his now-famous doctor's thesis, in which he suggested that the wave-particle duality might extend to the behavior of electrons as well as to light and x-ray quanta. Up until this time physicists felt sure that a beam of cathode rays was simply a corpuscular stream of electrons moving in accordance with Newton's laws of motion, as corrected in the high-energy region for relativistic effects.

De Broglie suggested that the relationship between the wavelength of the wave aspect of an electron and the momentum of the particle aspect of the electron ought to be the same as that already found to hold for x-ray quanta, namely, that wavelength equals Planck's constant divided by momentum. This suggestion made possible a simple interpretation of the existence of discrete energy levels in atoms, which in Bohr's theory was simply postulated in order to get agreement with spectroscopic facts.

We are all familiar with the fact that a stretched string in a musical instrument vibrates freely at a particular frequency such that the length of the string is just equal to half a wavelength of the wave of that frequency which might travel on the string. Then it can vibrate also at double this frequency, so the length equals two half-wavelengths, or at triple the fundamental frequency so the string's length equals three half-wavelengths, and so on. Similar rules apply to the modes of vibration of other continuous bodies such as the stretched membrane of a drum. De Broglie argued by analogy that, if the motion of electrons was somehow governed by an associated wave motion, then the allowed orbits in an atom must be governed by mathematical restrictions similar to those which determine that vibrating bodies can vibrate only in a certain discrete set of modes of vibration.

It turns out, on these views, that the de Broglie wavelengths of electrons which have been accelerated by a potential drop of a few hundred volts will be of the same order as that of x-rays.

This suggests that electrons, too, ought to show diffractive scattering by the regularly spaced layers of atoms in a crystal. In 1927 electron diffraction was discovered in New York by C. J. Davisson and L. H. Germer, working with the scattering of low-energy electrons by a single crystal of nickel, and independently that same year by G. P. Thomson in England, who worked with the scattering of higher energy electron beams by polycrystalline materials. These experiments fully confirmed the idea that electrons are scattered from crystals like a wave motion having the wavelength that was predicted by de Broglie. At the same time a new tool for crystallographic studies, supplementing that of x-ray diffraction, was made available.

A few years later it was shown experimentally that beams of hydrogen molecules and of helium atoms were also governed by de Broglie wave principles when scattered by crystals. This was done by Otto Stern, now a distinguished resident of Berkeley, who was then professor of physics in Hamburg, Germany.

In consequence of these experimental discoveries and many associated theoretical developments, physicists now believe that the wave-particle duality applies to all things in nature, be they light quanta, electrons, protons, or entire atoms and molecules. With larger things, the wavelength becomes so small that the wave aspect escapes observation, which is why all ordinary motions appear to be governed entirely by the particle formulation originating in Newton's laws of motion.

Matrix Mechanics. In 1925, Werner Heisenberg in Göttingen discovered a new mathematical way of treating problems in atomic physics. It was called matrix mechanics because quantities which in Newtonian mechanics are represented by ordinary numbers are represented in this theory by an abstract kind of mathematical entity known as a Hermitian matrix.

This theory caused physicists a lot of trouble. Up to then practically none of them had ever studied matrix algebra. It is true that the mathematicians knew about matrices but, under pressure from the physicists to teach them only what they needed to know, the mathematicians had not talked about matrices when physicists were around. Max Born, the 1954 Nobel prize winner in physics, was in Berkeley from Göttingen in 1925 as a visiting professor, and he lectured on matrix mechanics. What a rough time he gave us as we tried to grasp the strange new ideas of matrix mechanics.

Then, in the spring of 1926, what a relief it was when Erwin Schrödinger's rival wave mechanics came on the scene, and we could avoid the difficulties of matrix algebra. And what a surprise it was in the summer of 1926 when Carl Eckart, in Pasadena, and also Schrödinger himself discovered that the two theories were identically the same. They were simply dressed up in such totally different mathematical costumes that it took some time before their identity was recognized.

In the early fall of 1926 I left Berkeley to study the new quantum mechanics with Born in Göttingen. There the great mathematician, David Hilbert, used to delight to tell us how he had told the Göttingen theoretical physicists of the close relationship between matrix algebra and certain boundary value problems of differential equations. If they had followed up this lead they might have discovered wave mechanics before Schrödinger.

In those days Hilbert used to say, "Die Physik wird zu schwer für die Physikern"—physics is becoming too difficult for the physicists.

In 1927 the pace of discovery in theoretical physics was probably greater than in any other year in the history of the science. Every issue of the leading journals had at least one paper of great importance. There was the more general formulation of the laws of quantum mechanics that was made principally by P. A. M. Dirac in England and John von Neumann in Germany. There was the development of the quantum theory of the radiation field by Dirac and the relativistic form of the quantum theory of the electron, which led to the prediction of the existence of the positively charged electron or positron, that was discovered a few years later by Carl Anderson in Pasadena.

Arnold Sommerfeld laid the foundations for the whole

modern theory of metals and semiconductors by applying the quantum mechanical methods to the treatment of the free electrons in a conductor. W. Heitler and F. London applied quantum mechanics to the theory of the covalent chemical bond between two hydrogen atoms and showed that this atomic theory could at last meet the needs of the chemists. This gave rise to a wide program of developments, which resulted in the award of the 1954 Nobel prize in chemistry to Linus Pauling of the California Institute of Technology.

Heisenberg showed how the new quantum theory could account for the extremely strong interactions between the electrons in iron, cobalt, and nickel, which give rise to the strong magnetic effects shown by these elements. Many other discoveries of great importance were made among which may be mentioned the final clarification of the low-temperature heat capacity of gaseous hydrogen. It had long been known that this had something to do with quantum restrictions on the rotation of hydrogen molecules, but David M. Dennison showed the solution of this problem leading to the discovery of two stable forms of hydrogen gas known as orthohydrogen and parahydrogen.

Things were happening at such a pace that all the physicists, young and old, were suffering from acute mental indigestion. In the spring of 1928 when I taught a course in quantum mechanics for the first time at Columbia University, I remember that the late Bergen Davis summed it all up by saying, "I don't believe you young fellows understand it any better than I do—but you all stick together and say the same thing."

Statistical Theories. Going back a bit, it was in the fall of 1926 that Max Born took a decisive step in supplying the hypothesis that provided a general basis for interpretation of the mathematical formalism of quantum mechanics. We had a mathematics of wave motion that was somehow associated with the motion of the electrons or other atomic particles. The big question was What is the basic relationship between the associated wave motion and the behavior of the atomic particles?

Born's answer, which was largely the basis of the award of the 1954 Nobel prize in physics to him, was that the theory does not and cannot make precise predictions about the motion of the particles, but that it can make only predictions about the relative probability of appearances or motions of different kinds. In particular he postulated that the square of the amplitude of the de Broglie waves at a particular place gives the relative probability of finding a particle in that place. This is a radical and revolutionary idea in its implications, and fundamental disputes among physicists still rage regarding its basic meaning. Nevertheless, it must be realized that this idea of a statistical interpretation of the waves as describing probabilities of behavior of the particles has now stood the test of time for more than a quarter-century and lies at the foundation of all modern atomic physics.

Physical science got its start with the precise astronomical predictions resulting from the dynamical theory of the solar system. These many quantitatively verified results exercised a dominating influence on physical thinking. All physics was assumed to be reducible to a fully deterministic description of motions, such that, given a full description of the situation as of now and sufficient calculating skill, one could calculate precisely what will happen at all times in the future.

Prior to 1926 statistical theories had been used in physics. Statistical methods were used to give an over-all average description of the heat motions that give rise to the thermal properties of matter. But in all such theories it was supposed that there really exists an underlying fully deterministic reality, and that statistical methods are used by choice for simpler descriptions rather than by fundamental necessity.

The questions now arise: Is there really an underlying fully deterministic description of the phenomena of atomic physics that has so far eluded our observations and theory-making because of some basic incompleteness that may be remedied in the future? Or, on the other hand, is there some inherent limitation in the world and our possible ways of observing it such that our knowledge of events is fundamentally restricted to observations and conclusions of a statistical character?

In the fall of 1927, Heisenberg provided an analysis of the processes of measurement that strongly favors an affirmative answer to the second question. Later analysis by Bohr in 1928 extended these ideas. The essence is that on an atomic scale the processes of observation necessarily introduce uncontrolled disturbances, and it is these which give rise to the over-all uncertainties that make fully deterministic knowledge impossible. If one refrains from observing, he makes no disturbance but remains ignorant of the data needed for deterministic calculations. Observations can be arranged in ways that increase the precision of knowledge of one variable but only at the price of introducing more uncertainty into the knowledge of a complementary variable.

The analysis of Heisenberg and Bohr provides a deep insight into the nature of limitations on knowledge of deterministic behavior, which seem to be truly fundamental. Most physicists today accept these views and regard the statistical element of the theory as an intrinsic feature of the world in which we live. Classical determinism on this view is an ideal limit toward which our knowledge can approach in large-scale phenomena where the quantum limitations become unimportant corrections.

But one physicist of outstanding importance steadfastly thinks otherwise. He is Albert Einstein. At the very outset he expressed himself by saying "Der lieber Gott würfelt nicht." In American vernacular we would say "the good Lord doesn't shoot craps."

Born's book, *Natural Philosophy of Choice and Chance*, quotes a letter Einstein wrote in 1947 in which he says, "the statistical interpretation . . . has a considerable content of truth." However, he goes on to say, "I am absolutely convinced that one will eventually arrive at a theory in which the objects connected by law are not probabilities, but conceived facts as one took for granted only a short time ago." With characteristic modesty he concludes then by saying

> Zur Begründung dieser Überzeugung kann ich aber nicht logische Gründe, sondern nur meinen kleinen Finger als Zeugen beibringen, also keine Autorität, die ausserhalb meiner Haut irgendwelchen

Respect einflössen kann. [I cannot provide logical arguments for my conviction but can only call on my little finger as witness, which cannot claim any authority to be respected outside my own skin.]

Whether all the data of experience can be codified in terms of fully deterministic relations I do not know, of course, but unquestionably it is useful to have such organization of knowledge carried to its furthest limits. The history of science is filled with facile generalizations and the kind of oversimplification that fails to qualify what would be true if properly qualified. Think of the many pages of disputatious writings on free will and determinism!

In my view physics has nothing to say on this one way or the other as an issue related to human conduct. It was an unwarranted extrapolation in the first place to pass from the planetary successes of classical mechanics to extreme mechanistic determinism for human actions. It is equally incorrect to argue from the statistical determinism of quantum mechanics any support for the idea of free will in human behavior.

Nuclear Physics. By 1927 the principles of quantum theory as we know them today were pretty well developed. In the 27 years since then the ideas of quantum physics have been so closely identified with all the progress that has been made in physics and chemistry that it is not possible to discuss quantum physics separately from progress as a whole in these sciences.

The entire theoretical structure of nuclear physics is cast in quantum mechanical terms. This new branch of physics has never been handled in any other way. The application of quantum mechanics to problems of the internal structure of the nucleus was initiated in 1928 with the discovery of the theory of alpha-particle radioactivity by George Gamow in Göttingen and independently by the late Ronald Gurney and myself in Princeton.

This theory provides one of the most extreme examples of the use of probability ideas. According to classical mechanics, it is not possible for a particle to be in places where its total energy is less than its potential energy. In quantum mechanics this impossibility is changed into an improbability. An alpha particle in a uranium nucleus collides with the wall surrounding the nucleus some 10^{20} times a second. According to quantum mechanics it has a very slight chance of getting through the wall, even though it does not have energy enough to get over it. This chance is extremely small, amounting to only about one chance in 10^{36}. In consequence, the alpha particle remains in the nucleus on an average about 10^{9} years before the spontaneous disintegration occurs. Nevertheless, the statistical feature of the theory shows up in that some uranium atoms disintegrate in a very short time, whereas others have lasted for many thousands of years without disintegrating.

This same theory of barrier leakage applied in reverse indicated that light elements could be made to undergo artificial transmutations using particles accelerated with voltages much lower than had been estimated to be necessary. This gave a strong stimulus to the experimental investigation of nuclear reactions which began in the early 1930's.

Quantum mechanics has also provided the concept of saturable exchange forces between fundamental particles, an idea that is foreign to classical ideas but appears to be essential in the further development of the theory of nuclear structure. Relativistic quantum mechanics, as I have already mentioned, provided the prediction of the existence of the positron and provides the theoretical basis for calculations of many of the basic processes that occur in the region of high-energy physics—that is, the physics of particles having energies of several hundred million to billions of volts, a branch of physics that is extensively studied here in Berkeley.

From quantum mechanical theories concerning exchange forces between protons and neutrons, H. Yukawa in 1936 was led to postulate the existence of a hitherto undiscovered kind of particle, called the meson, intermediate in mass between the electron and the proton. Experiments in recent years have shown that there are in fact many kinds of mesons, with complicated interrelationships, whose study is today one of the most important topics in fundamental research in physics.

In spite of all these successes and many others too numerous to mention here, the record is not one of complete success. Very early in the modern period, namely in 1927, Dirac took the decisive steps toward the development of a quantum thory of the electromagnetic field and had a number of significant successes with the theory as he developed it. Heisenberg and W. Pauli extended the theory, and many others have worked on it.

This theory, or rather this family of theories, in various forms, however, suffers from a fatal defect in that many of the important problems of physics have no solution. When the solution is carried out, they lead to divergent integrals that give infinity for a formal answer to a problem that ought to have a finite solution. A large amount of study has gone into efforts to remove this difficulty but with little success. Therefore the quantum theory of the electromagnetic field remains today in an unsatisfactory state. Probably the difficulties can be overcome only by some radical revision of the fundamental ideas that is as revolutionary in its nature as the ideas of the present theory seemed when they were first developed in 1927.

The past half-century has been an exciting period of enormous fruitfulness in the development of physics and chemistry. Today a greater effort, measured both by adequacy of the equipment and numbers of well-trained men, is going into the investigation of the fundamental nature of matter than ever before in the world's history. We may expect therefore that the next 50 years will bring a development of our knowledge and our ideas that is even greater than has occurred in the first half of the present century. If this happens, the physics of the year 2000 will be as strange and unforeseeable by us today as the physics of today would have seemed to the physicists of 1900.

The most spectacular development in physics in recent years has been the discovery that a remarkable number (thirty, in fact) of elementary particles exist. Only nine of these particles were known before World War II! Today part of the mystery surrounding elementary particles has been removed by a combination of elegant experiments and powerful, if unconventional, theoretical analysis, and it is no longer fashionable to call K mesons and hyperons "strange particles." The purpose of this selection "is to systematize, as far as possible, our knowledge in this field, following more or less the historical order of the discovery of these particles and the evolution of concepts associated with them. These concepts are emphasized because they are closely connected with the physicist's notions of the structure of space and time." A careful reading of the selection is in order both because of the intrinsic interest of the subject and because it makes accessible perhaps the most profound and exhilarating aspect of contemporary physics.

Abdus Salam was educated at the University of the Punjab and at Cambridge. A theoretical physicist, he has contributed to quantum electrodynamics and the interpretation of elementary-particle phenomena. Elementary Particles originally appeared in the British journal **Endeavour.**

Abdus Salam

ELEMENTARY PARTICLES

The concept of an elementary particle has arisen from man's age-old search for the ultimate, fundamental, and indivisible units of which matter is composed. The nineteenth-century chemist came very near to the end of this quest with the realization, on the basis of the periodic table of the elements, that all matter, of whatever form, was made from 92 different types of atoms. With the work of J. J. Thomson and Rutherford at the beginning of this century came the belief that all these 92 different types of atoms were themselves made from just two elementary particles, the electron and the proton. These are stable, indivisible particles with unique masses and have the following properties:

1. The electron is a very tiny chunk of matter, with a mass of 10^{-27} g; the proton has a mass some 2,000 times greater.
2. The electron carries a negative charge of about 10^{-10} e.s.u.; the proton a positive charge of exactly the same magnitude.

The work of Planck and Einstein soon added to this list a third elementary particle, the photon. They recognized that the radiation energy of an electromagnetic field exists in the form of discrete units, which were called photons. On this view, a beam of light consists of a stream of photons, all travelling with the same velocity.

The electron, proton, and photon interact with each other in the following manner:

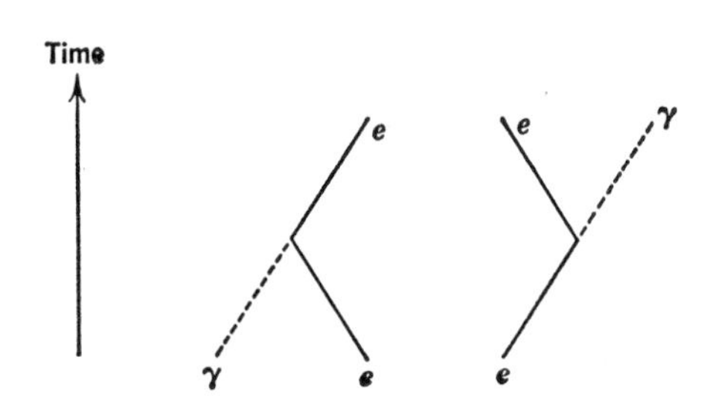

Figure 1

1. According to Maxwell's classical theory, all charged particles emit or absorb electromagnetic radiation when accelerated; according to Planck and Einstein's view, electromagnetic radiation exists in the form of photons. This means that electrons or protons emit or absorb photons. Figure 1 is a space-time picture of this emission or absorption process. On the right, an electron (solid line) is emitting a photon (dotted line); on the left, an electron absorbs a photon.

2. According to Maxwell's theory, one charged particle attracts or repels another charged particle by first producing an electromagnetic field in the surrounding space, and this field in turn acts on the second charged particle. On this present view this is visualized as an emission of one (or many) photons from one electron and reabsorption by the second (as shown in Figure 2).

3. The emission or absorption of photons and their exchange between two electrons or an electron and proton must proceed in accordance with what are called conservation laws. These require that:

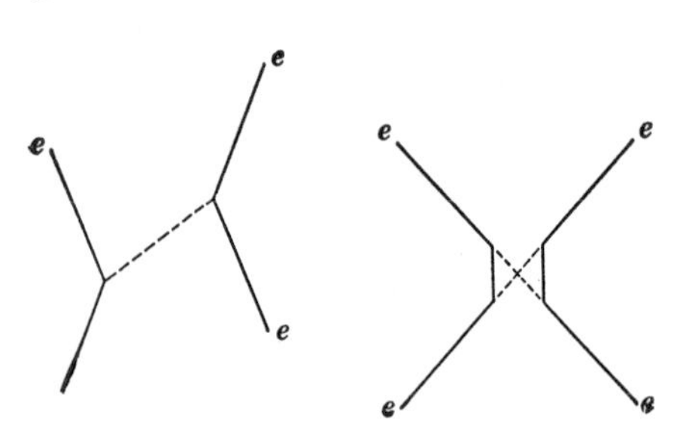

Figure 2

(i) In any physical process, *(a)* the total charge Q, *(b)* the number of electrons N_e, and *(c)* the number of protons N_p, must be the same before and after the interaction.

The number of photons at the beginning, however, can be different from that at the end.

(ii) In any process, *(a)* the total energy *E*, *(b)* the total momentum *P*, and *(c)* the total angular momentum *J* of all the particles must remain the same before and after the interaction.

These so-called conservation laws are experimental. They can, however, readily be linked with ideas about the structure of space-time. One can show that saying that momentum and energy are conserved is equivalent to saying that the results of an experiment are independent of where in space and when in time it is performed. This is the principle of translation symmetry of space-time. It can also be shown that saying that angular momentum is conserved is equivalent to saying that the results of an experiment do not change if the entire experimental set-up is rotated through any angle. This is the principle of rotation symmetry of space.

To give a precise meaning to the concept of conservation of angular momentum, it was found necessary to assign an intrinsic angular momentum (spin) to every elementary particle. Specifically, one has to ascribe a spin of 1 unit to the photon and a spin of ½ unit to the electron and to the proton. To fix one's ideas about intrinsic spin one may roughly conceive of an electron (or a proton) as a spinning top. If the electron is moving, its axis of spin may, to take a special case, be along the direction of motion. In that case, the spin may appear clockwise or counter-clockwise to someone looking along the forward path of the particle. In other words, the electron may move and spin like a right-hand screw (right-polarized electrons) or like a left-hand screw (left-polarized electrons). In a beam of free electrons, half will be right-polarized and half left-polarized.

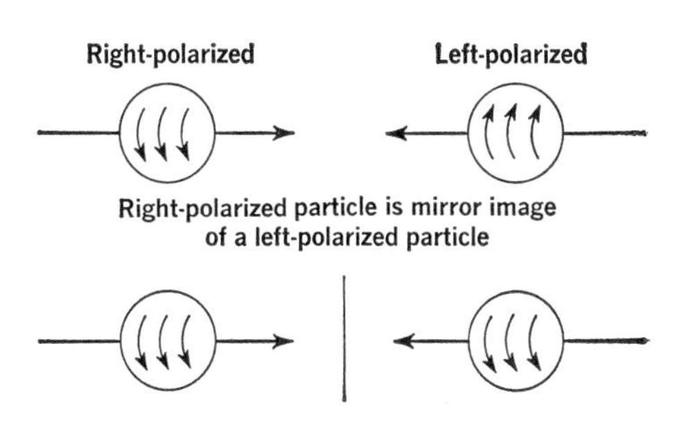

Figure 3

Clearly, a right-spinning or a right-polarized electron is a mirror image of a left-spinning or a left-polarized electron. This important point will be referred to later.

To these conclusions about space-time structure P. A. M. Dirac's work carried out during 1928 added a new and deep concept, for he could show on general grounds that all particles in nature must exist in pairs. To every particle there corresponds an anti-particle of precisely the same mass and spin, but of opposite charge. Thus the existence of the negative electron implies the possible existence of a positive anti-electron (the so-called positron); if the proton exists, so must an anti-proton. From the existence of the hydrogen atom we may infer that an atom of anti-hydrogen can exist with precisely the same energy levels.

Further, Dirac showed that when a particle and anti-particle collide both disappear, their energy, momentum, and angular momentum going into photons. Conversely a photon, under suitable circumstances, can produce a pair consisting of a particle and an anti-particle. Figure 4 gives a space-time picture. On the right, a photon produces a pair consisting of an electron and a positron. On the left, an electron-positron pair disappears with the emission of a photon. To take account of this we must modify two of our conservation laws, namely that N_e = constant and N_p = constant, to read $N_e - N_{\bar{e}}$ = constant and $N_p - N_{\bar{p}}$ = constant. Here $\bar{e}$ denotes positron, $\bar{p}$ anti-proton, etc.

This work of Dirac was among the most momentous in the history of physics. It revealed a deep symmetry in nature. It provided a mechanism by which electron-positron pairs could be created or annihilated. Not long after Dirac's work came the brilliant experimental confirmation of pair-creation by photon showers from C. D. Anderson and P. M. S. Blackett.

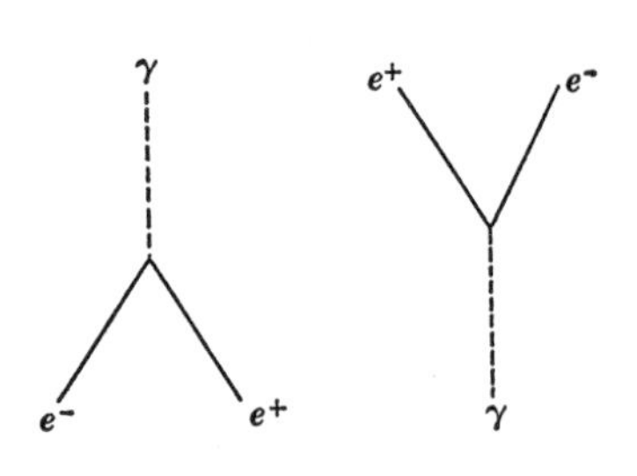

Figure 4

Recapitulating, at this stage we have considered five elementary particles: the photon, the positive and the negative electron, and the positive and the negative proton. The electron-electron or electron-proton force can be understood completely on the basis of the charge on these particles and an exchange of photons between them.

The next development in the subject came with the realization that the proton-proton force is only partly explained by the above picture. When two protons are close to each other by less than 10^{-13} cm, a much stronger force arises between them, the so-called nuclear force. This force is stronger than the electromagnetic force, produced by exchange of photons, by a factor of 100. At about the same time came the discovery of the neutron —our sixth elementary particle—and the realization that all atomic nuclei contain about as many neutrons as protons. The neutron is about as massive as the proton, but differs from it in being chargeless. To a very good approximation the proton-neutron force is equal to the proton-proton force. The neutron and the proton could in fact be considered two states, chargeless and charged, of the same basic particle.

The neutron was destined to enrich the concepts in the subject in a very surprising way. It is slightly heavier than the proton, and in about twelve minutes a free neutron decays into a proton and an electron. In this decay the total energy, momentum, and angular momentum before and after the decay did not seem to balance. Here indeed was a searching test of the theoretical physicist's faith in the concepts he had himself created. If one gave up the demand that these conservation laws should hold, one would have to revise one's ideas about the structure of space-time. To resolve this dilemma W. Pauli suggested that in neutron decay a further neutral particle of zero rest-mass must be emitted which carries away the missing energy, the missing momentum, and the missing angular momentum. This particle was called the neutrino. The discovery of the neutron thus introduced two new elementary particles, the neutron itself and the neutrino.

But is the neutron an elementary particle? The particles we have dealt with so far, the electron, the proton, the photon, and even the neutrino, are all stable, indivisible particles. This is not true of the neutron. To be sure, on the nuclear time scale the neutron decay is a very slow process. The other types of process we have considered, such as photon absorption and emission, take place in about 10^{-19} second. On this time scale neutron decay is certainly very slow. Nevertheless, the fact of the decay remains and forces us into the following compromise. We must divide all fundamental interactions into three classes:

1. Nuclear interactions, which give rise to *p–n*, *p–p*, and *n–n* forces. These interactions are the strongest we know of in nature.

2. Electromagnetic interactions, which give *p–e* and *e–e* forces. These are medium strong.

3. Weak interactions, which are responsible for the decay of the neutron.

The relative strengths of these interactions are in the ratio of $1 : 10^{-2} : 10^{-12}$. To the extent that the weak interactions can be neglected, the neutron is elementary, stable, and indivisible. To the extent that the electromagnetic interaction can be neglected the neutron and the proton are identical. Thus all the particles we have considered are elementary, but some are more elementary than others.

Our survey has now brought us to 1935, when H. Yukawa started to ponder over the problem of the specifically nuclear force. We have seen that the electromagnetic interaction of charged particles can be represented as arising from exchange of photons. Yukawa argued that, in complete analogy with this, the proton-neutron force must also be produced by an exchange of some new type of particles, which he called mesons. From the characteristics of the nuclear forces Yukawa deduced that:

1. Mesons must possess mass. They ought to be about 300 times as massive as electrons.

2. Unlike photons, mesons may be charged or neutral.

3. Like photons, mesons should be emitted or absorbed singly by the protons or the neutrons.

4. In suitable circumstances one such particle could create a proton–anti-proton or neutron–anti-neutron pair. Conversely, nucleons and anti-nucleons would annihilate each other, the energy and momentum going into mesons (Figure 5).

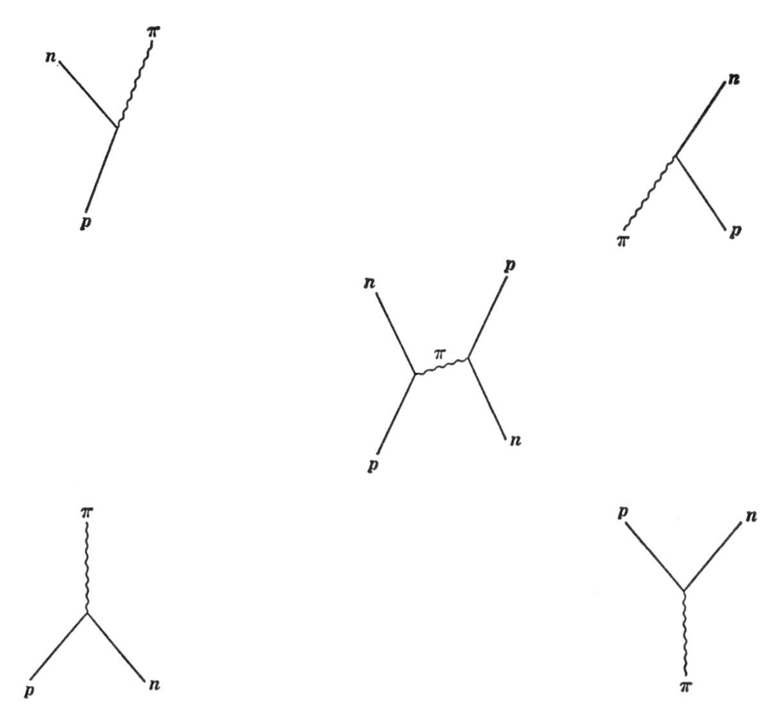

Figure 5 Solid lines represent protons or neutrons; wavy lines represent mesons. Notice the similarity of meson-nucleon interactions to photon-electron interactions in Figures 1 and 2.

The experimental discovery of mesons by C. F. Powell in 1947 forms part of the exciting annals of physics. The Yukawa particles are nowadays called π-mesons (π^+, π^0, π^-, according to charge).

Considering the strong interactions in more detail, at this stage the nuclear force arises between the two nuclear particles (p, n) and the three π-mesons (π^+, π^0, π^-). As remarked before, the nuclear force is much stronger than the electromagnetic. Thus to one part in a hundred, charge on a particle is irrelevant in considering reactions within the nucleus. To a very good approximation, then, the proton and the neutron are identical particles, as also are the three π-mesons. The fact that there are three π-mesons equivalent to each other immediately suggests that we should formally treat these three as components of a vector in a three-dimensional space. To distinguish between this abstract space and ordinary space we call this new space the isotopic space. The equivalence of the three π-mesons is then formally stated as the consequence of rotation symmetry in the isotopic space. As previously noted, rotations are connected with angular momentum, and we can, analogously with ordinary space, assign an intrinsic isotopic "spin" I_z to π-mesons. On this basis π^+ corresponds to $I_z = 1$; π^0 to $I_z = 0$; π^- to $I_z = -1$. Applying the analogy to the nucleon, which exists in two equivalent states (the proton and the neutron), we may assign $I_z = \frac{1}{2}$ to the proton and $I_z = -\frac{1}{2}$ to the neutron. Just as in ordinary space rotation symmetry implies conservation of angular momentum, so in isotopic space, rotation symmetry implies conservation of isotopic spin.

In any nuclear interaction, then, not only energy, momentum, and angular momentum, but isotopic spin should be conserved. But there is one important difference between this new conservation law and the other conservation laws. Clearly the electromagnetic interaction, in so far as it distinguishes charged particles from neutral particles, violates rotation symmetry in this space, and thus the law of conservation of total isotopic spin is only approximate.

Three new particles have now been added to our list. The same question as for the neutron arises again. Are these stable particles? The answer is no, and the decay of all these three particles presents novel features.

Consider π^- first. One might have expected that this particle would decay into an electron and a neutrino. A π^- could convert virtually into an anti-proton neutron pair, and this pair would then disappear, giving an electron and a neutrino. For some very inexplicable reason this does not happen. Instead, nature completely confounds us. The π-meson decays into a new particle, called the μ-meson, and a neutrino. This new particle, the μ-meson, is about 200 times as heavy as the electron. The strength of this decay interaction is identical with the interaction responsible for neutron decay.

The π-meson mystery does not stop here. In about 10^{-6} second the μ-meson itself spontaneously decays into an electron and two neutrinos. Quantitatively, once again it seems to be the same interaction as is responsible for the π-decay. Without hesitation one may say that the μ-meson is the most mysterious particle in physics. We do not know any good reason why it should exist, nor do we know why it should have such a large mass.

So far we have considered developments before 1947. In the last few years, following a brilliant discovery by C. C. Butler and G. D. Rochester, eight new particles have been discovered, and we must now consider these. They fall into two distinct categories:

1. There are six particles, each heavier than the proton, and designated Λ^0, Σ^+, Σ^-, Σ^0, Ξ^0, and Ξ^-. These all decay into a proton or a neutron, the decay strengths again being quantitatively the same as are those responsible for n, π, and μ decays. Since a proton or a neutron is one of the end products in the decay, there still is a conservation law for heavy particles. It now, however, reads $N_p + N_n + N_\Lambda + N_\Sigma + N_\Xi - (N_{\bar{p}} + N_{\bar{n}} + N_{\bar{\Lambda}} N +_{\bar{\Sigma}} + N_{\bar{\Xi}}) =$ constant, where N is the number of particles of the type designated by the subscript.

2. There are also particles, with masses intermediate between the nucleon and the π-meson, which finally decay into electrons and neutrinos. These are the K^+ and K^0 particles.

These eight particles presented certain unexpected features and for a number of years were called "strange" particles. From the copiousness of their production it seemed clear that their mutual interactions were strong in our technical sense. We have seen that isotopic spin is the distinguishing feature of strong interactions. It seemed appropriate to assign to these particles isotopic spin values and to demand that in their interactions isotopic spin conservation should hold. This assignment was made partly on theoretical and partly on phenomenological grounds by M. Gell-

Mann and K. Nishijima in 1953. The results were indeed startling. Some of these are:

1. In any collision process involving π-mesons and nucleons, not only can these "strange" particles be produced, but there must always be at least two of them. For example, $\pi^- + p \rightarrow \Sigma^- + K^+$.

2. In this same collision it is possible to produce $\Lambda^0 + K^0$, $\Sigma^0 + K^0$, or $\Sigma^- + K^+$, but never $\Sigma^+ + K^-$, even though the total charge, the heavy particle number, etc., all balance on both sides of the reaction. The explanation of this in terms of isotopic-spin conservation law is immediate. We notice from Table II that the total I_z value for $\pi^- + p$ is $-1 + \frac{1}{2} = -\frac{1}{2}$. For $\Sigma^- + K^+$, for example, it is also $-1 + \frac{1}{2} = -\frac{1}{2}$. For $\Sigma^+ + K^-$, however, $I_z = +\frac{1}{2}$, and thus this reaction cannot take place. A Pythagorean at this stage may well exclaim "Number rules the Universe." As with the former predictions cited, every one of the predictions made by the Gell-Mann-Nishijima theory has been verified.

To summarize all our findings:

1. Strong interactions take place between p, n, Λ^0, $\Sigma^{0\pm}$, Ξ^{0-}, $\pi^{0\pm}$, $K^{0\pm}$. These are characterized by the following set of conservation laws (Table I):

(i) Conservation of charge Q.
(ii) Conservation of heavy particle number $N_p + N_n + \ldots - (N_{\bar{p}} + N_{\bar{n}} \ldots) =$ constant.
(iii) Conservation of energy momentum. Space-time translation symmetry.
(iv) Conservation of spin. Space-time rotation symmetry.
(v) Conservation of isotopic spin. Isotopic space rotation symmetry.
(vi) Particle–anti-particle symmetry.

Subject to these rules, any interaction that can take place does take place.

2. Medium strong interactions involve electromagnetic interaction of all charged particles $p^\pm$, $\Sigma^\pm$, $\Xi^\pm$, $\pi^\pm$, $e^\pm$, $\mu^\pm$. These interactions are responsible for π^0 and Σ^0 decay in times $\sim 10^{-17}$ seconds. The conservation laws are the same here, save for (v).

TABLE I COMPARISON OF STRONG, ELECTROMAGNETIC, AND WEAK INTERACTIONS

	Strong (10^{-22} sec) $p, n, \Lambda, \Sigma, \Xi, \pi$, K	*Electro-magnetic* (10^{-18} sec) $p, \pi^{\pm}, \Sigma^{\pm}$, $K^{\pm}$, $\Xi^{-}, e^{\pm}, \mu^{\pm}, \gamma$	*Weak* (10^{-10} sec) $n, \pi, \mu, \Lambda, \Sigma, \Xi$, K decay
1. Charge conservation	√	√	√
2. Heavy particle conservation	√	√	√
Space-time			
3. Translation symmetry	√	√	√
4. Rotation symmetry	√	√	√
5. Space-reflection symmetry	√	√	×
6. Time-reflection symmetry	√	√	?
7. Isotopic space rotation symmetry	√	×	×
8. Particle–anti-particle symmetry	√	√	×

3. Weak interactions, which are responsible for the spontaneous decay of all particles except p, e, n, and the photon. The conservation laws are again (i) to (vi) except for (v), which is peculiar to the strong interaction.

We now come to the most recent act in our drama, bringing us up to January 1957. I have mentioned the translation and rotational symmetries of space-time. I have omitted to mention two further symmetry properties associated with space-time, namely space-reflection symmetry and time-reflection symmetry.

Consider space reflection or mirror reflection first. Since in a mirror a right hand reflects as a left hand, space-reflection symmetry is the same as right-left symmetry. The concept that right and left are indiscernible dates back to Leibniz, who first gave it a precise formulation. From Leibniz's day up to January 1957 it was accepted that there is no inner difference between right and left. Before proceeding, let me state the precise form in which the law of space reflection had been formulated. Just as Dirac showed that for any particle there must exist an anti-particle, so the law of space reflection asserts that if a particle exists the one obtained by reflecting it in a mirror must also exist. If a reaction can take place, the corresponding reaction seen in a mirror is also a physically possible one. Thus if right-polarized neutrinos can exist, so also must left-polarized neutrinos. Just as space-time rotation symmetry leads to conservation of spin, space-reflection symmetry leads to conservation of what is known as "parity."

The space-reflection symmetry or parity conservation principle is philosophically appealing. Even more important than any philosophical argument, the principle is known to hold for all strong and electromagnetic interactions. In the summer of 1956 C. N. Yang and T. D. Lee pointed out that there had until then been no experiment to prove or to disprove it for weak interactions, and they suggested a number of experiments which might clinch the matter. So firm was the belief that the principle must hold for all interactions that W. Pauli wrote to V. Weisskopf on 17th January, 1957: "I do *not* believe" (the *not* is heavily underscored by the writer) "that the Lord is a weak left-hander, and I am ready to bet a very high sum that the experiments will give symmetric results."

The experiments were completed two days after Pauli wrote. They have since been repeated all over the world. They showed unequivocally that in weak interactions there is no right-left symmetry. More precisely, the experiments showed that right-polarized neutrinos exist but left-polarized neutrinos do not. On reflecting a neutrino in a mirror one sees nothing.

It is sobering to think that the experimental results could have been discovered ten years back, for the evidence existed on all the photographic plates recording π^+ and μ^+ decay. If reflection symmetry holds, relative to the direction of motion of μ-mesons, the same number of electrons should be emitted in the forward as in the backward direction. If anybody had bothered to count the numbers he would have discovered the asymmetry. On January 27th, 1957 Pauli wrote:

> Now after the first shock is over I begin to collect myself. Yes, it was very dramatic. On Monday, the 21st, at 8.00 P.M. I was

> supposed to give a lecture on the neutrino theory. At 5.00 P.M. I received 3 experimental papers. . . . I am shocked not so much by the fact that the Lord prefers the left-hand but by the fact that he still appears to be left-right symmetric when he expresses himself strongly. In short the actual problem now seems to be the question why are strong interactions right and left symmetric.

Explaining to a classicist friend the magnitude of the revolution that had occurred in physics, I asked him if any classical writer had ever considered giants with only the left eye. He confessed that one-eyed giants have been described, and he supplied me with a full list of them; but they always sport their solitary eye in the middle of the forehead. In my view, what we have found is that space is a weak left-eyed giant.

One can perhaps give the deeper reason why right-left symmetry should be violated whenever a neutrino is emitted. It can be shown that an exactly zero mass for the neutrino is incompatible with right-left symmetry. We have lost the symmetry principle, but perhaps gained an exactly zero mass for the neutrino. Today the gain seems unimportant compared with the loss, but a few years hence we may think differently.

The time-reflection principle asserts symmetry between past and future; in our formulation it does not make statements about causation but merely such statements as that: The number of K's and Σ's produced in $\pi^- + p$ collision is the same as the number of $\pi^- + p$ produced in K, Σ collision. It is known that the principle holds in strong interations. We strongly suspect that it also holds for electromagnetic interactions. There is no experiment yet to test it for weak decays. One may remark that if the principle holds in weak decays, the left-eyed giant, on looking into a mirror, will see not a right-eyed giant but a right-eyed antigiant.

The entire development presented here is based on the assumption that the structure of space and time is that given by the special theory of relativity. The reason for ignoring the general theory of relativity is that the gravitational force is an even weaker one than any that have been considered. It has a strength

TABLE II ELEMENTARY PARTICLES

	Particle	*Rest mass*	*Spin*	I_z	*Decay time (sec)*	*Decay products*	*Anti-particle*
1.	γ	0	+ 1		∞	Stable	γ
2.	e^-	1	±½		∞	Stable	e^+
3.	μ^-	207	±½		10^{-6}	$e^- + \nu + \bar{\nu}$	μ^+
4.	ν^0	0	+½		∞	Stable	$\bar{\nu}$(spin −½)
5.	p^+	1836	±½	½	∞	Stable	$\bar{p}$
6.	n^0	1839	±½	−½	10^3	$p + e^- + \bar{\nu}$	$\bar{n}$
7.	Λ^0	2180	±½	0	10^{-10}	$p + \pi^-$ or $n + \pi^0$	$\bar{\Lambda}^0$
8.	Σ^+	2331	±½	1	10^{-11}	$p + \pi^0$ or $n + \pi^+$	$\bar{\Sigma}^+$
9.	Σ^0	2331	±½	0	10^{-18}	$\Lambda^0 + \gamma$	$\bar{\Sigma}^0$
10.	Σ^-	2345	±½	− 1	10^{-10}	$n + \pi^-$	$\bar{\Sigma}^-$
11.	Ξ^0	2590	±½	½	10^{-10}	$\Lambda^0 + \pi^0$	$\bar{\Xi}^0$
12.	Ξ^-	2590	±½	−½	10^{-10}	$\Lambda^0 + \pi^-$	$\bar{\Xi}^-$
13.	π^+	273	0	1	10^{-8}	$\mu + \nu$	$\pi^-(I_z = -1)$
14.	π^0	264	0	0	10^{-16}	2γ	π^0
15.	K^+	966	0	½	10^{-8}	$\mu + \nu, 2\pi, 3\pi$	$K^-(I_z = +½)$
16.	K^0	966	0	−½	10^{-10}	$\pi^+ + \pi^-$ or $\pi^0 + \pi^0$	$\bar{K}^0(I_z = -½)$

of 10^{-34} in the units used above, and to an excellent approximation its effects can be neglected.

Turning to some of the problems in the physics of elementary particles, we ask why there are just these particles. Are there still more particles to be discovered? In the case of particles possessing strong interactions we believe we understand the deeper reason for their existence in terms of the isotopic spin space. Why this space exists we do not know; but, granted its existence, it would seem that we have already discovered all particles possessing strong interactions, except possibly for one particle. This is a rash statement. Such statements have been made again and again in the history of physics and have always proved false, and I must qualify it by saying that the isotopic group may admit other particles, but they will all probably have lifetimes shorter than 10^{-19} second.

We still do not know the deeper symmetry principle associated with particles falling in the electromagnetic and weak interaction categories. There may well, for example, be more companion particles of the μ-meson. In fact, all we know about the particles that fall in these two categories is that their interactions violate some of the strong interaction symmetries. These interactions seem in a sense to have a negative role. There must in nature be a hierarchy of symmetry principles, some of which are dearer to nature's heart than others.

All our remarks on whether further particles are likely to be discovered or not depend, of course, on whether there exist further categories of interactions besides the three mentioned. If there do, naturally there will be whole classes of new particles. This question is connected with the existence of conservation laws. So far, we believe that four conservation laws hold universally. Are there further interactions weaker still, for which these also break down? Cosmologists in their theories of continuous creation have already suggested that energy and momentum are indeed not conserved when the still weaker gravitational interaction is considered. From the present point of view this hypothesis becomes entirely plausible.

On looking through the table of elementary particles there is only one thought in my mind: how deeply privileged our generation is to have been presented with this fascinating challenge. People speak of the multiplicity of elementary particles—they even give them outlandish names like "strange" particles; they shake their heads in disapproval of "weak" laws. I believe these are but stepping stones to an inner harmony, a deep pervading symmetry. The μ-meson may seem out of place today. When we discover its real nature we shall marvel how neatly it fits into the Great Scheme, how integral a part it is of something deeper, more profound, more transcending. Faith in the inner harmony of nature has paid dividends in the past. I am confident it will continue to do so in the future.

From the time of their discovery in the early years of this century, cosmic rays have been actively studied from a number of rather different points of view. Some investigators consider cosmic rays a prime source of the high energies required in fundamental particle research. For others, their enticements lie in the radioactive isotopes (such as tritium and carbon 14) that they produce in the atmosphere, in the clues they provide as to the structure of the galaxy, in the indications they give of solar activity, or in the hazards they present to space travelers. All in all, cosmic radiation is a fascinating field, and one that has regularly turned up new mysteries as fast as the old ones are solved.

Serge A. Korff has spent thirty years in hot pursuit of cosmic rays, the past twenty at New York University. His specialty is the neutron components of both primary and secondary cosmic radiation, and his instruments have counted neutrons at sea level, atop mountains, in high-altitude balloons, and in research rockets. He also has done pioneering work in developing the "proportional" counters used in detecting nuclear particles, particularly neutrons. Korff is an ex-president of the Explorer's Club. In the following selection, first presented as a Sigma Xi lecture, he surveys the geophysical and astrophysical aspects of cosmic rays in a clear, direct style that brings out the underlying order in the diversity of phenomena that are involved.

Serge A. Korff

THE ORIGIN AND IMPLICATIONS OF THE COSMIC RADIATION

Cosmic rays have been known for about half a century. The fact that we are only today beginning to understand some of the problems associated with them indicates the order of magnitude of the complexity of the problem, and the degree to which we were dealing with phenomena with which we had little familiarity. Our opinions have gone through a series of changes as we have slowly realized the true nature of the factors involved. For example, in the early 1920's the general opinion about cosmic rays was that they were of the nature of gamma rays, of some hundreds of Mev's in energy, and that most of the secondary particles at sea level were electrons. Contrast this with the fact that it has been proved that the majority of primary cosmic rays are protons, with energies tens to thousands of times the previous hundreds of Mev's, and that the secondary particles reaching sea level are mostly mesons. We see then just how revolutionary has been the change of view which modern detection techniques have made possible.

It is the purpose of this article to review our present thoughts about the radiation, about the mechanisms operating to produce it, and about the interesting astrophysical implications suggested by its presence. Further, we are today on the threshold of a new era in which we shall see important developments that follow from the use of the radiation as a tool of geophysical investigation. In this discussion we use the word "Geophysical" in its broadest sense, to include not only the science of our earth, but also the many fascinating, important, and complex solar-terrestrial relationships.

Review of Known Facts. Any acceptable theory of the origin of the radiation must explain the main features which characterize the cosmic rays. We shall briefly recapitulate these and indicate how each was determined. In so doing we have the great advantage of hindsight, and need not follow developments chronologically. Briefly, an acceptable theory must provide a mechanism which will generate radiation within the following characteristics.

First, the composition of the radiation. We know today that the primary radiation reaching the earth is, by number, mostly protons. A smaller number of alpha particles is also present, and a numerically much smaller number of heavy nuclei. The exact percentages are still being disputed by the experts, and differences of opinion exist. To quote a figure, for the purposes of this article, and with which some experts will disagree, most experts consider that the primary radiation is by number, 70% to 90% protons, 29% to 9% alpha particles, and somewhat under 1% heavy nuclei. The primary radiation contains few, if any, electrons or photons. By definition, it cannot contain unstable particles, such as neutrons or mesons, for these would have decayed in flight. Neutrons might reach the earth from the sun, but not from outside the solar system.

The data cited above on the identity of the primaries are secured principally through the use of photographic emulsions. These emulsions are flown to great heights in balloons, and, when recovered and developed, show tracks which can be identified and counted. The presence of heavy nuclei in the primary radiation was discovered by those emulsions.

Second, the energy of the radiation. The energy of the primary radiation lies mostly between 10^9 and 10^{18} electron volts (e.v.) per particle. Neither the upper nor the lower limit is exactly established. There may be some lower energy particles with energies of 10^8 e.v. or even less, and the upper limit is hard to determine exactly. Today, experimenters consider that 10^{18} e.v. is a proved value, and this author has even heard the figure 10^{20} e.v. seriously discussed. Such an energy is indeed huge for a nuclear particle. It would enable a single proton to lift a mass of one kilogram a meter against gravity.

The energy of the cosmic ray particles is measured, in the interval between 10^8 or 10^9 e.v. and 10^{12} e.v., by their deflection in the earth's magnetic field. The theory of the deflection was worked out by LeMaitre and Vallarta. The energy distribution manifests itself as the latitude effect in the radiation. The latitude effect has been measured in a series of world surveys by Millikan's and Compton's groups and by others. At energies in excess of 10^{12} e.v., the deflection produced by the earth's field becomes immeasurably small, and another method is required. This method is the study of "extensive showers." A high energy primary particle produces an extensive shower of secondary particles. Fortunately, cascade theory enables the distribution of particles in such a shower to be calculated. Careful experiments have substantiated the correctness of the theory. From the counting rates of counters which are separated by considerable distances, the primary energies can be inferred. Counter separations of 100 meters or more have been used for high energies with success, and a few experiments have been made at considerably greater separations. At large separation, the experimental difficulties become great since the travel times of the pulse from widely separated counters become comparable with the resolving time of the electronic components. However, as techniques improve, it seems reasonable to predict that before long we shall be able to prove conclusively whether particles in the very high energy brackets do or do not exist, and if so how many there are. In the lower energy brackets we are on safe ground and have quite accurate figures.

Recently with the aid of the rockets it has been possible to obtain measurements of the primary cosmic ray intensities. Rockets can go up to a sufficient altitude so that the magnitude of the hump produced by secondary particles can be evaluated.

The third feature of the radiation which a theory must explain is its remarkable constancy with time. A cosmic ray meter at any place on the earth's surface shows a radiation which has fluctuations of only a few per cent, after the usual meteorological effects have been allowed for. The diurnal wave is less than two tenths of a per cent in amplitude, and some observers consider that it has never been proved conclusively to exist at all. Similarly, no appreciable variation with sidereal time has been found except perhaps for a small effect in the extensive showers, which again some observers find but others claim is still within the error of the measurement. Long period changes over several years have been found to exist, in the excellent series of measurements made by Forbush with the Carnegie meters distributed at many different places all over the world. However, these changes are of the order of two or three per cent, and seem to show a connection with the 11-year sunspot cycle.

Clearly the absence of a marked 24-hour wave imposes on any theory the requirement that (*a*) the source shall be far away and preferably distributed about in many places, or (*b*) if the source is near, that a scrambling mechanism must be invoked which will be capable of completely scrambling the directions of even the most energetic components. A possible scrambling mechanism would be an interplanetary magnetic field. Yet such a field would have to satisfy two apparently mutually exclusive criteria. The field would have to be strong enough to bend the high energy particles but it must also be small enough so that we do not measure it here on earth with our best magnetometers. We measure no such field. It is today thought that an interplanetary field of the order of a few microgauss may exist, so small as to be impossible to measure directly. Such a field would not be sufficient to scramble the directions of the high energy part of the cosmic ray spectrum.

The radiation does show fluctuations, and the study of those changes is most interesting. We shall discuss these in detail later. But the fluctuations have a known cause, and the theories of origin must explain the non-varying part.

The fourth feature which characterizes the radiation and which presents a unique problem to the theories of origin is that of the total intensity. The total energy which arrives at the earth in the form of cosmic radiation is about the same as that of starlight. This amount is either very large or very small, depending on how it is considered. If one compares this radiation to the amount of energy arriving in the form of sunlight, it is very small. The reason is that we are near a source of energy, the sun. However, if we consider that starlight is the sum total of the output of all the luminous bodies in the universe put together, then the total is seen to be vast indeed. The problem of whether the total amount should be regarded as large or small therefore depends on whether the earth, as far as the cosmic rays are concerned, may be thought of as occupying a unique place near a source, or whether it occupies an average, typical place in a widely distributed system. If the earth is near a source of radiation, then the total amount of the cosmic radiation is quite unimportant. But if the earth occupies a representative typical place, such that if it were at some other place quite far from here it would receive approximately the same amount of energy, then we have a very difficult problem. In this case, we must look for a source of cosmic rays which must be able to produce as much energy as all the luminous surfaces of all the stars combined.

Further, our sun is in a part of a vast aggregation of stars, a galaxy. There are many millions of other galaxies at various distances from ours. The amount of starlight we receive is typical of what one receives inside a galactic system, and far greater than one would receive at an average point out in intergalactic space. Cosmic rays may also be characteristic of this place inside a galaxy. If cosmic rays should turn out to pervade all space, the problem will be more difficult by six orders of magnitude. Since galaxies have an average separation of about a hundred times their diameters, the total volume which they occupy is one millionth of all space. If cosmic rays were truly intergalactic, then we should be forced to conclude that there is a million times as much energy in this form as in all other forms put together. As we shall see, present evidence suggests that this is not so, and that cosmic rays are galactic phenomena, typical as also is our light radiation, of a place in an arm of a galaxy.

A Review of Possible Mechanisms of Origin. We pass next to considering what possible mechanisms could have given rise to radiation having the characteristics which we have cited above. Many years ago it was suggested that the radiation might have its origin in microscopic, atomic, or nuclear processes. Today we know that this solution is out of the question, for the most energetic possible nuclear process would be the complete annihilation of a heavy nucleus, and the annihilation of the heaviest we know would produce only of the order of 2.5×10^{11} e.v. This energy is far too small to account for the observed cosmic ray energies, which may go up to amounts of a million or more times this. Therefore we can consider nuclear energy as infinitesimal in the scale which we have to explain.

Since the above argument excludes all microscopic processes as totally insufficient we must next consider macroscopic processes. Charged particles can be accelerated in fields. Of these, there are both electric and magnetic. The electric case is quickly also ruled out. Space is too good a conductor, and if large potential differences existed between parts of space, such as would give rise to large electric fields, currents would flow and charged particles would move so as to restore electrical neutrality. To maintain the radiation we should then have to introduce a vast mechanism which would be required to bring about a separation of charges, and which would have to continue to do so. No one has seriously suggested any mechanism of this type. We turn for consideration then to magnetic fields.

In the case of magnetic fields, the situation is totally different. In the first place, for a charged particle to gain energy in a magnetic field, it must move through a field which is not constant. A simple illustration is the field in a betatron which varies with time. If we seek, we find such varying fields in a number of different forms and places. Not all of them will do the trick, however. Let us consider a few cases.

There are large magnetic fields in sunspots. We can measure the fields, and their rate of growth, by the Zeeman effect in sunspot spectra. We find spots which in some cases grow up to as much as 5000 gauss in a single day. Both the magnitude of the field and its rate of growth are sufficient for accelerating cosmic ray particles up to energies of 10 or 10^{12} e.v. Since our sun is not a particularly large star, it may be, as Swann has suggested, that on super-stars there are super-spots, and that these could produce energies which might account for the upper parts of the energy spectrum also. However, the sunspot solution as a source for all cosmic rays immediately runs into two difficulties. First, as far as our own sun is concerned, since our sun is near, the absence of any 24-hour wave in the radiation makes it improbable that our own sun is the source. It is true that certain large fluctuations can be traced to solar origins, but it is unlikely that the sun would send radiation around to the dark side of the earth with exactly the same intensity as on the sunlit face. Further, to assume that cosmic rays originate in distant sunspots on super-stars is to assume that the output of the disturbed spot areas is as great as that of all the luminous non-disturbed spot areas put together, which is certainly untrue for our own sun and scarcely believable for other stars.

Recently Babcock has discovered some very amazing stars, which are called the magnetic Babcock-type stars. In these, the whole star shows a strong magnetic field, which quite rapidly changes to an equally strong field in the opposite direction. No explanation of these curious properties has yet met with wide acceptance, but it is clear that such stars also could serve as cosmic ray accelerators. Again, however, the total energy argument is against these, for there are very few such stars, and it seems impossible to ascribe all the cosmic ray energy to a few stars.

Similarly there are the rotating magnetic double-star systems. The Swedish astrophysicist Alfven has calculated that double-star systems, if both stars have even small magnetic movements, could accelerate charged particles. However, in this case the acceleration would be at the expense of the angular momentum of the system, and if one were to ascribe all the cosmic rays to such systems, then all such systems would long since have exhausted their rotary kinetic energy and run down.

We come finally to one other magnetic field, which has several advantages. That is the galactic field. It is easy to show that there should be a weak field throughout most of the galaxy. There is a great deal of matter, dust, and gas atoms spread throughout the galaxy. An appreciable part of this matter is photoionized by being near hot stars which emit quanta of the requisite energy. We also know that the various clouds of dust and other matter are in motion, both in random motion with respect to one another and in a general rotary motion with respect to the center of the galaxy. Such motion of charged particles will set up the necessary magnetic fields, and easy calculations show the magnitude of such fields to be of the order of a few microgauss. The field will vary from place to place, both in magnitude, in direction and in time rate of change. Let us examine how such a galactic field would affect charged particles.

The original calculations of this effect were made by Fermi, who showed that the fields were sufficient to accelerate particles to cosmic ray energies. But two more extremely important features followed. The first is that galactic fields can account not only for cosmic ray energies but for the shape of the spectrum.

The energy spectrum of the cosmic radiation is described by an empirical power law formula with a negative exponent (approximately varying as E^{-2}) which may vary somewhat as one passes through various energy intervals. Its general form can be understood by saying that there are progressively fewer cosmic ray particles in each energy interval as one goes to progressively higher energies.

Cosmic ray particles in space will of course from time to

time make collisions on atoms of gas, or on dust particles or on stars in space. Such collisions will result in loss of energy by the cosmic ray particle, the amount ranging from a small loss of energy for a "near miss" on the nucleus of a free gas atom, to complete absorption on colliding with a star. The amount of energy lost depends on (*a*) the projectile, (*b*) the target, and (*c*) the energy of the particle. The amount of matter in space is known, and the mean free paths can be calculated for each type of collision. It will here suffice to say that collisions with stars are rare events; and that the mean free time between nuclear collisions with atoms is on the average a million years. In the galactic field theory the actual spectrum is a survival spectrum, characterized by those particles which by chance have not lost energy through collisions staying around longer and getting progressively more and more energy from the field. Another way of looking at this model is to consider that particles are making inelastic collisions with fields, and that in some of these collisions the particles gain energy. Naturally there will also be collisions in which the particles lose energy, but these particles disappear from the system and are of progressively less importance.

The second important feature of the galactic origin is that this time we have the entire rotational kinetic energy of the galaxy to draw upon, and therefore for the first time we have a source which has enough energy to supply the observed total. Actually it is not necessary to draw upon this vast supply and, in fact, the excellent organization of the galaxy shows that not much energy has been withdrawn from its supply of angular momentum. The clouds of dust and gas near hot stars are often in rapid turbulent motion, the turbulence being produced by the tremendous outpouring of energy from these hot stars. Some of these stars are radiating at such rates that they cannot be very old. This large radiative output is presumably the result of previous gravitational accumulation of dust and gas by the star. The expansional energy of the ionized luminous cloud is itself quite sufficient both to provide the necessary varying fields and the total energy.

Some other interesting consequences follow from this view. If cosmic rays are of galactic origin, we do not face the insuperable problems which we cited earlier for an intergalactic radiation, namely, a total energy a million times greater than that of the luminous thermal radiation. Further, the composition of the radiation makes sense, for we should expect the radiation to be composed of the same material which we know to be abundant in the universe, namely, mostly hydrogen (protons), substantially less helium (alpha particles), and a small amount of the heavier elements. This is the normal qualitative statement of the cosmic abundances although quantitatively there are somewhat more of the heavy nuclei than normal cosmic abundance would suggest. Further, heavy nuclei cannot have made any collisions at all, for they would have been fragmentized, since cosmic ray energies are far greater than nuclear binding energies. Protons on the other hand could have survived collisions.

The galactic field mechanism requires some sort of "injection." Particles can be accelerated by galactic fields if they start out with appreciable energies. The energies they must have are of the order of their "rest energies," M_0c^2. At such energies the energy-loss per collision is a minimum. For a proton this is about 10^9 e.v., which is just about the bottom of the observed cosmic ray spectrum. The injection is necessary because of the collisions mentioned above. At lower energies, a particle will lose energy by ionizing collisions faster than it gains energy from the field. The galactic process therefore has a definite starting potential. Fermi's latest mechanism requires somewhat less injection energy than does his first model, because of the greater rate of gain of energy. As it happens there are many injectors. All the mechanisms we have cited above, sunspots, superspots, magnetic stars, and possibly also supernovae, will inject particles at the requisite energy into the galaxy, whereupon the galactic field takes over, and provides the acceleration to the really large energies. All particles, and there will be many, with less than this minimum of energy will simply not be accelerated and will form a part of the low energy debris in space. The composition of the material injected will be that which is cosmically available. If supernovae are injectors, and if the suggestions made by some students of the subject about the "cooking" of heavy nuclei in supernovae are correct, then we may in fact find somewhat more heavy nuclei in the cosmic ray mass spectrum than in the standard galactic abundance tables. Incidentally it is not the supernova explosion in itself which would bring particles up even to injection energies. A supernova, spectacular though it is, is still a low-energy process. But the act of blowing out a huge cloud of material, much of which is ionized, will set up strong but local electric fields since the ions and the electrons will presumably not all move at the same speed. It is these electric and the consequent magnetic fields which can in certain circumstances accelerate particles. The processes involve that super-complex subject, magneto-hydrodynamics of heavily ionized gases.

If the galactic magnetic field is a gigantic betatron, then in all probability the various mechanisms we have cited, such as the Babcock stars and the sunspots will be the ion-sources, and will inject into the field these particles which the field will then accelerate. Further, the absence of electrons and photons from the primary radiation is explained, for photons are lost by being able to escape from the galaxy and electrons do not survive owing to their high rate of energy loss upon making radiative as well as ionizing collisions with the matter in space. In the language of nuclear physics, electrons have a large cross section for energy-dissipating collisions.

Consider next the curvature of the particle orbits and the problem of the entrapment of the radiation in the galaxy. The theory of relativity gives a relationship, between the energy for "relativistic" particles, that is for particles whose energy is very large compared to their rest-energy, M_0c^2, and their curvature in a magnetic field,

$$HR = 3 \times 10^{-3} E$$

where H is the magnitude of the field in gauss, R is the radius of curvature in cms, and E the energy in electron volts. Note that this is a relativistic formula and will give quite wrong results if applied to a "classical" particle at slow speeds. For fields of a microgauss, i.e., for an H of 10^{-6} gauss, and an energy of say 10^{12} e.v., the formula gives a radius of 3×10^{15} cm. The sun is about 1.5×10^{13} cms from the earth, so the curvature is quite small on the cosmic scale, being only 200 times the earth sun distance. A particle of energy 10^{18} e.v. has a curvature in such a field of 3×10^{21} cms. Now a light year is about 10^{18} cms. Hence such a particle has a radius of curvature of about 3000 light years. This figure is of the order of the thickness of the spiral arm of the galaxy, and suggests that particles of this energy would still be confined to the galaxy. An interesting effect occurs at the higher energy, say 10^{20} e.v., where the radius becomes larger than the thickness of the galaxy. At these energies we should expect some change in the cosmic ray distribution, and in the observed spectrum, for such rays would be able to escape from the galaxy if the plane of their orbit was at right angles to the plane of the galaxy. Further, we should expect some time-variations, for a given point on the earth's surface will at times be directly in the galactic plane, and at other times the galaxy may be on the horizon. This situation would introduce some of the directional effects known to be absent in the lower energy part of the radiation. These high energies are today just on the edge of what can be observed, and it will be most interesting and extremely revealing to see whether the spectrum changes as one goes to these energies and whether the particles show a variation with time which is not present in the lower brackets. This experiment is therefore one of the most promising cosmic ray experiments, and one which could tell us much about all the various factors. With present techniques it is extremely difficult, but it represents a most challenging new observation, and the one from which the most important new directions can be gained. Indeed it would seem at present that this study would provide for us one of the really vital keys to the structure of the universe.

Astrophysical Implications: Steady-state Solutions or Alternative Long Term Implications. We may also say a word about the astrophysical implications contained in the galactic acceleration picture of cosmic rays. There are two quite different possibilities, first that cosmic rays are in equilibrium today, being produced, accelerated, and absorbed, so that we are measuring a part of a long-term equilibrium process, and the second that cosmic rays are residual from an original catastrophic explosion. The latter possibility has been considered at length by LeMaitre. Today's opinion strongly leans in favor of the first of these alternatives. The Fermi picture of injection by such events as supernovae, super-sunspots, magnetic stars, and other mechanisms at moderate energies, followed by an acceleration to cosmic ray energies by the galactic fields, and eventual disappearance by absorption due to collisions with matter, either diffuse or in stars, is a "steady state" type of solution. The amount of the galactic field needed for the acceleration is sufficient to cause the rays to be trapped in the galaxy, and suggests that if we measured cosmic rays in intergalactic space, we should find that its intensity there was much less than within the galaxy.

If alternatively it should turn out that cosmic rays were residual from an explosion which took place perhaps when the universe in its present form came into being, then certain other consequences might be expected to follow. Since there is enough matter in the galaxy so that cosmic rays would perhaps survive for a million years or so at present densities, we must have the bulk of the radiation outside the galaxy, or it could not have survived for the approximately five billion years which have passed since the original explosion. In this event, the total amount of energy in the form of cosmic rays as we have mentioned earlier is a million times greater than the energy being emitted by the thermally hot luminous surfaces of all the stars in the universe. This would in turn impose very odd properties upon the original explosion. We should have to have an explosion in which the radiation was generated in enormous amounts at a time after the matter had already separated appreciably, for while today in intergalactic space the mean free time of a cosmic ray particle is longer than the five billion years since the explosion, during the dense phase the free times were shorter. The curves cross at about one per cent of the present age of the universe, i.e., at perhaps fifty million years, and at time previous to this, the free time between collisions is smaller than the total time elapsed since the initial instant. In other words, it is hard to see how the radiation could have survived the first fifty million years, and easy to see how it could have survived in the later periods.

Geophysical Aspects of the Cosmic Radiation. SOLAR FLARE EFFECTS: We may next consider the geophysical aspects of cosmic radiation, a subject which will undoubtedly see great development during the next decade. In this first case we shall be dealing with the fluctuations in the cosmic radiation and not with the constant portion. We know that large fluctuations occasionally occur, a spectacular recent one being that which took place on February 23, 1956, when the neutron intensity at and near sea level abruptly rose by 600 per cent, and then returned to normal in about 4 hours. The fluctuation was reported by observers all over the world, and while the amplitude varied with latitude and altitude, the time and general form of the increase is generally agreed upon. It is quite clear that, on this occasion, superposed on the normal pattern, some additional radiation reached the earth from the sun, and that this radiation included some particles with energy enough to penetrate the earth's field at the equator, and produce a large number of neutrons as secondaries.

This increase in cosmic ray intensity took place at the same time as the appearance of a solar flare, and was also accompanied by notable disturbances in the ionosphere and in a normal auroral activity. While it has not been established that it is actually radiation from the flare itself that produces the effect, the name "flare effect" has been used to identify the type of disturbance. It is of course possible that the radiation originates in disturbed regions on the sun adjacent to the flare itself, and that the flare is merely another manifestation in a certain frequency interval of a disturbed condition and an abrupt emission maximum. Flares are generally associated with sunspots, although not coextensive with them, but, rather, both are indicators of non-equilibrium disturbed areas on the sun. It is clear that the increases in cosmic ray intensity are manifestations of an intermittent and occasional charged-particle emission from the sun. The charged particles have energy enough to penetrate to sea level and to produce the large observed number of secondary neutrons. It is known that these occasional bursts of charged particle radiation produce brilliant auroral displays and show effects in geomagnetism. They undoubtedly produce other geophysical effects and a study of them promises much new information.

MAGNETIC STORM EFFECTS: There is also a different kind of fluctuation which occurs from time to time. This is a decrease in the observed radiation instead of an increase, which decrease takes place simultaneously with a magnetic storm. The intensity curves look very much like the inverse of the "flare effects" mentioned already, except that they persist for a day or two instead of an hour or two. The intensity drops abruptly several per cent, then slowly recovers to its original value. The curves of the earth's magnetic field do likewise. Actually, it is the fact that both the radiation and the field show a decrease which is the clue to what is happening. In this case we have a change in the cutoff produced by the earth's field. If the limiting energy admitted by the field changes, then a differing amount of radiation will enter. These decreases are known as the "Forbush type decreases" after the investigator who has observed more of them than anyone else and who has done much to explain their nature. In this case the effect is again due to charged particle radiation which arrives from the sun, particles with comparatively low energy. These particles are trapped in the earth's field and form a "ring current" around the earth, moving in almost stable orbits. Owing to their motion they set up a field of their own and this field when added to the earth's field determines the limiting cutoff energy of radiation entering from outside. We may thus say that the charged particle radiation alters the earth's field and this in turn modulates the incoming radiation which originated far away. Eventually the particles dissipate and move off into space, and the situation returns to normal.

EFFECTS OF THE COSMIC RADIATION ON TERRESTRIAL ISOTOPE DISTRIBUTION: Another interesting effect is that of the changes which the cosmic rays produce upon the isotopes in the atmosphere, the oceans, and the crust of the earth. The first of these to be discovered was the formation of radiocarbon, predicted in 1940 in the paper by Bethe, Korff, and Placzek. Cosmic ray neutrons, produced as secondary particles in the atmosphere by the original radiation, are captured by nitrogen nuclei to form the radioactive isotope of carbon, the isotope of mass 14. This isotope has a long half life, something over 5500 years. By the application of some very well thought-out techniques, Libby and his colleagues have actually not only identified the radiocarbon in nature, but also have made quantitative estimates thereof. Since this carbon in the atmosphere mostly becomes attached to oxygen to form carbon dioxide, and since the carbon dioxide is ingested by plants and animals and is incorporated in their biological structures, and further, since this process stops at the time of the death of the specimen, the percentage of radiocarbon among the normal carbon atoms in its system can be used to establish the date at which the specimen stopped metabolizing. The use of this important dating tool by archaeologists is too well known today to need further elaboration. It has been used for dating wood from Egyptian tombs, charcoal from old kitchen middens and for finding the dates at which trees are pushed over by glaciers, to mention but a few. This use is an interesting illustration of the normal function of pure research and of how such pure research leads into unexpected applications. Who would have imagined, had he started out to find a better method of dating wood in ancient tombs, that the thing he should do was to study the absorption properties of cosmic ray secondaries high in the atmosphere with the aid of neutron counters flown in free balloons from sites thousands of miles away from his specimens?

Another isotope produced by cosmic rays in the atmosphere is that of radioactive hydrogen, tritium. This substance also is produced by the cosmic ray neutrons. Since it has a much shorter half life, a bit over twelve years, and since it enters inanimate as well as the life cycle of living matter in a different manner from carbon, it too can be used as a dating tool, with quite differing characteristics and limitations. It may help us, for example, to date ice in glaciers, or to study the speed with which water moves at great depths in the ocean. Further, since tritium decays into helium three, and helium three is easily detected in and distinguished from normal helium four, we now have still another dating tool. It is probable that all the helium three in the atmosphere is of cosmic ray origin, and its rate of escape from the atmosphere and total accumulation may tell us something about the average temperature which has existed in the atmosphere at remote times in the past. Helium three may also be identified in solid objects. It is possible that a study of the distribution of helium three inside meteors will tell us about the origin of these objects, or perhaps about how long they have been circulating, or alternatively, about the intensity which cosmic rays have had at times in the distant past.

Further study by the author and by others has shown that there are many other isotopes also produced by the cosmic rays. The point is that the primary radiation has more than enough energy to break up the nuclei which it hits in the atmosphere, and that therefore we should expect to find spallation products of all masses less than those of the normal constituents of the atmosphere. Since argon 40 is present in air to the amount of about a per cent, we shall find quite a collection of different fragments of mass 40 or less. The first of these, phosphorus 32, has already been identified by a group of Brazilian investigators. Beryllium 7, a spallation product of the lighter but more abundant nitrogen and oxygen nuclei, has also been reported. It may confidently be anticipated that many new isotopes will be found in the years to come and these will each open up new and interesting vistas in research.

In addition to effects in the atmosphere, some cosmic ray neutrons reach sea level. The fraction near the surface of the earth is much smaller than the number in the high atmosphere, but all the neutrons produced are eventually captured by nuclei,

Fusion power, which refers to the energy liberated when two light nuclei join together to form a heavier one, has awesome potentialities. The problem of realizing these potentialities is equally awesome, however, and despite brilliant and imaginative efforts throughout the world, it remains unsolved. Like writings on elementary particles and space exploration, those on fusion power are full of excitement, of the feeling that success is just over the horizon—which it may or may not be. Regardless of whether current approaches to fusion power will bring it into being, there is no doubt that they have been immensely fruitful in enlarging our knowledge of plasmas and their interaction with magnetic fields. Nearly all the matter in the astronomical universe is in the plasma state, and many of the key workers in fusion power are peculiar combinations of astrophysicist and engineer. Richard Post came to controlled thermonuclear research from wartime work on underwater sound and a postwar association with Stanford's linear accelerator. He is currently with the Lawrence Radiation Laboratory of the University of California. Fusion Power was initially published in **Scientific American.** For a fuller, though still nontechnical, discussion of this subject, **Project Sherwood,** by Amasa S. Bishop (Addison-Wesley, 1958, and Anchor Books), is recommended.

Richard R. Post

FUSION POWER

The effort to "tame" the hydrogen bomb reaction–to harness the energy of nuclear fusion for controlled power–is gaining momentum in many countries of the world. It is proceeding quietly, behind a screen of official secrecy, but nonetheless vigorously and on a substantial scale. Every nation has come to recognize that this research effort may well be the most important in the history of mankind. The ultimate stakes are so high, for nations individually and mankind collectively, that a growing sense of urgency and determination is infusing the work of the several nations on this problem.

The upsurge of our industrial civilization in the first half of the 20th century was founded upon fossil fuels–coal and oil. But there are many "have-not" nations, and even countries rich in these fuels are now seeing rapid inroads into their reserves. At this juncture uranium has come to the rescue as a hope for the future. Already electrical power is beginning to flow from the first nuclear fission plants. The United Kingdom expects to go over to fissionable fuels for most of its energy needs within a few decades, and many other countries are laying plans to follow suit; even the U.S., with its great reserves of coal, is spending hundreds of millions of dollars to prepare for turning to fission power at a not too distant date.

The world's uranium and thorium, it is estimated, represent an energy reserve somewhere between 10 and 100 times larger than its remaining coal. Even so, fissionable fuels, too, are an exhaustible supply. At the rate at which the world's energy needs are expanding (the U.S. has doubled its electrical power requirements every eight years) practically all of the economically recoverable uranium, as well as coal, might be exhausted within another century or so. Fission power also presents a more immediate problem: namely, disposal of its radioactive wastes. If the present power needs of the U.S. were all supplied by fission reactors, we would have to dispose each year of an amount of radioactive fission products equal to that from the explosion of 200,000 atomic bombs; by the year 2000, with increased use of power, the radioactive wastes would come to the equivalent of eight million atomic bomb explosions per year! It is clear that the problem of safe disposal of radioactive ashes and gases in the coming age of fission power will soon become staggering.

All this helps to explain the drive, if not race, to find out whether thermonuclear power can be tapped and put to work. If the fusion reaction can be made to yield power, it will solve forever both the fuel supply problem and the problem of radioactive wastes. The basic fusion fuel, deuterium, is as inexhaustible as the oceans, and fusion produces no appreciable amount of radioactive by-products.

The Fusion Reaction. Nuclear fusion is not exactly a new phenomenon. It has been generating the power of the sun and other stars for billions of years, and physicists discovered the fusion reaction in the laboratory before they did fission. But to create and control fusion power on the earth is a problem of a totally different order from harnessing fission. It is undoubtedly the most difficult project ever presented to scientists and engineers. This article is a report of the publishable progress made so far.

In the 1920s and 1930s physicists working with particle accelerators found that by accelerating protons (hydrogen nuclei) and other light nuclei to high enough energies (many thousands of electron volts) they could break through the nuclear electrical repulsion and force the projectiles to fuse with light nuclei in a target. The fusion releases energy, because part of the mass of the fusing nuclei is transformed into energy according to Einstein's famous equation $E = mc^2$. But in this sort of bombardment a great deal of energy has to be put in to make a few nuclei fuse. There can be no net yield of energy from fusion unless it proceeds by a self-sustaining reaction, as, for example, in the interior of the sun.

What is needed to produce a self-sustaining reaction? Here it is apropos to compare fusion with fission. The fission chain reaction is analogous to the explosion of TNT. A mechanical shock is sufficient to cause TNT to start exploding; the shock wave produced by fracture of its unstable molecules then touches off one molecule after another. Similarly in a fission chain-reaction the trigger for the successive fissions is supplied by neutrons, each fission releasing neutrons to attack more fissionable uranium nuclei. In short, heat or kinetic energy plays no part in promoting the chain reaction.

A continuing fusion reaction, in contrast, is analogous to the familiar process of combustion. In ordinary burning, molecules combine (*e.g.*, hydrogen with oxygen, forming water), and their chemical reaction releases energy. To stick together or fuse, the molecules must collide violently, which means the material must be heated. Three conditions are needed to burn a chemical fuel and harness its heat to do work: (1) the fuel must be raised to its ignition point; (2) there must be enough of it to sustain a continuing reaction; (3) the energy released must be tapped in a controlled manner—*e.g.*, to heat water or to drive a piston. Now precisely the same conditions are needed to make a nuclear fusion reaction go and do useful work. The great difference is that for a fusion reaction the ignition point is rather high—hundreds of millions of degrees centigrade!

This one condition—the attainment of which was quite unthinkable on the earth until recently—underlies all our problems. From it stems a whole train of formidable questions. Unfortunately it seems that no one crucial experiment will tell us whether a solution is possible, as the first fission chain reaction did. We shall have to go through a long series of experiments to solve one problem after another. Most of them have to do with quantitative questions, that is, numbers. There never was a field in which the numbers were more imposing—or more important.

The Fusion Fuel. Our first concern is the fuel. The most interesting candidate is deuterium, a heavy isotope of hydrogen, found in ordinary water. The nucleus of the deuterium atom consists of one proton and one neutron. When two deuterium nuclei (deuterons) collide with enough energy to fuse, one deuteron grabs either the proton or the neutron of the other—the chances are 50-50. If it fuses with the proton (freeing the neutron), it forms helium 3, releasing about 3.25 million electron volts of energy. If it combines with the neutron (this time liberating its partner's proton), it yields about four million electron volts and becomes hydrogen 3, or tritium, the radioactive isotope of hydrogen. A deuteron and a tritium nucleus (triton) will fuse more readily than two deuterons, and this reaction releases more energy. Tritium is therefore another potential fuel for thermonuclear reactors. It would have to be manufactured, however, as plutonium is, because there are only trace amounts of tritium in nature. One possible method of breeding tritium is to expose lithium to slow neutrons: on capturing a neutron, lithium splits into tritium and helium 4.

Complete "burning" of the deuterons and their products (tritium and helium 3) in a thermonuclear cycle would produce

Figure 1 Fusion reactions, which promise to be useful for production of power, are shown schematically. At top two deuterons merge to form a tritium nucleus (triton). Second is the equally probable reaction in which the deuterons form helium 3 and a neutron. Third, a deuteron combines with a triton to form helium 4 and a neutron. At bottom a deuteron fuses with helium 3, producing helium 4 and a proton. The amount of energy released in each reaction is listed at its right. Protons and neutrons are designated as p *and* n.

about seven mev (million electron volts) per deuteron burned. This corresponds to 43 million kilowatt-hours per pound of fuel. By comparison gasoline, one of the best chemical fuels, yields about six kilowatt-hours per pound. Although only a small fraction of the hydrogen in natural water is deuterium, still the deuterium in one gallon of ordinary water has an energy content equivalent to 350 gallons of gasoline! The oceans contain enough deuterium to supply the world with fuel for billions of years, even at a power demand 1,000 times the present figure. For use in our atomic energy program in the U.S., according to published figures, we are already producing an amount of deuterium which would be sufficient to supply the nation's total energy needs many times over if it could be burned as fuel. The cost of extracting deuterium from water is low enough so that deuterium would be less than 1 per cent as expensive as coal as a fuel. And finally, the nuclear burning of deuterium and tritium produces only inert gases, avoiding any problem of waste disposal.

Deuterium, then, represents the "ultimate fuel." But its great promise is matched by the equally great difficulty of finding a way to burn it!

The burning of thermonuclear fuel in an uncontrolled manner has been achieved with all too well known success in the hydrogen bomb. But the problem of producing a controlled fusion reaction is quite different. Let us see what the necessary conditions are. The best way to do this is to follow an imaginary experiment.

The Plasma. We take a liter of deuterium gas confined in a vessel made of a mythical material which is capable of withstanding the enormous temperatures and pressures that will arise in the course of the experiment. At room temperature and normal atmospheric pressure the deuterium gas-molecules are wandering about in the vessel with an average kinetic energy of about one 25th of an electron volt, or a velocity of about 3,000 miles per hour. Of course no fusion reactions are taking place. Now we heat the gas to 5,000 degrees C. At this temperature we no longer

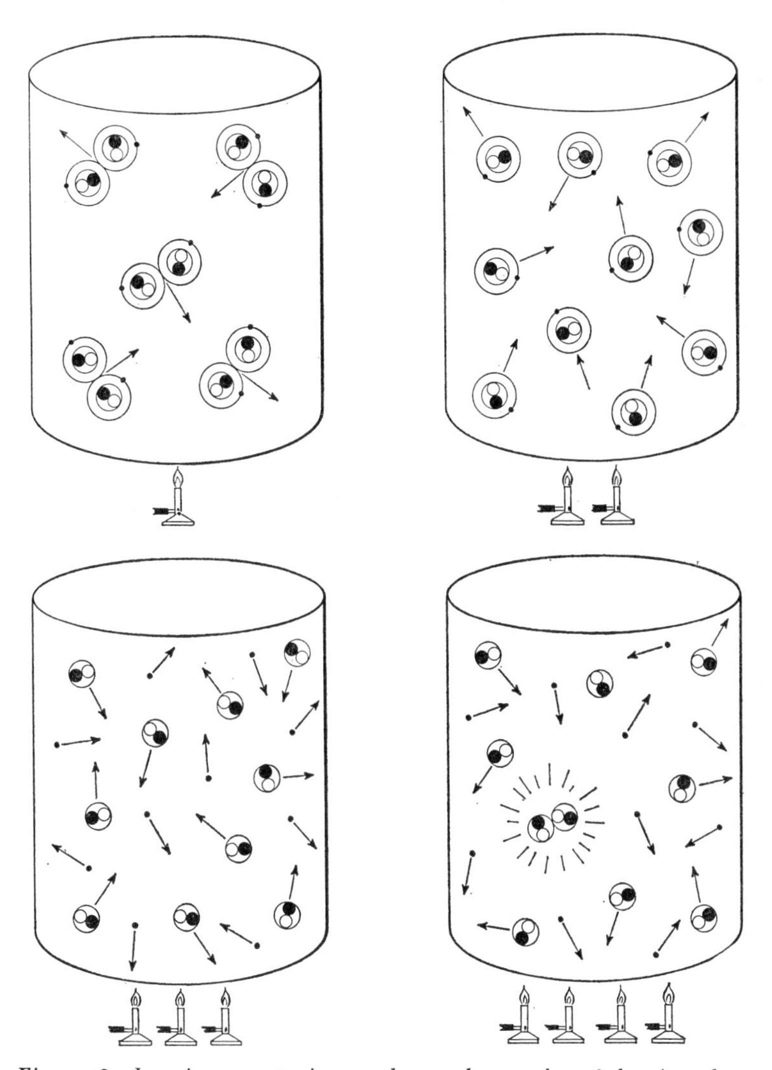

Figure 2 Imaginary experiment shows the results of heating deuterium gas. At top left the gas is at room temperature and atmospheric pressure of 15 pounds per square inch. Heated to 5,000 degrees centigrade (top right), *the diatomic molecules have split to form deuterium atoms and the pressure is 600 pounds per square inch. When the temperature is raised to 100,000 degrees* (bottom left), *atoms are ionized, forming a plasma of electrons and deuterons. The pressure is 20,000 pounds. At a temperature of 100 million degrees (and a pressure of 22 million pounds) some deuterons can fuse, releasing energy, but the reaction is still not self-sustaining.*

have molecules: the violence of their collisions has broken them apart into deuterium atoms. The pressure has risen to about 40 atmospheres (600 pounds per square inch), and the average velocity of the atoms is about 40,000 miles per hour. But we are still very far from the velocity needed to make two nuclei fuse.

Next, let us jump to 100,000 degrees. The remarkable properties of the mythical wall material are very much needed now, for any real material would long since have vaporized. Now the deuterium atoms of the gas have been broken down to the electrically charged nuclei (deuterons) and electrons: in a word, the gas has become what is known as a plasma. The gas pressure has risen to 1,500 atmospheres. The average velocity of the electrons is 10 million miles per hour, and even the much heavier deuterons are moving at the great speed of 170,000 miles per hour. Yet the deuterons still do not have sufficient energy effectively to overcome their mutual electrostatic repulsion. At this temperature there would be only about one fusion in the liter of plasma every 500 years! We still have a long way to go before we shall reach the ignition temperature of a mass of deuterons.

At one million degrees, the rate of fusion reactions will increase more than a billion billion times, but the total energy output will still be too small to be detected–only a few millionths of a watt per cubic centimeter. At 100 million degrees, however, the reaction rate will become really respectable. The pressure then will have reached the staggering value of 1.5 million atmospheres. The electrons will be traveling at 90,000 miles per *second*, and the deuterons at 1,500 miles (around the world in 16 seconds). Essentially all of the deuterons will react with one another rapidly (within a fraction of a second), and their reactions will release energy at a fantastic rate–about 100 million kilowatts. But we shall not yet have arrived at the kindling point: to sustain the reaction we shall still have to put in more energy than the fusions release. Only at about 350 million degrees will the "fire" (*i.e.*, thermonuclear reaction) become self-sustaining.

This imaginary experiment brings out several important points. First, we need extremely high temperatures, though when we speak of high temperature here we are not thinking of heat in the usual sense but of the kinetic energy of the gas particles. Second, we could not even think of using the fuel at ordinary gas concentrations. If we are to keep the energy output and pressure of the gas within controllable bounds, we must start with a thin gas at a density much lower than at atmospheric pressure—somewhere in the neighborhood of one 10,000th of an atmosphere. But what a thin fuel this is! In a laboratory a gas at this density would be considered practically a vacuum.

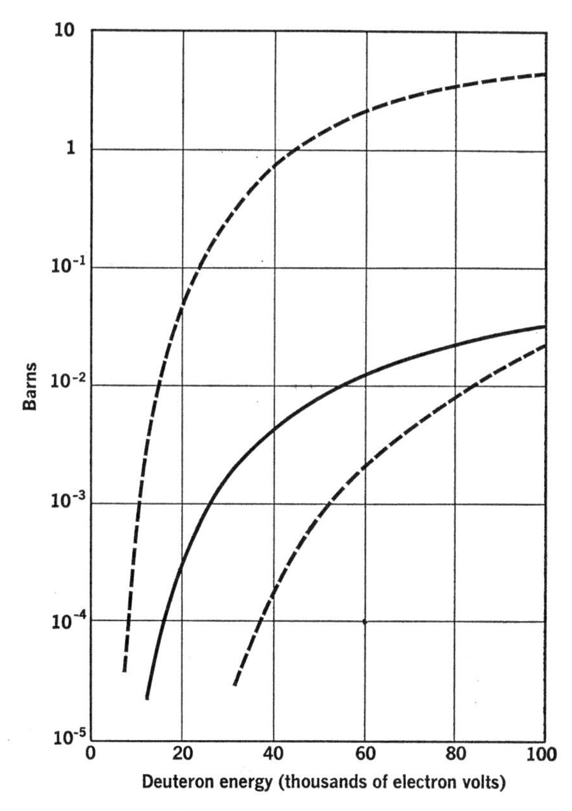

Figure 3 Cross sections or probabilities of fusion reactions, as they vary with particle energy, are plotted for fusion of deuterium and tritium (top), *deuterium and deuterium* (middle) *and deuterium and helium 3* (bottom). *A barn is an area of 10^{-24} square centimeter.*

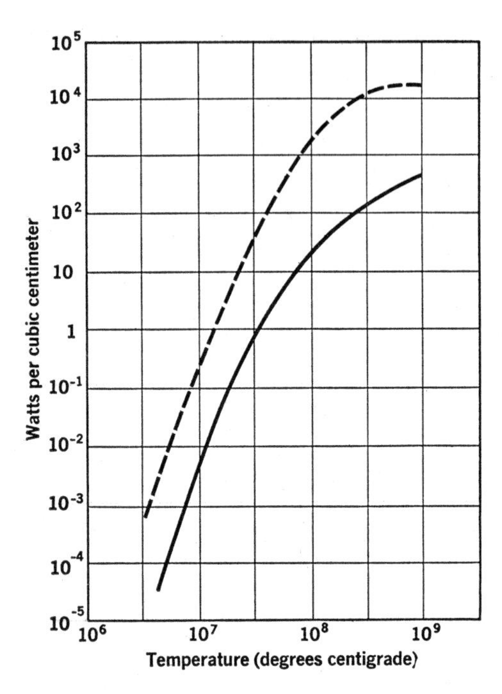

Figure 4 Fusion-power output of plasma at one 10,000th of atmospheric density is plotted against temperature. Upper curve is for deuterium-tritium fusion; lower curve, for deuterium-deuterium.

One of the interesting consequences of using a very low density is that even though the plasma is very hot in terms of the speed of its particles, its heat *content* will actually be very small. A liter of deuterium plasma one 10,000th of an atmosphere in density would, at a kinetic temperature of 350 million degrees, have a heat content amounting to 18,000 calories—about enough to heat a small cup of coffee.

To calculate the rate of fusion power production from a hot plasma it is only necessary to know the reaction cross sections and to insert these as data in the theory of thermonuclear reactions in a hot gas. However, calculations of this kind, important as they are in specifying the required physical conditions, shed no light on *how* to heat a gas to thermonuclear temperatures or on whether the reactions, once initiated, could be made self-sustaining. This latter question depends on how much of the energy will be lost by radiation and other mechanisms. In the sun, the energy generated within its huge volume is sufficient to maintain the reactions in spite of the radiation loss from the surface. If we could build a fusion reactor as big as the moon, we would not need to worry particularly about energy losses. But for a reactor of practicable size this is our key problem.

Let me first mention the unavoidable losses that must be lived with. These are the losses by radiation from the plasma—primarily in the form of X-rays emitted when electrons collide with nuclei. Now at a temperature of 100 million degrees, one cubic centimeter of dense matter would radiate energy at the unbelievable rate of three million million million kilowatts! But fortunately the rate of radiation drops very rapidly as the density of the matter falls. At the low density we have been considering, the radiation loss becomes comparatively small. The energy yield of fusion reactions increases rapidly with rise in temperature, and it will outstrip radiation losses at a temperature above 50 million degrees in the case of the deuteron-triton reaction and above 370 million degrees in the deuteron-deuteron reaction. These, then,

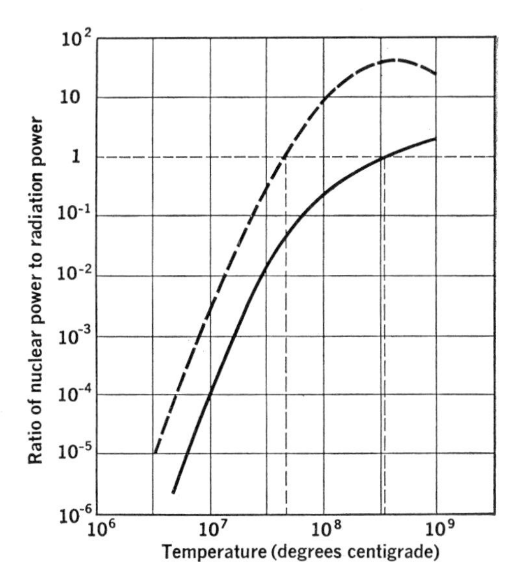

Figure 5 Ignition temperatures, where nuclear power equals radiated power, are indicated by broken vertical lines for deuterium-tritium (upper curve) *and deuterium-deuterium* (lower curve).

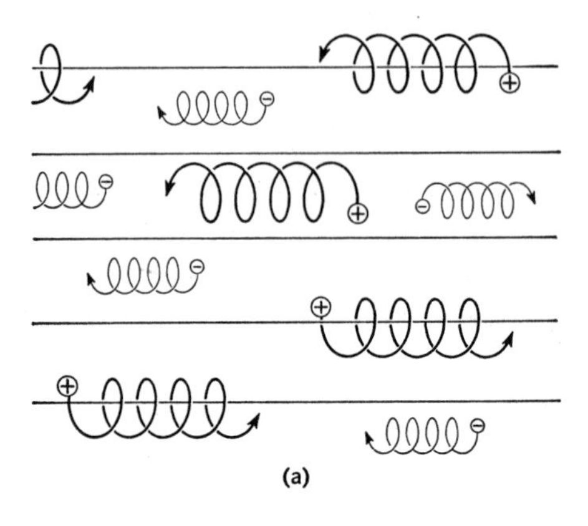

(a)

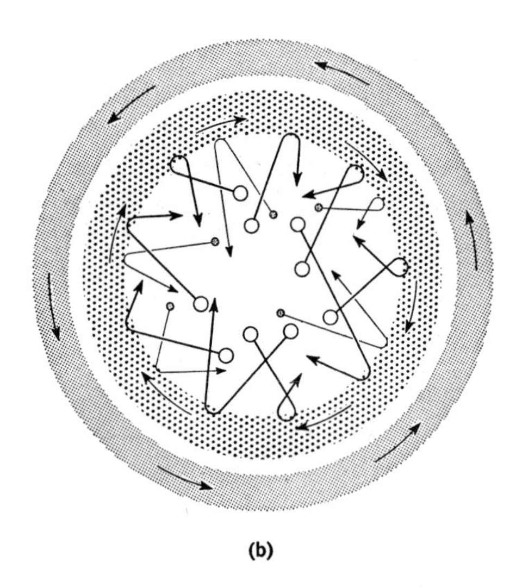

(b)

Figure 6 (a) *Paths of plasma particles in a magnetic field are helixes. Positive particles go counterclockwise; negative particles, clockwise looking in the direction of the field.* (b) *Plasma is contained by a magnetic field* (dotted ring) *which prevents escape of particles. Outer arrows show current in coil; inner arrows, current from deflected particles.*

are the ignition temperatures of the respective fuels. But the plasma must be very pure, because nuclei of higher elements (above hydrogen and helium) greatly accelerate the rate of radiation. A surprisingly small amount of impurities could poison a very large volume of plasma. For example, the metal in the head of a pin, if vaporized, would be quite sufficient to poison several railroad tank cars full of plasma. It is clear that purity will be a prime requirement in any controlled-fusion reactor.

Of the other class of energy losses—the ones we can and must reduce—the most serious is dissipation of particle energy to the walls of the reactor. We have to have a closed chamber, to hold out the atmosphere and keep our gas at low density. But consider the particles in this gas. They are so widely dispersed in our near-vacuum that each deuteron, in its random wanderings, travels thousands of miles on the average before it encounters another deuteron (or a triton). It has a far greater chance of hitting the walls of the container first. Yet if it does, this collision will immediately damp its energy. Obviously we cannot allow the particles of the plasma to touch the walls. Contrary to a common impression, the reason is not that the plasma will vaporize the walls (it does not contain much heat) but simply that contact with the walls would instantly cool the plasma and quench the reaction.

This, then, is the nub of the problem: How to confine a very hot gas within a material chamber (for at least a fraction of a second) without allowing any appreciable amount of it to reach the chamber walls. Posed in this way, it sounds like a science-fiction problem, quite unsolvable in any real world. But as is now well known, about a decade ago an ingenious solution emerged—namely, the plasma might be confined within a magnetic field, serving as a kind of furnace liner in the chamber to keep the particles away from the walls.

The Magnetic Bottle. The idea rests basically on the simple fact that a strong magnetic field will deflect charged particles from a straight path. Now a hot, high-pressure plasma could, under the proper circumstances, generate an internal magnetic field of its own strong enough to exclude the externally applied field. Inside such a plasma the particles would therefore move in straight lines. But at the boundary of the plasma they would be deflected back into it by the outside magnetic field. The magnetic lines of force, acting like elastic rubber bands, could resist considerable pressure. If the magnetic field were made strong enough, it should form a magnetic "wall" able to contain a high-pressure plasma, just as a steel cylinder holds a high-pressure gas. According to the theoretical calculations, a field with a strength of 50,000 gauss, for example, could withstand a plasma pressure of 100 atmospheres, and a field 10 times stronger (which has been achieved in laboratories) could support a pressure of 10,000 atmospheres.

A fusion reaction sustained in such a magnetic bottle could never "run away," as the fission chain reaction may. If the plasma pressure became stronger than the magnetic field, it would rupture the magnetic wall and the plasma would touch the material chamber wall, which would immediately quench the fusion reaction. By the very nature of the beast, then, a fusion reactor could never explode; it could only collapse.

The simplified picture we have been considering should not be taken to mean that the magnetic bottle would be leakproof. Actually the plasma and the magnetic field would gradually penetrate and intermingle with each other, and the plasma would eventually escape completely unless replenished. Fortunately this leakage should be slow enough, according to the theory, to permit the achievement of a self-sustaining fusion reaction. But, as we shall see, a magnetic bottle does not always behave as the simple theory predicts. The interactions between a high-temperature plasma and magnetic fields are a difficult problem in fundamental physics, and they have given rise to a new field of study which might be called "experimental astrophysics."

The Pinch Effect. So much for the theory. How could we actually make a magnetic bottle? It occurred independently to many

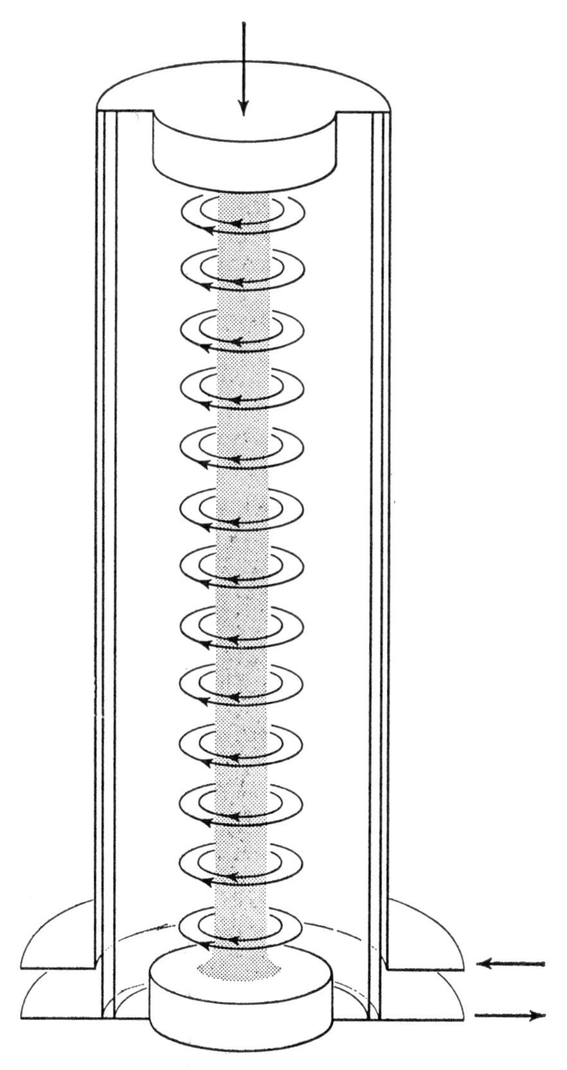

Figure 7 Pinch effect occurs when a large electrical current is sent through a plasma in a cylinder. Circular magnetic lines of force set up by the current contract and pinch the plasma into a narrow channel (shaded column). *The straight arrows show the direction of the current.*

investigators that an obscure electrical phenomenon known as the "pinch effect" might provide the answer. This effect, first produced experimentally only about a decade ago, requires a very large electrical current. When such a current is passed through a conducting gas in a tube, it sets up a magnetic field which tends to pinch the gas and pull it away from the tube walls. The magnetic lines of force circling the gas compress it by their tension. Since a plasma is an excellent conductor of electricity, the pinch effect looked like an attractive and ready-made means of forming a magnetic bottle.

Theoretical calculations showed that it would take a very large current indeed—millions of amperes—to confine a plasma of high temperature and low density. Not discouraged by this fact, investigators in many countries carried out experiments with simple pinch tubes. They applied a high voltage to a low-pressure gas in an insulated tube and produced an electrical discharge. This ionized the gas, and heavy current then began to flow. As they hoped, the pinch made its dramatic appearance. But with it also came a blow to their hopes. The pinch lasted only a millionth of a second or so; no sooner had the column of plasma been compressed than it writhed violently and drove itself to the tube wall. Furthermore, the tighter the pinch, the faster it destroyed itself.

This was not hard to understand, and in fact was predictable theoretically. Two different types of instability can develop. In the first place, any small kink in the pinched column will grow rapidly, because the magnetic pressure is stronger on the concave side of the kink (where the lines of force are crowded together) than on the convex side. The second cause of instability is a kind of "sausage" effect. The plasma tends to pinch or neck itself off at one or more points along the column, and thus cuts itself into pieces.

Incidentally, in connection with the latter phenomenon there is an interesting story which illustrates how hopes can suddenly rise and just as suddenly fall in an important but uncharted field of research such as the fusion power enterprise. When investigators first produced strong pinches in deuterium

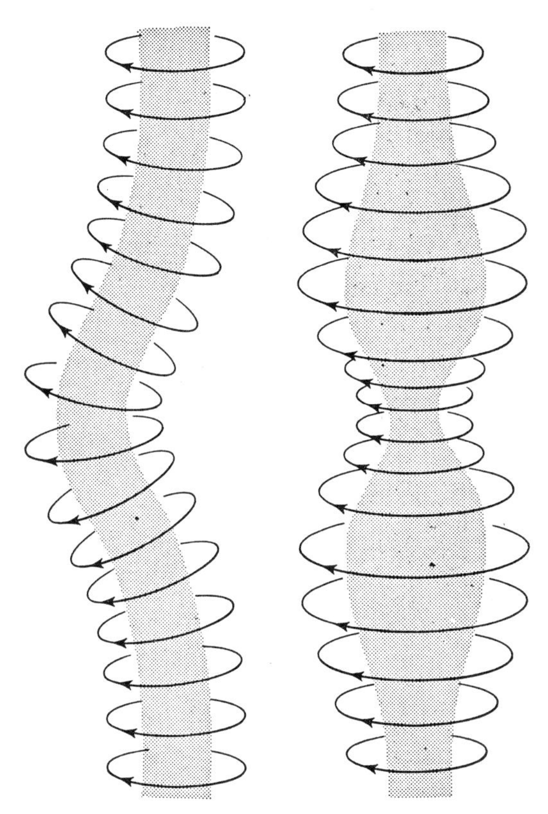

Figure 8 Instabilities in a pinched plasma arise from kinks (left), *where the magnetic lines are crowded on the concave side, and constrictions* (right), *where the field is also crowded.*

gas, they were delighted to discover bursts of neutrons—evidence of fusion reactions in the plasma. They thought they had reached thermonuclear temperatures momentarily. But on analysis they had to conclude that it was merely some obscure electrical effect, associated with the violent disruption of the pinch by the sausage instability, that had accelerated a few deuterons to fuse.

How could the pinch be stabilized? Theoretical investigations published in the U.S., in the United Kingdom and in the U.S.S.R. have suggested a possible answer, although they have

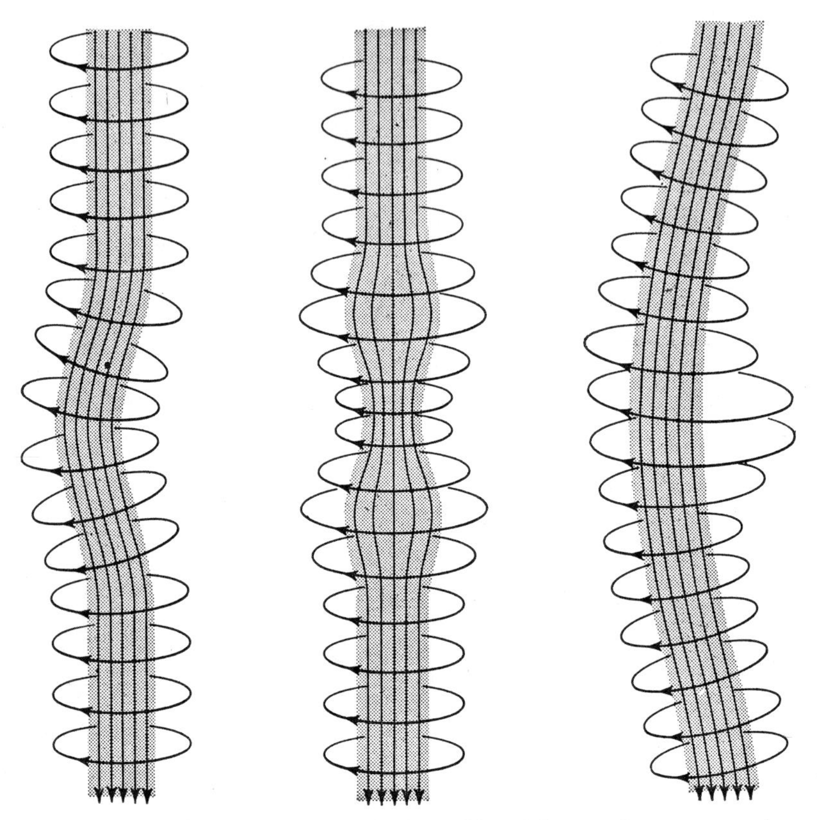

Figure 9 Stabilized pinch might be achieved by putting a magnetic field (long arrows) *through a plasma. Tension would straighten kinks* (left) *and mutual repulsion would resist constrictions* (center). *Circular lines hold plasma away from conducting wall* (right).

not yet shown how the physical conditions necessary to make it work could be achieved. The idea is to create not only a pinching magnetic field around the plasma but also a strong longitudinal magnetic field *within* the plasma column. The internal field would act as a kind of stiffener. If a kink started to develop, it would tend to stretch the interior lines of force, and their elastic resistance would pull out the kink. Similarly if the sausage type of constriction tried to pinch into the column, the internal lines of force would resist being squeezed together and thus would prevent collapse of the column.

There is a third type of instability which could destroy a plasma column: namely, a long, gentle bend of the column that would grow in strength and push the column to the chamber wall. However, this could be counteracted by using a conducting material for the walls of the tube. Since a conductor acts as a barrier to a magnetic field, the magnetic field lines around the plasma column would be crowded against the wall where the bent column approached it, and the resulting back pressure would push the column back toward the center of the tube.

I should make clear that the straight pinch columns illustrated here are simplified systems which merely exemplify the principles. In practice it would probably not be desirable to try to produce a stable pinch in a straight tube, for several reasons: among other things, the electrodes at the ends of the tube would have a cooling (*i.e.*, quenching) effect on the plasma. Pinch experiments have already been performed with other shapes. One of these is a doughnut-shaped tube in which currents are induced and can circulate without bumping into a solid surface. A high voltage applied to the winding around a large iron transformer core in the tube produces an electrical discharge in the gas, which

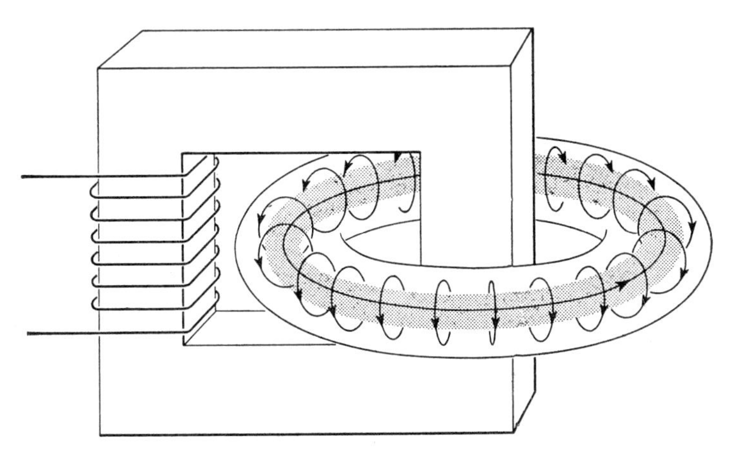

Figure 10 Doughnut-shaped pinch tube is made by threading a transformer core through a hollow ring containing plasma. Current through the winding at left causes a strong induced current in the plasma, which is then pinched by its own circular magnetic field.

then functions as a one-turn secondary winding. Very heavy currents can be induced into the plasma in this way.

Besides the pinch effect, other possible methods of forming a magnetic bottle are being investigated, in the U.S. and no doubt in other countries. Most of the current research on the fusion power problem involves experiments in very complicated electromagnetic phenomena–the behavior of a high-temperature plasma in various magnetic field configurations. It is extremely hard work, taxing all the resources of our present technology. As I have mentioned, there is little likelihood of anything like a sudden "break-through" to a radically simpler approach. Since we shall make headway only by many mutually reinforcing studies and by the development of new and unusual techniques, it is evident that progress would be more rapid if the various nations involved joined in a cooperative exchange of information on all phases of the research.

Tracing the Wisp. We are having to learn for the first time how to handle and manipulate rapidly huge quantities of electrical energy, and to build big, extremely clean vacuum systems. One of the thorniest problems is measurement. It is hard enough to create a hot plasma in the first place, but to find out what it is doing, once created, is sometimes still harder. Some new measurement techniques have already been developed. To measure the density of a plasma there is a new "microwave interferometer" using beams of millimeter radio waves as probes. The temperature of the plasma is assessed by studying its X-ray emissions, its radio "noise" and its escaping particles or reaction products. Somewhat surprisingly, a very hot plasma emits little visible light. But it has been possible to make spectroscopic studies of cooler plasmas, in which the atoms are not completely stripped of their electrons. These measurements not only indicate the temperature but also tell the velocity of the plasma's motions, by the Doppler shift. And simply by measuring changes of the magnetic field during an experiment we can get information about the temperature, density, shape and velocity of plasmas as they are formed.

To appreciate the observation problem you have to picture the scene of the events we are studying. Most of the experiments on high-temperature plasmas are carried out within antiseptic vacuum systems surrounded by conductors carrying large and rapidly varying electrical currents. And what we have to detect are the whims of an invisible, short-lived wisp of near-nothingness somewhere in the bowels of this apparatus!

Tapping the Power. Plainly it will be several years before any fusion reactor is developed to the point where we have to face the final problem of extracting its power. But of course some thought has already been given to this matter.

If the fuel is a mixture of deuterium and tritium, the lion's share (80 per cent) of the energy released by the fusion is carried off by the neutron emerging from the reaction. This energy would be tapped by trapping the fast neutrons and feeding the resulting heat to a steam system generating electricity in the conventional way. Since such a reactor would have to breed more tritium, the neutrons would probably be trapped in a breeding blanket of lithium surrounding the reactor. Some of the electrical power generated would have to be fed back to the reactor to maintain the magnetic bottle.

If the fuel is deuterium alone, we have the intriguing possibility of turning the energy output directly into electricity. In the deuteron-deuteron fusion, 66 per cent of the energy released is imparted to the charged reaction products—helium nuclei and protons. It is quite possible that conditions could be arranged so that most of these particles stayed trapped within the plasma. In that case the heated and expanding plasma would tend to push outward against the magnetic field, and by the use of properly arranged circuits this motion could in principle be made to generate a current. In other words, in pushing against the magnetic field the expanding plasma would do work, just as steam expanding against the piston of a steam engine does work. In the case of the plasma the piston would be the "wall" of the magnetic field, and the linkages converting its energy into useful work would be electrical circuits instead of rods and wheels. It is possible that the efficiency of this engine might be much higher than that of the conventional steam cycle, for the thermodynamic principles that limit the efficiency of ordinary heat engines would not apply.

In the last analysis the feasibility of fusion power probably will hinge primarily on the size of the reactor. Very likely many potentially workable reactor schemes will have to be rejected on the basis that they would be impracticably large. On the other hand, "pocket-edition" fusion reactors are simply out of the question, on theoretical grounds. The fusion power plants of the future, if they are ever realized, will in all likelihood be large central stations for generating electrical power.

Growing Hopes. The scientists working on the fusion power project in the U.S. confidently believe that all the problems will eventually be solved, for, difficult though the problems are, they now see no really fundamental barrier standing in the way of ultimate success.

I want to mention a few of the milestones that have been passed, insofar as secrecy restrictions permit. The first group to consider the possibility of obtaining fusion power through the magnetic confinement of a hot plasma, so far as we know, were Enrico Fermi, Edward Teller, James Tuck and others at the Los Alamos Scientific Laboratory. Although they advanced their ideas around the end of World War II, no extensive experimental work was started in the U.S. until about 1951, when programs began under Tuck at Los Alamos and Lyman Spitzer at Princeton. Scientists in the United Kingdom apparently had launched some work two or three years earlier, and the U.S.S.R. may have started about the same time. In 1952 the U.S. Atomic Energy Commission sponsored a large conference on controlled-fusion reactions. In the same year a program was initiated by Herbert York at the University of California Radiation Laboratory in Livermore. Smaller programs have since been set up at the Oak Ridge National Laboratory and New York University. Within the past year two substantial programs have been initiated with private capital: at the General Atomics Laboratory in San Diego, Calif., and at the General Electric Research Laboratory in Schenectady, N.Y.

Among other countries known to be engaged in studies of controlled fusion are France, Germany, the Netherlands and Sweden. It is abundantly evident that the search for fusion power is taken seriously in all parts of the world. The nature of the problems being faced, the time it will no doubt take to solve them, and the importance of the goal to be won are compelling reasons to hope for the growth of international cooperation in the research.

If the reader of this article is left with the impression that the search for fusion power is at once the most fascinating, the most difficult and potentially the most important peacetime scientific effort ever undertaken, he will be sharing the opinion of the many scientists now working on this problem.

No longer the exclusive property of science fiction, the exploration of space has become a matter of importance to science and the general public both. Even the world's governments have recognized the challenge of space, in some cases devoting as much attention to it as to hog prices. Remarkable advances in our knowledge of the earth's environment in space have already been made: the discovery of the Van Allen zones of energetic ions, for example, has had an enormous impact on theories of cosmic rays, the aurora, and geomagnetism. Late in 1958 the Select Committee on Astronautics and Space Exploration of the United States House of Representatives requested the RAND Corporation, an independent, nonprofit research organization largely devoted to long-range planning for the Air Force, to prepare "an authoritative study in lay terms which would set forth clearly the present and definitely foreseeable state of the art of space flight." The resulting report, called **Space Handbook** (Modern Library Paperback P51), was prepared under the direction of Robert W. Buchheim; Scientific Space Exploration is its twenty-seventh chapter.

The RAND Corporation

SCIENTIFIC SPACE EXPLORATION

Most of the information that man is able to obtain about the universe comes to him in the form of electromagnetic radiations. Some of these radiations he can see with the naked eye. But visible light represents a very small part of the total radiation spectrum (see Figure 1); the Earth is constantly being bombarded with other forms of "light," which are invisible to the human eye.

If we spread out the entire radiation spectrum as it occurs in nature, we find that a star like the Sun concentrates most of its energy in a relatively narrow band stretching from the near ultraviolet into the infrared portion of the spectrum. That is, most of the Sun's energy is visible to us by optical means. In addition, however, very high energy radiations of short wavelength in the form of X-rays, gamma rays, and cosmic rays are present, as well as radiations of low energy and long wavelength, all of which are invisible to the eye. The eye is sensitive only to those radiations that fall within a small band of wavelengths. Radiations whose wavelengths are longer or shorter than those to

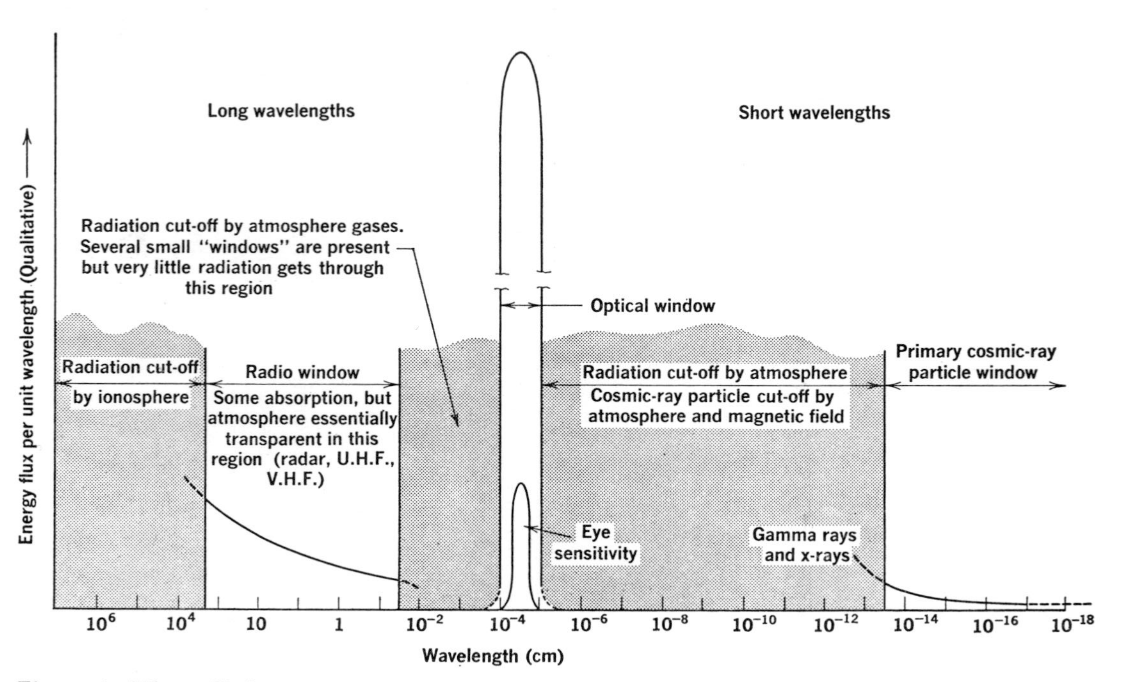

Figure 1 The radiation spectrum

which the eye can respond must be "seen" with other sensors.*

We can see into these hidden parts of the spectrum by using various kinds of detectors. Properly coated photographic plates, for example, allow us to look part of the way into the infrared region, and they also permit us to look into the ultraviolet, X-ray, and gamma-ray regions of the spectrum. Other devices, such as photoemissive cells, photoconductors, and bolometers, allow us to peer farther into the infrared, while Geiger counters, scintillation counters, etc., permit us indirectly to "see" gamma radiation and some of the high-energy cosmic rays that come through the atmosphere. Radio antennas, of course, provide us with means to look into the longer wavelength portion of the radiation spectrum.

While we have developed sensors that will enable us to see and measure much of this very short and very long wavelength energy, we have not been able to exploit them fully because only a part of the energy in these portions of the spectrum reaches the Earth. Much of it is blocked or deflected, absorbed or screened out by the Earth's atmosphere and magnetic field.

Atmospheric turbulence, air currents, and eddies make the images of the celestial bodies shimmer and dance about on the photographic plates of telescopes, so that we can only see a blur where we should see a sharp picture. The biggest telescopes on Earth normally operate with an effective resolution which is about one-twentieth of the theoretically obtainable value.

Low-energy radio waves are reflected and absorbed by the electrons and ions of the ionosphere, and never get through the atmosphere. In fact, most of the radio-frequency energy that envelops the Earth cannot penetrate the ionosphere.

The Earth's atmosphere is completely opaque also to wave-

* We can, of course, produce many of these radiations, or forms of energy, on Earth. Radio and radar transmitters, light bulbs, X-ray equipment, and nuclear explosions all produce electromagnetic energy in different parts of the radiation spectrum. We cannot, however, as yet produce the highest energy cosmic rays, which are really solid particles moving at tremendous velocity, here on Earth.

lengths shorter than a few millimeters, and it does not "open up" until one reaches the near infrared, where ordinary light and heat rays exist. At still shorter wavelengths, because of the influence of ozone and other atmospheric gases, the Earth's atmosphere blots out the ultraviolet radiation from the Sun and the other Stars. The so-called soft X-rays emitted by the Sun can only penetrate the outermost layers of the Earth's atmosphere. The atmosphere in general is opaque to X-rays and to gamma rays. Only the most energetic cosmic rays succeed in penetrating the Earth's atmosphere down to the ground, so that information about the lower energy primary cosmic rays is not available on the surface of the Earth. Moreover, the Earth's magnetic field repels low-energy primary cosmic rays and is another factor in keeping them from reaching the ground.

In fact, the plight of the Earth-bound observer until now may be likened to that of a man imprisoned in a stone igloo with walls and roof 10 feet thick. At the time of his imprisonment, a small hole in the roof directly overhead was his only connection with the outside world. Since then, through a great deal of labor, aided by ingenuity, he has been able to enlarge this roof opening slightly, and also to bore two small holes in the wall close to the ground, on opposite sides of his prison. Through these three "windows" comes all the information that he is able to obtain about the world around him, and it is with this meager knowledge, coupled with his imagination, that he must construct a picture of the outside world.

Applying this idea to the radiation spectrum in Figure 1, we may say that man's knowledge of the universe has come to him through three "windows" in the spectrum. Through a radio window he "sees" a wide range of radio frequencies from different types of celestial objects: the Sun, the planets, possibly other stars, clouds of gas in our own galaxy, exploding stars, and outside universes. Through an optical window, he has been able to obtain other information about the universe with the aid of telescopes, spectroscopes, cameras, etc. And finally, there is the cosmic-ray window, through which still other bits of information have come to him. Except for these apertures, however, the wall of the atmosphere shuts him in.*

Fundamental Problems. A prime question of concern to astronomers is the composition of the universe; that is, the relative abundance of different species of atoms. The most abundant elements in the universe are thought to be the lighter ones: hydrogen, helium, carbon, nitrogen, oxygen, neon, etc. Unfortunately, their strongest spectral lines are in the far ultraviolet region of the radiation spectrum, which can never be observed from the surface of the Earth. While indirect methods have given us some preliminary data, the fundamental questions of how much of these substances exists and whether the stars differ in composition from one another must still be considered as unsolved. The answers would be of the utmost importance to astronomy. These spectra, especially in the bright and very hot stars, could be observed with apparatus in the few-hundred-pound satellite-payload range, and the results telemetered to Earth with equipment that is now available. The total amount of information that must be transmitted to obtain the first spectroreconnaissance of the stars is in fact quite small, and useful observations could be done within today's technology.

Obviously, the nearest star, the Sun, is worthy of the most detailed study. This is true not only because the Sun is the prime source of the Earth's energy, but because the ultraviolet, X-ray, and gamma-ray radiation of the Sun will be controlling factors of man's environment in space, and they may provide hazards to man's survival which are of a nature still unknown and unsuspected.

Moreover, the effect of the Sun's ultraviolet radiation dominates the ionization of the outermost atmosphere of the Earth,

* The areas beneath the curves in the three open regions indicate the amount of energy at various wavelengths that reaches the Earth. While the total quantity of energy that reaches us in the form of visible light is quite high, the amounts in the radiowave and cosmic-ray portions of the spectrum are relatively low. Most of these energies lie in a region of the spectrum to which we are denied access from the ground.

which has an important effect on communication, and possibly a very much more important one on the weather. The gain for pure scientific research, however, that could be obtained through detailed observation of the solar ultraviolet spectrum will come mainly in explanations of the origin of the hot outermost layers of the Sun. While the surface of the Sun is at a temperature of about 6,000° C., the temperature rises as one goes out from the Sun, reaching at least a million degrees at a distance of some 20,000 kilometers from the Sun's surface. We have no explanation of the origin of this heating; we do not know where the Sun's outer envelope stops, and there is a good chance that the Earth itself is immersed in this corona.

The Sun is subject to violent storms, manifested by so-called sunspots, prominences, and solar flares. These disturbed outer regions of the Sun have an important effect on the Earth's ionosphere, geomagnetism, and, in the long run, ordinary weather. It is technically feasible to map the Sun in terms of its emissions in the ultraviolet or even soft X-ray portions of the spectrum. Such observations, unobstructed by the atmosphere, would provide us with a detailed history of what happens during solar storms and flares. Pictures could be telemetered back on a more-or-less continuous basis, providing warning of solar disturbances which could affect the Earth.

To obtain a true picture of the total cosmic-ray energy enveloping the Earth, particularly that which reaches us from the Sun during solar storms or flares, it will be necessary to reach beyond the atmosphere and through the Earth's magnetic field to a distance of perhaps 25,000 miles. The longer wavelength primary cosmic radiation, where in fact most of the cosmic-ray energy is concentrated, must be investigated experimentally if we are to obtain information about the origin of these particles, their effect on the Earth and its inhabitants, and the hazards they may present to space travel.

The question of photographing other objects in our universe from space, and the possibility of our finding new kinds of objects, is an important one. Even low-altitude orbiting satellites, and certainly high-altitude satellites, would permit us to make detailed observations of the structure of the surfaces of the planets and the composition of their atmosphere. At the present time there are indications from ultraviolet measurements made from Naval Research Laboratory rockets that there are in space large clouds of gas of an unknown nature which shine in the ultraviolet. A photograph of even minimum resolution taken in the far ultraviolet would decide this question. In particular, astronomers have found that the most abundant element in the universe, hydrogen, is present throughout our Milky Way. This is detectable so far by radio observations only, although it is known that perhaps 10 percent of the total mass of our universe is in the form of gaseous hydrogen in space. Direct photographs, or spectra, of this interstellar hydrogen can be obtained once a vehicle has penetrated the atmosphere of the Earth, photography being important both in the ultraviolet and in the infrared.

Another very important question concerns the distribution of other systems of stars as one goes farther outward into space. Because of the apparent expansion of the universe, there is a shifting of the light emitted by distant objects toward the red portion of the spectrum, known as the "red shift." At the present time, external systems of stars, extragalactic nebulae, have been photographed out to distances of at least 2 million light years, and as far as we know, exist very much farther out into space. However, at great distances the red shift becomes larger and all the light of the system is shifted into the nonphotographable far infrared. There is no doubt of this effect, and what we do not know is how far out this red shift can be extrapolated. In particular, it is not necessary to photograph individual galaxies of very great faintness, but an important set of conclusions on the nature of the expansion of the universe and fundamental cosmology could be reached by merely measuring the total brightness in the far infrared of all of the galaxies together. Apparatus providing rough spectral resolution, so that quantitative measures of the brightness of the sky at many different wavelengths in the far infrared could be obtained, would perhaps settle some of the fundamental questions of the expansion of the universe, and the distance to which it stretches. This has an important bearing also on the age of our universe.

The subject of radio astronomy, which has grown rapidly in importance in the last few years, has already provided many scientific surprises. For example, the second brightest source of radio waves from outside the Earth turns out to be a pair of colliding galaxies at a distance of 300 million light years. Since most of the radio-frequency energy that occurs in nature does not penetrate the ionosphere, it can be measured only by probing above the ionosphere. Such investigations would greatly extend our knowledge of the total energy involved in radio emissions from these strange sources, perhaps giving us a clue to their origin.

One very important possibility considered by several scientists in recent years is that the existence of both extremely intense radio-frequency radiation and very high energy cosmic rays is an indication that we have still to discover some fundamental properties of the universe. One may speculate that the most fundamental processes in the universe are those involving extremely high energy particles, and that these may be produced by some as yet unknown physical mechanism. While tentative explanations of the origin of cosmic rays exist and suggest that they are merely matter accelerated to ultrahigh velocities, differing negligibly from the velocity of light, it would seem desirable to obtain a complete survey of the total electromagnetic and particle spectra at altitudes where the Earth is no longer a disturbing factor. Theories of the origin of the Earth have suggested that all matter was produced in a primeval explosion some 10 billion years ago. Are there any relics of this explosion available still in the form of very high energy radiation? Other theories suggest that matter is continuously produced in intergalactic space. Is this latter theory tenable? Are there any evidences in the radiations coming from space of the continuing creation of matter?

Experimental Programs. PRELIMINARY CONSIDERATIONS: Before mounting a large-scale attack on the space frontier, it is essential that we consider the interactions among possible experiments to be sure they are done in the proper sequence. It is conceivable, for example, that an early experiment, done merely because the means were available, could so alter the natural environment that other important experiments would no longer be possible. Experiments must be planned with due regard for leaving future parts of an overall program intact.

It must also be borne in mind that expensive scientific ventures in space will only be effective if backed up by adequate theoretical studies and laboratory research on the ground.

EXPERIMENTS IN SPACE BIOLOGY: Astronautics will provide new approaches to some of the fundamental problems in biological science. The study of terrestrial life forms in radically new environments (and perhaps even nonterrestrial life forms) will become possible, providing opportunities for increased understanding of the nature of the life process, how it originated, how it evolves and functions, and what forms it may assume under widely different environmental conditions. An experimental program in space biology should include:

Experiments to investigate the survival of micro-organisms under various atmospheric and space conditions.

Experiments to determine the astrophysical properties of micro-organisms.

By astrophysical properties are meant absorption coefficients, masses, sizes, etc.—in general, those properties which would give information on how the organisms would react to radiation fields and other forces affecting their transport and physical state in space.

Actual samples taken at various levels of the atmosphere and exosphere to determine the presence (if any) of micro-organisms; and, later, samples of the atmospheres and soils of other bodies of the solar system.

Survival studies should be conducted both in the laboratory

and in space. The laboratory experiments would entail subjecting bacteria, viruses, spores, and seeds to space-simulated conditions to determine the survival limits of organisms irradiated by X-rays, gamma rays, ultraviolet rays, and high-energy particles; and to determine the influence of temperature, absence of atmosphere, moisture, etc., on survival.

These laboratory tests should, of course, be supplemented by investigations under actual conditions in free space.

EXPERIMENTS WITH SOUNDING ROCKETS: Vertical rockets, of the Viking and Aerobee type, will continue to be useful, as in the past, for measurements of upper atmosphere phenomena and composition. They can also be used for high-altitude observations of the Sun, Moon, planets, and other celestial objects. (Balloons, of course, are also useful in this connection.)

EXPERIMENTS WITH SATELLITES: Uses of satellites for scientific observations have been mentioned under "Observation Satellites" and "Meteorological Satellites."

Satellites can remain in space permanently for long-term observation to altitudes of about 1 million miles, and would be most useful for continued mapping of the "radiation belt" disclosed by the IGY satellites.

Some experiments appropriate to satellites of various payload classes are:

Less than one hundred pounds:

- Cosmic-ray counters; mass spectrometer; measurements of total magnetic field, solar ultraviolet radiation, X-rays, and gamma rays.
- Observations of heat balance and albedo of Earth.
- Low-resolution pictures of Earth, Moon, and planets.
- Density, composition, and temperature in upper atmosphere and solar corona.
- Geodetic information from radio and visual observations of satellite orbits.
- Micrometeorite densities.
- Ionospheric density from radio signals.

Growth of spores or yeast in space.
Small mammals in a space environment.

One hundred pounds:
Small recoverable payload.
Higher resolution photographs of Earth, Moon, and planets; emulsion plates for detecting cosmic rays.
Measurement of vector components of geomagnetic field and its time variations.
Spectrum of the atmosphere of the Earth and Sun; hemispheric cloud observations.
Location of radiating points in space; cosmic radio noise at the low radio frequencies.
Tests of space environment on mammals.
Plant-growth cycle under weightlessness.

One thousand pounds:
Telescope to obtain spectra of planets, stars, and galaxies from far ultraviolet through infrared.
Combination meteorological satellite involving both television and infrared sensors.
Test of the general theory of relativity using atomic or molecular clocks.
Small animals in space in a closed ecological system.
Experiments to note animal body rhythms and activity in space.

Ten thousand pounds:
Larger animals and man in space.
Large telescopes for astronomical observation.

LUNAR VEHICLES: Some of the purposes to which lunar rocket experiments might be turned include measurements of—

The mass of the Moon. The current estimates of this quantity may be in error by as much as 0.3 percent, and substantial inconsistencies exist between mass estimates based on asteroid observations and those implied by data on the motions of the Earth's polar axis.

The Moon's magnetic field: At present we have virtually no knowledge whatsoever of the Moon's magnetic field. Data on the magnetic field of the Moon would allow us to make some progress in theories about the history of the Moon, the processes of its formation, etc.

The composition and physical properties of the lunar atmosphere.

The composition and properties of the lunar crust.

Lunar surface temperature and its variation with time and depth.

Surface radioactivity and atmospheric electricity.

Seismic properties of the lunar interior.

INTERPLANETARY VEHICLES: The measurements that might be made on other planets are generally the same as those pertinent to the Earth itself, as modified by the singular features of each planet.